SPC in the Office

SPC in the Office

by
Mal Owen and John Morgan

Greenfield Publishing

Greenfield Publishing,
P.O. Box 12
Kenilworth,
Warwickshire,
CV8 1ZS,
England.

First published 2000

ISBN 0 9523328 4 1

Printed and bound in Great Britain by Biddles Ltd., Guildford and King's Lynn

ACKNOWLEDGEMENTS

ACKNOWLEDGEMENTS

Real live case studies are an attraction in any book, and particularly when the text concerned relates to something too often seen as a technique which has limited value in an office.

If anything can convince the doubters it is a series of applications on how organisations, from the well known to those less in the limelight, have effectively used control charts.

The authors owe a debt to the following organisations who have allocated time and material in the development of this book:-

Aerospace Composite Technologies
BAE SYSTEMS
Bromley Council
GEC Marconi Avionics (Customer Support)
GEC Marconi Avionics
Kerry Milling
Napp Laboratories Ltd
NPI
NatWest UK
Ronaldsway Aircraft Company
Rover Finance
Spillers Milling
3M Healthcare
AUCS

Over the years we have also been assisted by countless others who have shown interest in SPC. We are grateful to these colleagues for their involvement in one way or another in providing an insight, making a suggestion or passing a comment. We never stop learning.

The case studies contained in this book have been reproduced as they were presented to the authors. No attempt has been made to change the style, or interpretation, of any of them.

CONTENTS

CONTENTS

CHAPTER 1   An introduction to SPC   **1**
1.1   An introduction   1
1.2   Listening to voices   1
    1.2.1   The view of the customer   1
    1.2.2   Understanding the process   2
1.3   Statistical Process Control   3
1.4   Some historical information   4
    1.4.1   Developments in the US   4
    1.4.2   Developments in Japan   5
    1.4.3   Recent developments   5
1.5   Variation   6
1.6   Looking at data in a different way   7
1.7   Detecting unusual features   8
1.8   Summary of symbols and formulae   10
1.9   Key points and summary   10

CHAPTER 2   An introduction to processes   **11**
2.1   Introduction   11
2.2   So what is a process?   11
2.3   The internal customer/supplier chain   11
2.4   Understanding the process   12
    2.4.1   Customer requirements   12
    2.4.2   Supplier requirements   13
    2.4.3   People, skills and knowledge   13
    2.4.4   Equipment and facilities   13
    2.4.5   Procedures   13
    2.4.6   Standards   13
2.5   Company-wide processes   13
2.6   Mapping and measuring the process   15
    2.6.1   Flowcharts   15
    2.6.2   Process stapling   16
    2.6.3   Asking questions   17
    2.6.4   Adding value   17
2.7   Processes and Business Excellence   18
2.8   Summary of symbols and formulae   20
2.9   Key points and summary   20

CHAPTER 3   The process and the customer   **22**
3.1   Introduction   22
3.2   The deployment flowchart   22

CONTENTS

3.3   The check sheet   23
3.4   Measuring the detail   24
3.5   Asking the right questions   26
3.6   CSFs and KPIs   27
3.7   The Balanced Business Scorecard   27
3.8   Customer requirements   28
        3.8.1   Service Level Agreements   28
        3.8.2   Targets   28
        3.8.3   Choice of SLA and target   29
3.9   Comparison with reality   30
3.10   Other issues   31
3.11   Summary of symbols and formulae   31
3.12   Key points and summary   31

CHAPTER 4   Getting the measure of processes   **33**
4.1   Introduction   33
4.2   Measurement   33
4.3   Traditional sources of information   33
        4.3.1   Manual records   33
        4.3.2   Computer-based records   34
4.4   Traditional methods of representation   34
        4.4.1   Bar charts   35
        4.4.2   Pie charts   38
        4.4.3   Line graphs or run charts   38
        4.4.4   Rainbow charts   38
        4.4.5   Glyph charts   39
        4.4.6   Other charts   40
4.5   Limitations of existing methods   42
4.6   Key points and summary   43

CHAPTER 5   Measuring the right things   **44**
5.1   Introduction   44
5.2   Measuring or counting?   44
5.3   Representing the data   46
        5.3.1   Representing the data   46
        5.3.2   Building the picture   46
5.4   What does the histogram tell us?   49
5.5   What doesn't the histogram tell us?   50
5.6   Variations in patterns   50
5.7   Measures of the position of a process   52
        5.7.1   The mode   52
        5.7.2   The mean   52
5.8   Measures of variation   55
        5.8.1   The range   55
        5.8.2   The standard deviation   56
        5.8.3   Interpreting the standard deviation   56
5.9   From run chart to control chart   58
5.10   Rules for special causes   58
        5.10.1   Rule 1.   Point outside the control limit   58
        5.10.2   Rule 2.   Run of seven   59
        5.10.3   Rule 3.   Unusual pattern   60

	5.10.4	Rule 4.	Middle third rule	61
5.11	Other issues			62
5.12	Summary of symbols and formulae			62
5.13	Key points and summary			63

CHAPTER 6   How to measure. The control chart – a step-by-step guide   64

6.1	Introduction		64
6.2	Defining the process		64
6.3	Collecting the data		65
6.4	Calculating results		66
	6.4.1	Sample calculations	67
	6.4.2	Calculation of central lines	67
	6.4.3	Calculation of control limits	67
6.5	Plotting and recording		67
6.6	Interpreting the chart		68
	6.6.1	Interpretation based on setting up the chart	68
	6.6.2	Interpretation when using the chart in an ongoing situation	71
	6.6.3	Moving from sheet to sheet	73
6.7	Summary of symbols and formulae		74
6.8	Key points and summary		74

CHAPTER 7   Which chart to use?   75

7.1	Introduction		75
7.2	Chart based on individual readings		75
	7.2.1	Data available	76
	7.2.2	Data not currently available and has to be collected	78
7.3	Chart based on samples		80
	7.3.1	Data available	82
	7.3.2	Data not currently available and has to be collected	82
7.4	Data which is classified into different categories		82
	7.4.1 Data available		84
	7.4.2 Data not currently available and has to be collected		84
7.5	Making the choice		86
7.6	Summary of symbols and formulae		87
7.7	Key points and summary		87

CHAPTER 8   The (X, Moving R) chart   88

8.1	Introduction		88
8.2	Some typical figures to work on		88
8.3	Defining the process		89
8.4	Collecting the data		89
8.5	The control chart format to be used		90
8.6	Recording data on chart		91
8.7	Carrying out the required calculations		92
	8.7.1	Sample calculations	92
	8.7.2	Calculation of central lines	93
	8.7.3	Calculation of control limits	93
8.8.	Recording numerical values on chart		95
8.9	Choosing scales for the charts		95
8.10	Plotting sample results		96
8.11	Drawing the central lines and control limits		96

CONTENTS

8.12	Interpreting the chart	99
8.13	Projecting lines ahead	99
8.14	Continue monitoring the process	100
8.15	Other issues relating to the (X, Moving R) chart	100
	8.15.1　Choice of correct formula for evaluating the standard deviation	100
	8.15.2　Limitation of the Moving R section of the chart	101
8.16	Summary of symbols and formulae	101
8.17	Key points and summary	102

CHAPTER 9　　The (X, Moving R) chart – CASE STUDIES　　104

9.1	Introduction	104
9.2	Water consumption – *Kerry Milling*	104
	9.2.1 Background to the company	104
	9.2.2 The project	104
	9.2.3 The control chart	106
9.3	Response times to task authorisation – *GEC-Marconi Avionics*	106
	9.3.1 Background to the company	106
	9.3.2 GEC-Marconi and SPC	108
	9.3.3 The project	108
	9.3.4 The control chart	108
	9.3.5 Conclusion	108
9.4	Recruitment selection tools – *Ronaldsway Aircraft Company*	108
	9.4.1 Background to the company	108
	9.4.2 Purpose of the application	110
	9.4.3 Introduction	110
	9.4.4 Current selection process	110
	9.4.5 Data collection and the SPC chart	110
	9.4.6 Conclusions	110
9.5	Daily call rates for sales personnel – *Spillers Milling*	111
	9.5.1 Background to the company	111
	9.5.2 Spillers Milling and SPC	111
	9.5.3 The project	112
	9.5.4 The sales operation	112
	9.5.5 The control charts	113
	9.5.6 The next step	113
9.6	Commercial vehicle maintenance costs – *Spillers Milling*	114
	9.6.1 Background to the company	114
	9.6.2 The project	114
	9.6.3 The control chart	114
	9.6.4 Future action	114
9.7	Absenteeism – *Organisation A*	117
	9.7.1 Background to the company	117
	9.7.2 Some background on the project	117
	9.7.3 Data collection	117
	9.7.4 Data analysis	117
	9.7.5 The control chart	117
	9.7.6 Further analysis	117
	9.7.7 Benefits of the project	117
	9.7.8 Conclusions	119
9.8	Scores for training courses – *Training for Excellence*	119
	9.8.1 Background to the company	119

9.8.2 Title and brief description 120
9.8.3 Choice of topic 120
9.8.4 Assessing course questionnaires 121
9.8.5 Collection of data 121
9.8.6 Analysis of data 121
9.8.7 Chart results 124
9.8.8 Any benefits obtained 126
9.8.9 Conclusions 127
9.9 Giving up smoking – *Organisation B* 127
9.9.1 Background to the company 127
9.9.2 Organisation B and SPC 127
9.9.3 The project 127
9.9.4 Data collection 127
9.9.5 The control chart 127
9.9.6 Conclusion 129

CHAPTER 10   The ($\overline{X}$, R) chart   130

10.1 Introduction 130
10.2 Some typical figures to work on 130
10.3 Defining the process 131
10.4 Collecting the data 131
10.5 The control chart format to be used 132
10.6 Record data on chart 133
10.7 Carrying out the required calculations 134
10.7.1 Sample calculations 134
10.7.2 Calculation of central lines 135
10.7.3 Calculation of control limits 135
10.8 Recording numerical values on chart 137
10.9 Choosing scales for the charts 137
10.10 Plotting the sample results 138
10.11 Drawing the central lines and control limits 138
10.12 Interpret the chart 139
10.13 Removing values resulting in special causes 141
10.14 Carrying out the required calculations 141
10.15 Drawing the new central lines and control limits 142
10.16 Interpreting the chart 142
10.17 Projecting lines ahead 142
10.18 Continue monitoring the process 142
10.19 Other issues relating to the ($\overline{X}$, R) chart 143
10.19.1 Choice of sample size 143
10.19.2 Improving the process 144
10.19.3 The R chart 144
10.20 Summary of symbols and formulae 145
10.21 Key points and summary 146

CHAPTER 11   The ($\overline{X}$, R) chart – CASE STUDIES   147

11.1 Introduction 147
11.2 Standard order processing times. – *Organisation C* 147
11.2.1 Background to the company 147
11.2.2 Targets 147
11.2.3 Initial measurement 150

CONTENTS

	11.2.4	Process improvements	150
	11.2.5	Process mapping	150
	11.2.6	Further activities	151
11.3		Do we pay our suppliers too early? – *Rover Finance*	151
	11.3.1	Background to the company	151
	11.3.2	Current practice	152
	11.3.3	Relevance of SPC project ot the department	152
	11.3.4	Data collection	153
	11.3.5	Calculation of theoretical payment date	153
	11.3.6	The measure of payment performance	153
	11.3.7	The control chart	153
	11.3.8	Savings	153
	11.3.9	The future	153
11.4		Response times to customer transactions at the counter	155
		– *NatWest – UK Retail Banking Services*	
	11.4.1	Background to the company	155
	11.4.2	Introduction	155
	11.4.3	Some background	155
	11.4.4	The project	156
	11.4.5	Collecting the data	156
	11.4.6	The control chart	156
	11.4.7	Analysing the results	156
	11.4.8	Future action	156
11.5		Company cars – *Spillers Milling*	158
	11.5.1	Background to the company	158
	11.5.2	Introduction	158
	11.5.3	Management actions	158
	11.5.4	Data collection	159
	11.5.5	The control chart	159
	11.5.6	Future action	159
CHAPTER 12		**The multiple characteristics control chart**	**161**
12.1		Introduction	161
12.2		Some typical figures to work on	161
12.3		Defining the process	161
12.4		Collecting the data	163
12.5		The control chart format to be used	163
12.6		Recording data on chart	163
12.7		Carrying out the required calculations	166
	12.7.1	Sample calculations	166
	12.7.2	Calculation of central lines	167
	12.7.3	Calculation of control limits	167
12.8		Recording numerical values on chart	167
12.9		Choosing a scale for the chart	168
12.10		Plotting the sample results	168
12.11		Draw the central line and control limits	169
12.12		Interpreting the chart	169
12.13		Projecting lines ahead	171
12.14		Continue monitoring the process	171
12.15		Further analysis	172
	12.15.1	Highlighting the major problem	172

12.15.2   Setting up a new control chart   173
12.15.3   Repeating the procedure   174
12.16   Other issues relating to the Multiple Characteristics chart   174
    12.16.1   Use of (X, Moving R) chart   174
    12.16.2   Classifying the data   176
    12.16.3   Number or value?   176
12.17   Summary of symbols and formulae   176
12.18   Key points and summary   176

CHAPTER 13   The multiple characteristics control chart – CASE STUDIES   178
13.1   Introduction   178
13.2   Errors in letter writing – *NPI*   178
    13.2.1 Background to the company   178
    13.2.2 Introduction   178
    13.2.3 The case study   178
    13.2.4 Background   179
    13.2.5 Collection of data   180
    13.2.6 Difficulties experienced in collecting the data   180
    13.2.7 Importance of the data   180
    13.2.8 Analysis of data   180
    13.2.9 Control chart   180
    13.2.10 Further action   182
    13.2.11 Deming's fourteen points   182
13.3   The analysis of weekly recorded shortages – *Aerospace Composite Technologies*   182
    13.3.1 Background to the company   182
    13.3.2 The company and SPC   182
    13.3.3 The project   184
    13.3.4 The control chart   184
    13.3.5 Future action   184
13.4   The analysis of downtime at an ATM – *NatWest – UK Retail Banking Services*   185
    13.4.1 Background to the company   185
    13.4.2 Introduction   185
    13.4.3 The case study   185
    13.4.4 The control chart   185
    13.4.5 Interpreting the chart   185
13.5   Service Order Invoice errors – *GEC-Marconi Avionics*   187
    13.5.1 Background to the company   187
    13.5.2 Introduction   187
    13.5.3 Data collection   187
    13.5.4 The control chart   187
    13.5.5 Future action   189
13.6   Complaints analysis – *Bromley Council*   189
    13.6.1 Background to the organisation   189
    13.6.2 Bromley Council and SPC   189
    13.6.3 The project   189
    13.6.4 Handling the data   189
    13.6.5 The control charts   191
    13.6.6 Studying the detail   191
    13.6.7 Tackling the problem   193
    13.6.8 Further charts   194
    13.6.9 Future action   195

CONTENTS

CHAPTER 14   Capability – can the process deliver?   **196**

14.1   Introduction   196
14.2   Two voices   197
14.3   How are the processes doing?   197
14.4   The C_p index   198
    14.4.1   Defining and interpreting the C_p index   198
    14.4.2   Calculating and recording the C_p index   200
    14.4.3   Limitations of the C_p index   200
14.5   The C_{pk} index   201
    14.5.1   Nominal is critical   201
    14.5.2   Calculating and recording the C_{pk} index   204
    14.5.3   USL or LSL is critical   205
    14.5.4   Cases where there is a natural upper or lower barrier   207
    14.5.5 C_{pk} calculations based on an ($\overline{X}$, R) chart   208
14.6   Capability for attributes   208
    14.6.1   First Run Capability (FRC)   209
    14.6.2   Defects per hundred units (DHU)   209
14.7   Making the choice   209
14.8   Control, capability and improvement   211
14.9   Misuse of capability indices   212
14.10   Summary of symbols and formulae   212
14.11   Key points and summary   213

CHAPTER 15   Journey to improvement – A framework for progress   **214**

15.1   Introduction   214
15.2   The Journey to Improvement   214
15.3   Select the problem –Step 1   216
15.4   Understand the current situation – Step 2   218
15.5   Identify and check the possible causes – Step 3   219
15.6   First review   220
15.7   Generate possible solutions – Step 4   220
15.8   Select the solution – Step 5   221
15.9   Plan and test the solution – Step 6   221
15.10   Second review   223
15.11   Implement and standardise the solution – Step 7   223
15.12   Assess achievements and lessons – Step 8   224
15.13   Final review   224
15.14   The 'Improvement Journal'   225
15.15   Key points and summary   225

CHAPTER 16   The journey to improvement – Some other tools   **226**

16.1   Introduction   226
16.2   Other problem-solving techniques   226
16.3   Brainstorming   227
    16.3.1   Some sensible ground rules   227
    16.3.2   Generating ideas   227
    16.3.3   Capturing ideas   227
16.4   Fishbone diagram   228
16.5   The Affinity diagram   230
16.6   The Interrelationship diagram   231
16.7   Force Field Analysis   232

16.8	The XY Grid	233
16.9	Paired comparisons and N/3	234
16.10	The Scatter diagram	235
16.11	Putting it together	236
16.12	Summary of symbols and formulae	236
16.13	Key points and summary	237

CHAPTER 17 Some further issues **238**

17.1	Introduction	238
17.2	Drifting processes	239
	17.2.1 The problem	239
	17.2.2 Step 1 Record the readings	239
	17.2.3 Step 2 Choose the scale	239
	17.2.4 Step 3 Plot the results	239
	17.2.5 Step 4 Calculate the 'line of best fit'	240
	17.2.6 Step 5 Calculate moving ranges	241
	17.2.7 Step 6 Calculate mean values	241
	17.2.8 Step 7 Determine control limits	242
	17.2.9 Step 8 Interpret for process control	242
	17.2.10 Inclined lines for ($\overline{X}$, R) chart	243
	17.2.11 Use of software packages	243
17.3	Process control measurement within the sales environment – *3M Healthcare*	244
	17.3.1 Background to the company	244
	17.3.2 From data to information	244
	17.3.3 The traditional view	245
	17.3.4 The new view	245
	17.3.5 Angled control limits	246
17.4	Cyclic processes	246
17.5	Invoice runs – *Napp Laboratories Ltd*	247
	17.5.1 Background to the company	247
	17.5.2 The project	248
	17.5.3 Invoicing procedure	248
	17.5.4 The control chart	248
	17.5.5 Potential savings	248
	17.5.6 Further action	248
17.6	Bunching	249
17.7	Analysing Goods Received Notes – *GEC-Marconi Avionics*	250
	17.7.1 The company	250
	17.7.2 Introduction	250
	17.7.3 The control chart	250
	17.7.4 Data collection	250
	17.7.5 Chart results	253
	17.7.6 Further analysis	253
17.8	Problems of sampling	255
17.9	Turnround times for Internal Release Notes – *GEC-Marconi Avionics*	255
	17.9.1 The company	255
	17.9.2 Introduction	255
	17.9.3 First attempts	256
	17.9.4 Where next?	256
	17.9 5 Training	256
	17.9.6 Further developments	257

CONTENTS

	17.9.7 Other issues	257
17.10	Recalculating control limits	260
	17.10.1 Recalculating limits for an ($\overline{X}$, R) chart	260
	17.10.2 Recalculating limits for an (X, Moving R) chart	261
	17.10.3 Recalculating limits for a multiple characteristics chart	261
17.11	Other attribute charts	262
17.12	Summary of symbols and formulae	262
17.13	Key points and summary	262

CHAPTER 18 Introducing SPC into an organisation – Problems and opportunities — **263**

18.1	Introduction	263
18.2	SPC and management	263
18.3	Starting the programme	264
18.4	Managing the fact	266
18.5	SPC and managing reporting – *Organisation D*	267
	18.5.1 Background to the company	267
	18.5.2 The project	267
	18.5.3 Management reporting	267
18.6	Some pointers to success	267
18.7	Training	270
18.8	Software or manual charts	272
18.9	SPC training software and management reporting– *Unisource*	272
	18.9.1 Background to the company	272
	18.9.2 The training	273
	18.9.3 Applications	273
18.10	Wider opportunities	275
18.11	Are we ready for change?	277
18.12	Key points and summary	278

Appendices — **279**

Appendix 1	Deming's 14 points	279
Appendix 2	Tables of constants and formulae	280
Appendix 3	List of reference books	282
Appendix 4	List of articles	283
Appendix 5	Other references	284

Index — **285**

Books from Greenfield Publishing and order forms — **293**

Further assistance — **298**

Reader feedback — **299**

FOREWORD

It may be that you are already familiar with SPC and are attracted by a resource that can help you in moving the SPC applications into newer areas. On the other hand, you may know nothing about the topic but the idea of improving office efficiency is appealing. Or you may already be familiar with earlier texts that have been produced in a similar vein and you like the practical, hands-on style, based on a mix of different control charts and various real-life case studies.

It really doesn't matter how you have found out about *SPC in the Office*. We are only too pleased that you have acquired the book.

What do you know about us, the authors? Some information on how we came together to develop this book will not come amiss.

In one sense the authors come from different backgrounds. One of us is grounded in managing business processes within the financial services industry before moving into training and consultancy. The other has extensive experience in introducing SPC techniques in a wide field of operations, increasingly in the service/administrative area. However, we both have a common concern regarding the lack of knowledge, at all levels and in most of the organisations we have worked with, as to what is meant by variation, how to control it, and, of much more importance, how to reduce it.

It does seem that people have misplaced and misguided views as to the use and applicability of statistics. The very word '*statistics*' spreads fear in the hearts of too many. Possibly the title of this book does not help. '*SPC in the Office*' is hardly an appealing title for any book, but there really is no choice. Various alternatives to '*Statistical Process Control*' have been proposed over the years, but there is no better combination of words to express what we are trying to cover in this book. We know that the word '*statistics*' also brings with it some passion, sometimes negative. The authors have recognised this, and have developed the text so that over the pages we trust that any fear becomes diminished.

We have tried to reduce this apprehension in different ways.

Firstly, we have assumed absolutely no knowledge of statistics. We have not assumed much knowledge of mathematics either. This does not mean that we are being patronising. We have sought to tread the delicate line between being helpful and considerate of those readers who really are put off by anything mathematical, yet at the same time providing material which is sufficiently technical and at the right level for those who feel comfortable with straightforward mathematics. What is certain is that the authors are not interested in any academic approaches to statistical theory. Goodness knows there are enough of those books about. Search in a University library or academic bookshop, and you will find these texts. Good luck to you, if you pursue these sources. Books relating to classical statistics are not referenced in the appendix, and no apologies are made for that. If we are truthful, books of this nature contain material that bears little, if any, relationship with the theory used in developing the control chart.

We would like to think that the book will appeal to both company senior executives and operational staff at the sharp end of the operation. This is not an easy balance. In the case of this book, you are the customer, and no doubt you will tell us in one way or another if we have achieved this objective.

In writing this book, the authors recognised the various options that were available when getting into the detail of control charts. Variable charts or attribute charts? Individuals or samples? Fixed sample size or varying sample size? Document faults or errors in documents? If we were not careful we would find ourselves producing a detailed SPC text covering all the options, and that was definitely what we did not want. If you are interested in accessing more detailed SPC books to help you, then they are there, and you will find appropriate references in the appendix.

Because we did not intend to write a book covering all the options, we have concentrated on just three types of control charts.

One chart, which allows us to deal with single readings such as weekly sales figures, takes priority. It is becoming clear that this single reading chart as it is called, or, in SPC terms, the (X, Moving R) chart, has been considerably under-utilised. The scope for using this chart is almost unlimited, and the various case studies shown in the book should help in making you aware of the potential for using this type of chart.

It does seem that when control charts are first mentioned in conversation, an association is often made with the control chart used when dealing with samples as opposed to individuals, - the ($\overline{X}$, R) chart. This chart has traditionally been associated with the mass production of engineering components, and your views might be similar. If we have got it right then this book should change that. There are now available some excellent examples of the application of this chart in office areas. The relevant chapters in this book should interest you.

Finally, and by no means least, we have the multiple characteristic chart. Typically this chart is not generally recognised, and certainly not conspicuous in office areas where it has considerable potential, latent up to now, in assisting an organisation in handling errors, complaints, and much more.

There are various interpretations and options available as to the way control limits are determined – not the actual mathematics involved but more the rationale behind the use of a control limit. It was Walter Shewhart who first devised a control chart and his colleague Edwards Deming who further progressed the idea. And so it is their views on control limits that we have used in the book. As well as adopting a tried and proven method, this also has the advantage of making things much simpler.

SPC is a measurement tool. It will help you to understand, manage and improve your processes, enabling you to make sense of a mass (or even as mess) of figures, and data.

However it is not an end in itself, and if SPC is to be used successfully, you will have to take action on the information it is giving to you. To help you determine the action needed, the book includes a step-by-step method for process improvement and problem solving, and a small but helpful tool kit to help you on your way.

The authors believe that the book has an attraction in at least three ways.

Firstly, we really have tried to keep things simple. If you feel that we have insulted you in doing this, then apologies are in order. We have adopted a view that it is better to aim at the level of those who have the greatest fear than those who possess an MBA, or a degree in statistics.

Secondly, the numerous Case Studies should prove both relevant and interesting. The various examples are based on genuine applications of control charts in non-manufacturing areas. There is a real spread of applications, perhaps sufficient in some cases to make you rethink your views on what you understand by SPC. The Case Studies are very readable, and illustrate how a particular type of chart has been used. That does not necessarily mean that the organisation concerned has introduced, and progressed, a complete company-wide programme based on utilising, and understanding, a control. chart. We don't claim that, and neither does the organisation involved. Nevertheless, the use of a chart in a particular context is a perfectly acceptable indicator of how powerful SPC can be.

Thirdly, since the book is called *SPC in the Office*, then you can expect the material to relate to office areas. There may be the odd mention of production processes, Japan, the Ford Motor Co, whatever, but that is only referencing the way in which SPC has developed and progressed. The book sets out to show readers that SPC is very appropriate to a whole range of activities outside of its traditional manufacturing base. The book also seeks to demonstrate that SPC is only a part, albeit an important part of what is needed in the improvement journey.

We do hope you find the book useful and informative. It should give you a guide as to how to become familiar with the nature of variation, and why it is imperative that we all understand the dangers of not understanding it. There is a strong criticism in the book of much to do with the way targets, quotas and Service Level Agreements are used. There is also a strong underlying criticism of a system of further and higher education, both in the UK and abroad, that does not recognise that education and training in SPC should be mandatory for all students.

It is outside the scope of the book as to how to deal with the latter. Both authors have enough experience of Britain's higher education system to recognise its shortcomings, in this respect, in providing the UK's future workforce, at whatever level, with a really useful tool to help them to manage their processes.

It is no wonder that Deming, Tribus and others despair. We need to prompt and provoke and maybe this book will help.

We owe a lot to those who have helped in the production of this book. Individuals in the various organisations who have co-operated in making case study material available. Various colleagues who have made comments and suggestions as to the contents and approach of the book. Without repeating earlier comments, there was a general consensus that in reducing the various options for control charts in order to keep thing simple, it did seem we have hit a sympathetic nerve.

Finally, we thank our respective families for their support. Writing a book of this nature, and collating the many case studies, has taken months. We would also like to thank Alex Weiss for his help in preparing the material for publication. Working with him has been a real pleasure.

We hope you like the final product. We would welcome any comments and would be pleased to hear from you. Details on how we can be contacted appear at the end of the book.

Mal Owen
John Morgan
May 2000

AN INTRODUCTION TO SPC

1.1 Introduction

A critical aspect of using Statistical Process Control is matching the needs of our customer with the measure of the process involved. Understanding the voice of the customer and the voice of the process is therefore essential, and detail on these requirements appears in Section 1.2.

A definition of SPC follows, together with some detail on the historical developments which have led to the technique being used increasingly in newer areas and, in particular, in an office environment.

Section 1.5 covers the need to understand variation and, more specifically, variation in business figures. This variation cannot be detected from business information when represented, as it so often is, in the form of rows and columns of numbers. Section 1.6 suggests how we can look at data in a different way by making use of a control chart. This leads naturally to the next section, which explains that the basic feature of a control chart is its ability to distinguish between natural changes in a process and unusual changes that need to be acted upon.

1.2 Listening to voices

Do you know why the Prince of Wales talks to plants? The theory is that by talking to them he shows that he loves them and cares for them, and in doing so, he believes he is developing a relationship that encourages growth.

These are pretty much the same set of reasons why we should be talking to customers.

1.2.1 The view of the customer

We need to show that we care about them, that we love them and want to develop a relationship that leads to growth, both for our business and our customers. More important than talking to our customers,

Fig 1.1 *The view of the customer.*

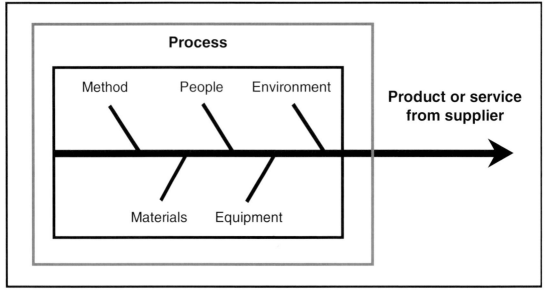

Fig 1.2 *A process as a combination of various factors.*

however, is the need to listen, a skill that all too often tends to be overlooked. In particular, we should remember to use our two ears and one mouth in roughly the same proportion.

We can listen to our customers in a number of ways including, for example, market research, customer satisfaction measurement and the monitoring of complaints. *Fig 1.1* provides a representation of the 'voice of the customer'.

Listening to, and understanding, the 'voice of the customer' is relatively easy. We might not always like what our customers tell us, but they do at least talk the same language, albeit jargon free! Understanding the 'voice of the process' is a lot harder.

1.2.2 Understanding the process

A process is a series of steps and actions that produce a product or service. All work is a process, and a process is a blend of method, people, environment, materials and equipment, as shown in *Fig 1.2*.

The process is always trying to talk to us, to tell us, for example, whether it is capable of meeting the customer's requirement.

Unfortunately, the process does not talk the same language. Nevertheless, we have to learn to understand it, since what we have to do is match the 'voice of the process' with the 'voice of the customer'. *Fig 1.3* illustrates a process that is trying to meet the customer's requirements.

The feedback from the customer and the process highlights a gap that needs to be closed. This is an aim that might be achieved either by improving the process, or through some marketing or public relations activity that changes the customer's perception. As we all know probably only too well, perception and reality can be different. While changing the customer's perception may be an option in the early stages of negotiating a customer's requirements, it is not an option which fits comfortably with a continuous improvement approach, and we should really be aiming to improve the process so that we can meet the customer's needs.

Listening to the 'voice of the process' is therefore essential.

The only effective way to do it is to measure the process and use Statistical Process Control (SPC).

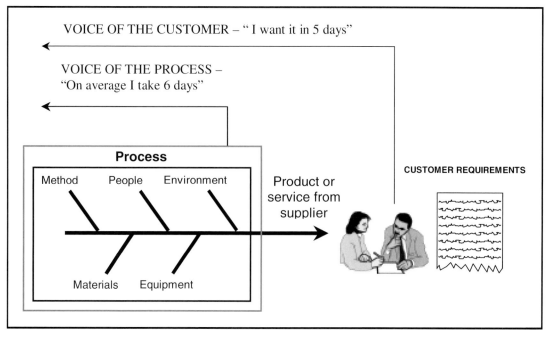

VOICE OF THE CUSTOMER – " I want it in 5 days"

VOICE OF THE PROCESS –
"On average I take 6 days"

Process

Method   People   Environment

Materials   Equipment

Product or
service from
supplier

CUSTOMER REQUIREMENTS

Fig 1.3 *A process that is trying to meet the customer's requirements.*

1.3 Statistical Process Control

So what exactly is Statistical Process Control?

It is best if we specify what we mean by the three words: *'statistical'*, *'process'* and *'control'*. We have a problem straightaway because for many people these words are enough to put them off. However, there is no real alternative. Some attempts have been made to use other words, but they do not really describe the programme in the same way.

'Statistical' implies the collection and representation of numerical data. In SPC terms it does not mean the classical theoretical statistics which many of us have encountered on one educational course or another. Nor does it mean the gathering of statistics in the form of tables of numbers. The statistical knowledge we make use of in SPC is well founded in theory, but we take that for granted. All the calculations we will carry out are based around the use of a control chart – a key element of SPC. And all the calculations are straightforward and simple.

'Process' means just that – a combination of method, people, environment, materials and equipment, as introduced in Section 1.2. In this book a process will be considered as an activity to do with an office in the widest sense.

'Control' means working on the process to make it predictable. Once the process is under control, we are then in a position to understand its capability. 'Control' has nothing to do with Big Brother.

Initially, when we first apply SPC, we are likely to be using it on the output of a process. For example, we could be using a control chart on the errors in a document at the end of an administrative process. As time goes on, we are likely to move the use of the chart to the characteristics of the process. For example, we could measure characteristics such as the time taken to carry out the administrative operation. Equally, it is important to work on improving the inputs to the process. For example, control charts could be used on characteristics of software used, the quality of the printer ribbons acquired, or

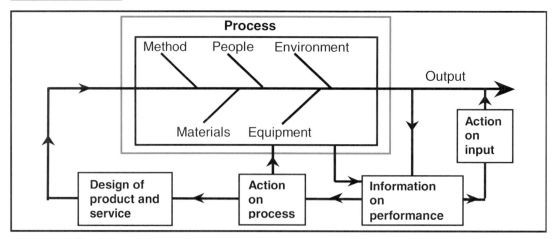

Fig 1.4 Feedback loop in improving a process.

the accuracy of forms sent in by customers, or others. There is considerable scope here for extending the SPC programme to your suppliers.

Fig 1.4 shows schematically how data from a process is used to improve it.

1.4 Some historical information

For many, the historical events associated with the development of SPC are well known. There is a danger of repeating too often material which is commonly available, and which is well referenced in the Appendix. On the other hand there is also a danger of mistakenly assuming that the reader is aware of the critical events which have resulted in an increased interest in applying SPC in an office environment. So that we can all start from the same level of understanding, therefore, a few sentences on the development of practical statistical thinking will probably help.

1.4.1 Developments in the US

In the early 1920s, Walter Shewhart devised the control chart when working at the Bell Telephone Company in the US. Further work led to the publication of his results in 1931. His text *The Economic Control of Quality of Manufactured Product* is now recognised as one of the major publications in the field. One of Shewhart's team at the Bell Telephone Laboratories was Dr. W. Edwards Deming, and it was Shewhart and Deming who further developed the use of the control chart in the US in the 1930s. Another leading US consultant, Dr. Joseph Juran, was also one of the team employed at the Bell Laboratories. Juran's approach to quality has placed far less emphasis on the use of control charts than that advocated later by Deming.

Interest in the control chart was heightened in the early 1940s due to the involvement of the United States in World War II. The control chart was used in the production of military equipment to improve the efficiency of the US war effort.

At the same time there was a need to increase the general awareness of the control chart and Shewhart, Deming and others ran a series of courses in the US on 'Understanding Variation'. In carrying out these training courses, it is unclear as to how much reference was made to the use of the control chart in administrative areas. Certainly there would have been an emphasis on the need to understand the process, the customer and supplier and a suitable measure from the process.

A significant change from Shewhart's time has been the use of the term SPC rather than SQC

(Statistical Quality Control). It reflects the wider use of the chart and the emphasis on measuring the process, whatever its nature, rather than the product. At the same time, there has been a move away from the traditional view of using the Quality Department to handle the programme.

The training courses referred to proved highly successful and were one of the major factors in establishing, in 1946, the American Society for Quality Control (ASQC), now known as the American Society for Quality (ASQ).

1.4.2 Developments in Japan

After the war, interest in the control chart faded in the US. There was little competition for American products because the rest of the world was devastated following the war effort. It was the Japanese who showed the value of controlling and reducing variation. As they began to practise the virtues of quality improvement as advocated by Deming, so they started to make inroads into the world market place. Deming carried out training assignments in Japan over several visits during the 1950s. His work was recognised by the establishment of the Deming Prize.

Deming's success in Japan was helped by a system of management which was at odds with the autocratic style so common in Western organisations. He knew that a control chart raised a series of management issues, and he began to develop a set of suitable guidelines that would support the introduction of statistical thinking into an organisation. These 14 Points for Management, as they became known, provide a sense of direction to senior management, and will be referred to at different times throughout the book. The 14 Points appear in Appendix 1.

1.4.3 Recent developments

In 1981, Deming appeared in an NCB documentary in the US entitled *If Japan can do it, why can't we*? Deming's appearance on the programme led to his involvement with the Ford Motor Company, and from that developed the insistence by Ford on the use of statistical methods, as laid out in the Ford Q101 programme. The SPC training initiative subsequently introduced into the UK had a significant effect in several ways. It brought out the lack of basic, practical statistical knowledge, which was evident across the workplace – from the boardroom to the shopfloor. It also prompted other organisations, outside the automotive industry, to introduce similar programmes based on using the control chart as a focus for improvement.

Deming died in 1993, having spent the best part of 50 years consulting with some of his country's major organisations, following on from his success in helping the Japanese. Other people are now carrying on the work. A leading advocate of Deming's thinking for the last 20 years has been Myron Tribus, previously Vice-President of Xerox. Tribus is particularly critical of business schools in that, for various reasons, they have shown little interest in introducing the Deming philosophy into their respective syllabuses. William Scherkenbach was Director of Statistical Methods at the Ford Motor Company, responsible for bringing in the philosophy of statistical thinking, and all that resulted from it. Alfie Kohn has spent time researching areas such as competition and rewards, and is promoting a radical rethink on how to handle such controversial issues. References to these consultants, and others, appear in the Appendix, and the books and articles they have produced provide excellent material for those who are interested in the wider cultural issues around SPC.

Traditionally, SPC has been used in manufacturing and, in textbooks, typical examples of its use are from the motor or chemical industries. Its potential in service industries, and in administrative areas generally is, however, enormous. A recent important development has been the stipulation of the Boeing Corporation to ask all its suppliers to introduce SPC and, in particular, apply it in office areas.

So how does it work? Like most improvement programmes, SPC works only if management behaviour and actions support it. That support starts with the acceptance that 'variation exists in everything'.

1.5 Variation

There is variation in our heights, in the colour green, especially in Ireland, in the number of words in the sentences of this book, and in the time different people take to read it. Things are not exactly the same, even if they appear to be so.

Importantly, there are two types of variation, known as 'common cause' and 'special cause' variation. SPC can help us to identify this variation and which type it is. Common cause variation, often referred to as natural variation, is just that – natural. We should expect it. We should not be surprised by it, and we should not react to individual examples of it. If we do, we are likely to make things worse and increase the amount of variation. Deming describes this as 'tampering' with the process.

When a process exhibits only natural variation, it is said to be in 'statistical control'. This does not necessarily mean that the results from the process are good. For example, accident figures may be running at a level of eight per day, and the control chart indicates that the natural variation tells us we can expect up to seventeen accidents a day. That can hardly be a cause for satisfaction.

The two views of variation can probably be best demonstrated by a simple experiment that you can try in the privacy of your own home, or perhaps at work with some colleagues. The first step is to write down the letter 'a' five times.

That in itself can form the basis for an interesting discussion on giving clear instructions in ensuring that the requirements are understood. Some of you will have written across the page, some down the page. Some will have used uppercase letters, others lowercase ones. One or two of you may even have written "the letter 'a' five times". Either way, look at your own 'a's. Are they the same? Almost certainly they will not be. They will probably all be slightly different.

This difference is common cause variation, and the process is in statistical control. If you repeated the exercise we could expect to see the same sort of variation. To improve the process, we could carry out a brainstorming session using a cause and effect diagram to generate ideas. The way forward might be to introduce the use of a template, for example, or a special pen. If you are not sure of what is meant by a 'brainstorming session', or a 'fishbone diagram', then refer to some of the reference books in Chapter 16.

SALES PERFORMANCE - **MAY**									
	LOCATION A					LOCATION B			
PRODUCT	Previous month	Target	Current month	Target	% change from last year	Previous month	Target	Current month	Target	% change from last year
1	34	30	37	30	-5.4	59	50	56	55	-7.6
2	260	250	230	250	3.3	226	250	267	250	12.8
3	75	75	65	70	0.4	125	130	133	135	5.9
4	3	2	4	2	2.7	16	15	18	15	-6.7
5	4678	4750	4978	5000	10.6	1657	1600	1753	1700	5.9
6	930	950	1006	975	2.9	975	1000	952	1000	-1.5
7	950	975	1100	1050	-3.9		975	950	975	-6.2
8	43	45	48	45	-2.8	75	75	78	85	8.4

Fig 1.5 A typical set of data which provides little useful information.

What might happen if we tampered with the process by reacting to an individual example of common cause variation? I might be your manager, and I might look at your letter 'a's and react by saying "Clearly you're not getting it right! Try writing with the other hand, and try a little harder!" The result is likely to show increased variation. Interfering in the natural pattern of results in this way is known as 'tampering', and management seems to do a lot of it.

Tampering can also take the form of pointless discussion. How often do you see reports that are simply a page of numbers that you are expected to make sense of, perhaps even make decisions on? A typical set of information, which is practically meaningless, is shown in *Fig 1.5*.

Figures relating to sales activity usually provide good examples. "This week's figures were better than last week's, but not as good as the week before that", or "Well it rained last Thursday, but the team did a great job this week!" Do you hear this type of comment in your company? It would be surprising if the answer is no. Almost certainly the differences in the weekly figures will be a measure of the natural variation in the process, and not due to a special cause. Using SPC can help us to make sense of the figures.

1.6 Looking at data in a different way

We might think that the data tells us something, but this is not so. We can make progress by presenting the data represented in *Fig 1.5* in a more visual form.

In *Fig 1.5* we have a typical set of row-by-column data. It relates to the sales performance for two locations for the month of May. Eight products are involved, and the table represents the actual sales, in number, together with some targets that have been set. Instead of using just the figures for one month, it is preferable to plot a graph, known as a run chart, using figures for a series of months. We will use figures for Location A and product 3, and the resulting run chart appears in *Fig 1.6*.

This makes it easier to spot any trends, but in itself does not tell us whether the variation is natural or unusual. We need a control chart to tell us whether any changes are part of the natural variation of the process, or whether they are unusual, due to special causes, and need to be looked at. Using the results from the process, we can calculate the mean of the first twenty points, represented by a central

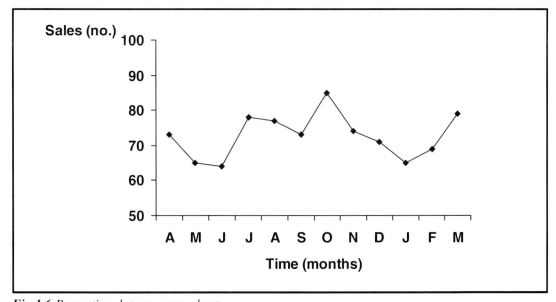

Fig 1.6 Presenting data as a run chart.

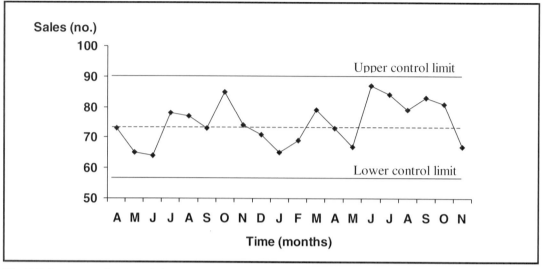

Fig 1.7 *A process that is exhibiting natural variation.*

line on the control chart, together with upper and lower control limits. These control limits, denoted by UCL and LCL, represent the natural, common cause variation of the readings. The detail of calculating central lines and control limits appears in subsequent chapters. The calculations are relatively straight-forward, and you should not worry about any mathematics involved.

The corresponding control chart for the sales figures appears in *Fig 1.7*.

The chart shows that our sales process is exhibiting variation, and that the variation that is occurring is all natural.

We know this because we can use the 'rules' of SPC to distinguish the type of variation. The detail on this appears in Chapter 5. At this stage, it is sufficient to say that if the readings all fall within the control limits, then they reflect natural variation. That will not always be the case. Other rules are available to suggest something unusual happening and these will be explained later.

If the process is exhibiting only natural variation, then it can be described as being in 'statistical control'. It is said to be 'stable'. So what does that mean? It means that the process results are predict-able and we will continue to get results that display variation within the control limits. So do not be surprised, and do not react to individual data items. As far as the process is concerned, these numbers are all the same. Note that because all our readings reflect a process that is under control, stable and predictable, it does not mean that the results are necessarily good. Indeed, there might be a very wide gap between the voice of the process and the voice of the customer. Because the process is stable, we can safely undertake a review of the whole process to find improvement opportunities.

Where action has been taken to improve the process, the chart should be updated to show the details. It is very important that charts are used in this way to provide a living record of what is happening. A 'clean' control chart probably is not being used properly.

1.7 Detecting unusual features

So how do we identify special cause variation? And what do we do when we find it? Special causes are identified in a number of ways. The most obvious is when a data item appears outside the control limits, as shown in *Fig 1.8*.

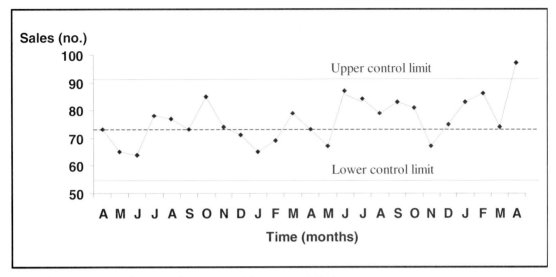

Fig 1.8 *Occurrence of a special cause outside a control limit.*

When that happens, we need to find the 'root cause' and take one of three actions. The options are to remove the data item from the chart, or to take action that either prevents the special cause from occurring again, or build it into the process if it is something good. Note that all special causes are not bad! Reacting to these options indicates a fair degree of understanding of a control chart, and how it operates. At this introductory stage, only a simplistic approach can be provided, but even so it should be helpful as a prelude of the more detailed explanation which will follow.

In *Fig 1.8*, for example, we might well know why the April sales figure is unusually high. A special promotion had taken place, coupled with the provision of a range of extra resources, which has resulted in a sales figure which is out of line with the previously expected values, and as a result outside the control limit. In SPC terms, this means that the sales value for the month in question is outside the system.

Sometimes, and more to our benefit, we can find a reason for an out-of-control signal which we can integrate into the system as part of an improvement programme. For example, if we find we have a very high sales figure, and we can find the reason for this, we are then justified in integrating this into the system and using it as part of an improvement strategy.

A special cause that we will be particularly pleased to see will be the proof that a change in the process has been successful. In *Fig 1.9 (overleaf)* we can see a situation where a process review has been carried out and improvement action taken. The figures in this case refer to the number of errors produced in sequential documents.

The subsequent results show a process running at a reduced level, reflecting an improvement in the process. The control chart has given us evidence of a change for the better, and the rules for interpreting a control chart, to follow in Chapter 5, are quite specific in indicating when such a change as this has taken place. Importantly, we can now recalculate the control limits, and start down a track that will perhaps highlight new special causes to be actioned.

Deming's message to managers came down to two words – 'reduce variation'. As you can see, that is exactly what we are trying to do, reduce the variation and bring the control limits ever closer together, as shown schematically in *Fig 1.9*.

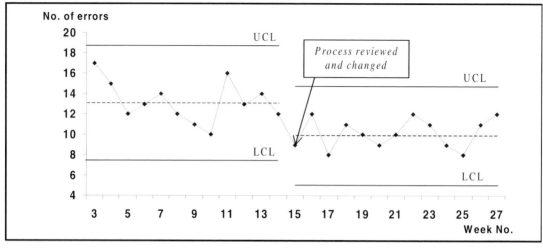

Fig 1.9 *New control limits set after a process review and improvement action.*

Before we look in more detail at the different types of control chart, their formulae, and how to interpret the results, it is worth taking stock of what we mean by a process. This is a critical issue relating to control charts because it is only comparatively recently that service companies and administrative areas have recognised that they have processes in the same way as manufacturing organisations have processes.

1.8 Summary of symbols and formulae

SPC   Statistical Process Control
SQC   Statistical Quality Control
UCL   Upper Control Limit
LCL   Lower Control Limit

1.9 Key points and summary

- The 'voice of the customer' is a measure of our customer requirement.
- A process is a blend of people, method, environment, material and equipment.
- SPC is a very effective 'voice of the process'.
- SPC uses a control chart to measure our process, control it, and then prompt its improvement.
- W. Edwards Deming introduced the control chart to the Japanese after World War II.
- SPC will work only when the culture of the organisation is supportive.
- Variation can be due to common causes and special causes.
- Common cause variation is the natural, expected variation in any process.
- Special cause variation is unusual.
- Replace typical statistics in row and column format by a series of control charts.
- Special causes, which are associated with improvement, should be integrated into the system.
- A control chart can provide visual proof of a change in the process.
- 'Reduce variation' is a key message to management.

The idea of a process has been introduced in this chapter. The next chapter concentrates on processes – why we need to understand them, measure them, and improve them.

AN INTRODUCTION TO PROCESSES

2.1 Introduction

It is outside the scope of this book to cover processes and process management in a fully comprehensive way, but it is important to provide some context, background and understanding. This chapter looks to do just that.

Section 2.2 provides detail on what we mean by a process, and this leads on naturally to an explanation of the internal customer-supplier chain. Customer and supplier requirements of a process are discussed in Section 2.4. The following section looks at the more extensive company-wide definition of a process. Flowcharting is a vital tool to be used when analysing a process, and Section 2.6 gives more detail on this. Various international quality standards are promoting the relevance of the process. Section 2.7 gives detail on how the EFQM's Excellence Model could be applied to a typical administrative organisation – an insurance company.

2.2 So what is a process?

As we have already said in Chapter 1, a process is a series of steps and actions that produce a product or a service. All work is a process, and a process is a blend of people, equipment, method, materials and environment. Years ago, in manufacturing, these five factors used to be referred to as the '4 M's' – manpower, machines, method and materials. Why was 'environment' not included? Equally, why did it take service organisations and, indeed, the back offices of manufacturing companies, so long to recognise that processes apply to them?

This description of a process, shown in *Fig 2.1*, applies to everything we do. Yes, everything! From getting up in the morning, to making a drink, from ordering stationery, to paying a customer's pension. These are all processes, and these processes can all be broken down into a series of steps.

So, all work is a process, whether it is in manufacturing, in administration, or in service.

2.3 The internal customer/supplier chain

When we start to break down our work processes into a series of steps, we recognise that processes involve other people and departments. Within our own organisation, these other people or departments can be described as internal customers or suppliers.

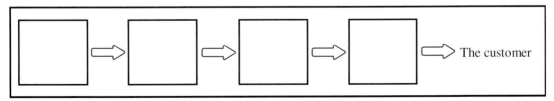

Fig 2.1 Representation of a process as a series of steps and actions.

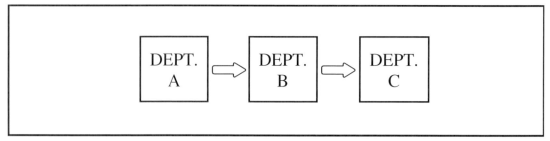

Fig 2.2 *Identifying internal customers and suppliers.*

In *Fig 2.2*, Department A produces something which is passed to Department B which produces something for Department C. The 'something' can be described as output. But it can also be described as input.

Department A's output becomes input for Department B. After Department B has worked on this input, it provides output for Department C. And, of course, this output becomes Department C's input.

The output and input could be anything from a customer enquiry needing various pieces of information to an invoice requiring authorisation and then payment. What is important here is to recognise that Departments A, B and C are involved in the process. They need to understand that. They need to recognise that this 'bigger process' exists and that they are a part of the process chain.

All too often, departments are working in a vacuum, unaware of this bigger picture and their role within it, either as a customer, supplier, or both.

In the example, Department A is a supplier and Department C is a customer. Department B is both a customer and a supplier at different points in the process flow. Understanding the process flow is a vital element in process improvement and in determining what needs to be measured.

2.4 Understanding the process

2.4.1 Customer requirements

Processes should be 'adding value' for the customer and should be seeking to meet the customer's requirements. All too often, processes don't have a clear, customer-focussed objective that is understood by the various parties involved in the process. One of the first steps in process design, therefore, should be to ensure an agreed objective for the process that Departments A, B, and C should be working together to achieve.

This will help ensure some hope of meeting the customer's requirements. However, to provide a more realistic chance, it's important to recognise that the process itself has requirements that need to be met. These are shown in *Fig 2.3* and begin with the customer.

In most things it helps if we know what we are trying to produce. So begin with the end in mind by clarifying the customer's requirements and developing an overall objective for the process. Once we know this, we can more easily ensure that Departments A, B, and C can focus their efforts on achieving the end result in the most effective and efficient way by having a common purpose.

The importance of understanding and agreeing requirements cannot be overstated. More often than not, a lack of quality or the need for rework are the direct result of not defining the requirement properly. Even on apparently simple things. A little extra time spent in clarifying requirements will help save time and potential upset later on.

If you don't believe this, ask yourself how often you either hear or say the words, "That's not quite what I meant!"

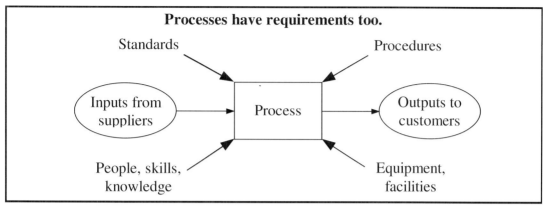

Fig 2.3 *Understanding the requirements of the process.*

2.4.2 Supplier requirements
Once the customer's requirements have been agreed, the next step is to determine your own requirements from suppliers. The same rules apply. Spend time to ensure the requirements are properly understood and agreed.

2.4.3 People, skills and knowledge
Management will need to ensure the right number of people are working in the process, and that they have the necessary knowledge and skills. If they do not, appropriate training needs to be arranged.

2.4.4 Equipment and facilities
Equipment and facilities will be needed to operate the process. These must be appropriate from day one and effectively maintained thereafter, and the working environment must be suitable for the activity. How often have you seen or experienced poor performance resulting from inadequate equipment, or out-of-date software, for example? And how often does this relate to apparently simple issues like having an efficient photocopier?

2.4.5 Procedures
The procedures must be developed, agreed and appropriately documented, and kept up to date. Importantly, they should be simple to follow and understand. Clear English and 'pictures' will help ensure they are used to good effect. Flowcharts are important here.

2.4.6 Standards
Standards will apply and will need to be clearly communicated, too. Like procedures, these should be documented in a way that is easy to understand. Similarly, if there is a budget involved or authority limits on certain actions, then management must ensure that the people in the process know the details and parameters in which to work.

2.5 Company-wide processes
As we mentioned in the previous section, it is important to recognise that processes within a team or department are often part of a much bigger process or system that goes across the company in a series of internal supplier and customer relationships.

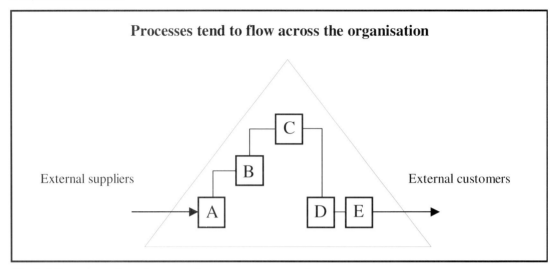

Fig 2.4 *Representation of process flow across an organisation.*

This example suggests that the process looks quite straightforward. It rarely is! The reality is that some systems will look more like a bowl of spaghetti, with a network of interdependent processes, as suggested in *Fig 2.5*.

In many companies, this complexity can be compounded by barriers between the different departments, and the existence of an 'over-the-wall' attitude or a 'them and us' syndrome. Typical symptoms of this will be comments like: "It's all right, it's their problem…they'll sort it out", or when they don't, "Don't they understand how important this is…what are they doing?" *Fig 2.6* illustrates how departments are typically seen as independent units within an organisation.

The problem is that each division or department has its own agenda, its own set of vertical objectives to achieve. The cross-company process or system will not have been considered, and the objectives of the bigger process, to service the customer, will be lost, or will be in conflict with local, vertical priorities.

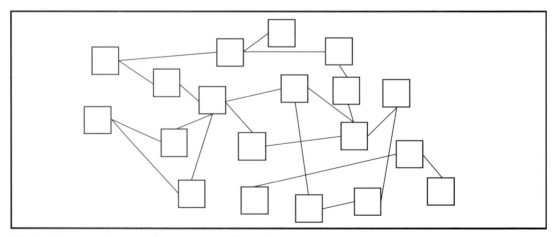

Fig 2.5 *Spaghetti junction is alive and well and living in many organisations.*

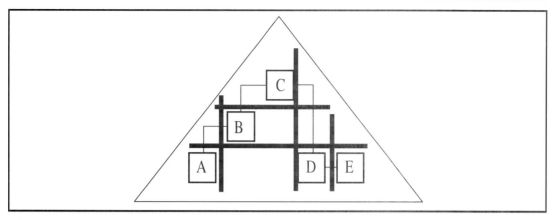

Fig 2.6 *Vertical objectives in conflict with the horizontal process objectives.*

The forgotten customer has to wait patiently, or perhaps not so patiently, outside of the picture. The common language of quality and a culture of continuous improvement can help to remove many of these barriers, though, of course, it is not difficult for people to put them up again. Everyone must play their part to achieve the common purpose.

Meeting the requirements of internal customers is fundamental to the success of a business in meeting the end customers' requirements.

2.6 Mapping and measuring the process

2.6.1 Flowcharts

Seeing the bigger picture becomes easier when you have painted or drawn one. So, if a picture paints a thousand words, then so too does a flowchart! It is simply a picture of the process – a picture that shows the work flow; a map that demonstrates where things are being actioned within that work flow.

It can help you see if a process looks complicated, like the bowl of spaghetti we mentioned. It can highlight the internal and external customer and supplier relationships, or 'process interfaces'. And it can provide a useful framework that prompts questions.

There are a number of different types of flowchart. The majority are quite simple and extremely useful. Others can be more complex, such as where they are being used as a specification for a computer system. And there are lots of different flowchart symbols – over fifty of them. But in the context of the continuous improvement journey, the advice is to keep things simple.

Use just one or two of the flowchart symbols or conventions. It is possible to produce a flowchart using only the 'activity box' but you might prefer to also use the 'diamond' to signify decision points.

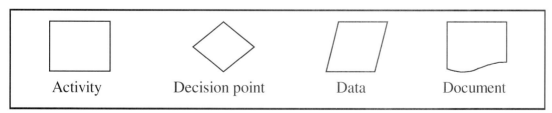

Fig 2.7 *Some commonly-used flow chart symbols.*

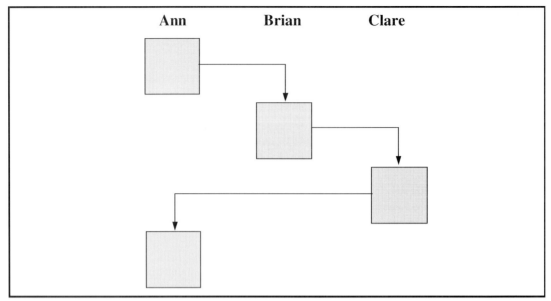

Ann **Brian** **Clare**

Fig 2.8 *A deployment flow-chart.*

In developing a flowchart try to involve all the people who work in the process, and use 'Post-its' – one for each step in the process. Using Post-its makes it very simple to move things around. And almost certainly you will want to, because undoubtedly there will be different perceptions on how the process should work. For existing processes it is also highly likely that the process is being carried out in different ways by different people, even within the same team or department.

In terms of the type of flowchart, use a 'deployment flowchart'.

A deployment-flow chart provides a logical breakdown of a process and the personnel and related activities that are involved at each stage. It is a very effective way of seeing who is involved in the process, and when. And it will make it easier to work out what needs to be measured.

Measurement is a key activity in quality and continuous improvement, but you need to know what to measure and where to do it. A simple example of a deployment flow chart is shown in *Fig 2.8*.

Departments A, B, and C, used in earlier examples, now become Ann, Brian and Clare.

Ann produces something for Brian, and so on. Each time someone else or another area is involved, the chart moves horizontally and down.

When this happens, there is a customer/supplier relationship, and even before we introduce measurement, the flowchart has provided the prompt for a number of questions.

Before asking those questions, the important thing is to recognise and understand the 'whole process' or 'system', and put your questions and ideas for improvement in the context of this bigger picture. One way of really understanding the process and the bigger picture is 'process stapling'.

2.6.2 Process stapling

Carrying out a process stapling exercise with a small team can be an ideal first step in developing or reviewing a flow chart.

Very simply, process stapling means taking a customer order, for example, and literally walking it through the entire process as if it were stapled to you. No matter where it goes, you go too, and in doing so you'll start to see what really happens in the process. Who does what, and why? How do they do it?

Where do they do it and when? You'll spot the frustrations in the process, the inconsistencies and the "Why on earth do we do this?" activities.

2.6.3 Asking questions

It is worth taking stock of how the flowchart not only paints a thousand words, but prompts a thousand questions too.

Rudyard Kipling's 'six honest serving men' provide an effective framework for a series of open questions.

> *I keep six honest serving men*
> *(They taught me all I knew).*
> *Their names are What and Why and When,*
> *And How, and Where and Who.*

Use them all, but particularly "Why?" And ask "Why?" five times, or as often as you need, to get the real answer which lies waiting beyond the initial, often superficial first response.

In order to challenge and improve processes, you should continually question each part of the process. Set out below are some typical questions that will be prompted by a flow-charting exercise. The list is not meant to be comprehensive.

- Who are the customers who have expectations of the process?
- What are their requirements?
- Why is the process done when it is done?
- Why are the tasks in the process carried out in that sequence? Are all the steps in the process really necessary?
- Why does that person or those people carry out the activity?
- What measurement is in place that will help assess performance and identify possible improvement opportunities? Think in particular of how you might identify and measure those parts of the process output that meet customer requirements.

Whichever questions you ask, try to make sure they are really the right questions. All too often, people have forgotten why something is done the way it is. And all too often, the reasons are no longer relevant! But nothing will change if the right questions are not asked.

2.6.4 Adding Value

In looking at the deployment flowchart, you're also likely to ask questions about whether the various process steps add value. There are 3 broad rules:

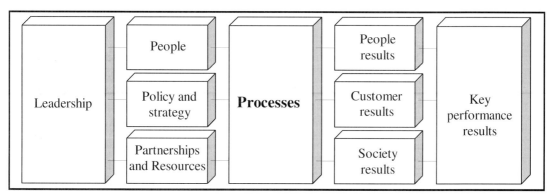

Fig 2.9 The EFQM's Excellence model.

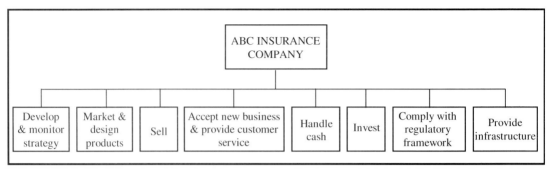

Fig 2.10 Possible key processes for an insurance company.

- The customer is interested in this step. In other words, the customers would be prepared to pay for it, if they knew about it.
- The step must either change the product or service in some way, or be an essential pre-requisite.
- The step must be actioned 'right first time'.

If the steps do not add value, then look seriously at how you can remove them.

2.7 Processes and Business Excellence

'Processes' is one of the nine criteria in the European Foundation for Quality Management's Excellence Model, shown in *Fig 2.9*.

The guidelines for self-assessment identify that "amongst the processes there will be those which are critical to the success of the business. These processes, which must be identified, will often cut across departmental and functional boundaries and will require particular attention."

These key processes are fundamental to the success of an organisation and should reflect the 'value chain' that's operating across it. Key processes provide the high level picture of an organisation and cut across functional boundaries. An example based on an insurance company is set out in *Fig 2.10*.

This model represents the value chain operating in the organisation, as shown in *Fig 2.11*.

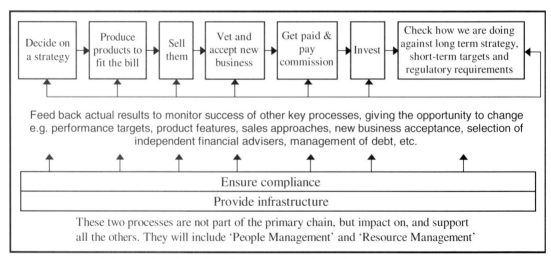

Fig 2.11 The model reflecting the value chain operating in an insurance company.

The generic framework of key operating and support processes shown in *Fig 2.12* was developed by the American Quality and Productivity Centre.

The key processes should be focused on the customers and each key process needs a clear objective, critical success factors (CSFs), and key performance indicators (KPIs). We will look at these in a little more detail in Chapter 3, but in simple terms CSFs are the activities an organisation must do well to be successful. KPIs are the measures that help an organisation assess how well they are performing the activities that they must do well.

These CSFs and KPIs should 'drill down' into an organisation through the many primary, secondary and tertiary sub-processes that exist under the umbrella of the vital few key processes, as shown in *Fig 2.13 (overleaf)*. The top section of the diagram shows six key processes corresponding to the operating processes identified in *Fig 2.12*. We will concentrate on 'invoice and service customers' as a key process, for which the primary processes might be 'invoice the customer', 'provide after sales service' and 'respond to customer enquiries'. The secondary processes for this last primary process could be 'respond to information requests' and 'manage customer complaints'.

Eventually, the key processes lead to the nitty-gritty step-by-step procedures of an organisation. If

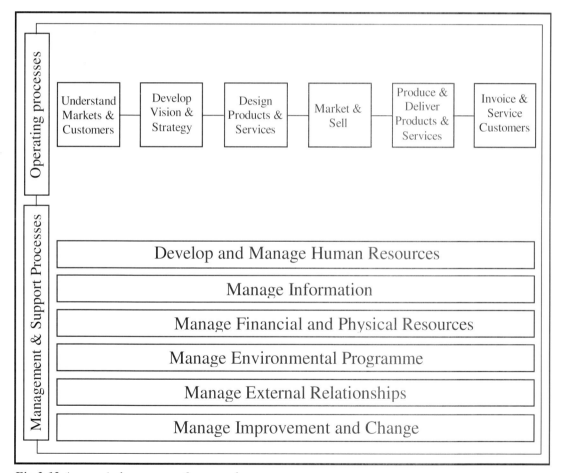

Fig 2.12 A generic key process framework.

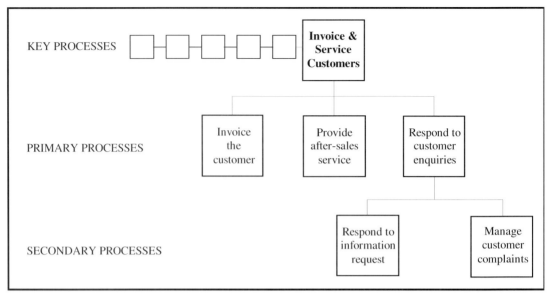

Fig 2.13 *Drilling down the sub-processes.*

the objectives, CSF's and KPI's have been effectively deployed, there will be a clear customer focus that ensures the organisation is working together and pointing in the same direction.

It is easy to get submerged in the detail relating the EFQM model, or any other. In the last couple of sections a lot of information has been provided relating to flowcharts and processes. The main reason for doing this is to make sure we really understand the process we are looking at. Once we have the process clarified, it opens up opportunities for measurement. For example, looking at the primary and secondary processes identified in *Fig 2.13*, we can ask:

- How long does it take to invoice this customer?
- How quickly can we provide after sales service?
- What is the response time for customer enquiries, requests for information and complaints?
- Were there any errors in carrying out these activities?
- Why was an after sales service requested?
- What is the pattern of customer enquiries?
- What type of complaints, and how many?

The need to define processes leads logically to the requirement to measure them, and hence the relevance of control charts. Much of the material on charts, which follows in further chapters, relates neatly to the detail covered in this chapter.

2.8 Summary of symbols and formulae

4M's   Manpower, machines, method, material
CSF   Critical success factor
KPI   Key performance indicator

2.9 Key points and summary

- Every activity is a process.
- Remember that the next person in the chain is a customer.

- We could be both a customer and a supplier.
- We need to understand the customer requirements.
- Suppliers also have requirements, which need to be met.
- Processes are typically company-wide.
- Eliminate barriers between people, sections and departments.
- Use flowcharts to track the process.
- Post-It notes can help in defining a process.
- A deployment flowchart is particularly useful.
- Track the process using process stapling.
- Ask "Why?" five times.
- The EFQM's Excellence Model refers to 'processes' as a key building block.
- Key, primary and secondary processes open up the detail of the organisation.
- Control charts are the only real way of measuring the process.

The idea of processes has been introduced, and CSFs, KPIs and measurement have also been referred to in this chapter.

More detail on these is also provided in the next chapter, within the framework of knowing what needs to be measured in the process.

THE PROCESS AND THE CUSTOMER

3.1 Introduction

In this chapter we develop some of the ideas introduced in Chapter 2 and introduce others which have to do with the relationship between the process and the customer.

More detail on the deployment flow chart appears in Section 3.2. A simple, yet very effective tool in collecting data is the check-sheet and Section 3.3 covers this. In the same section there is an explanation of the importance of the Pareto principle, and how it ties in nicely with the multiple characteristics chart. If we are to get to the detail of the process, then the latter has to be split into appropriate elements that are then measured. Again, the deployment flow chart can help, as shown in Section 3.4. There is a reminder of the importance of asking the right questions before relating Critical Success Factors (CSFs) and Key Performance Indicators (KPIs) to the control chart in Section 3.6. Section 3.7 refers to the Balanced Business Scorecard and the need for a balanced set of measures. Perhaps the most important part of the chapter comes in Section 3.8, where we discuss Service Level Agreements and targets. Finally, in Section 3.9, we show how data from a control chart enables us to make more sensible judgements on our processes.

3.2 The deployment flowchart

In Chapter 2 we identified that measurement is a critical requirement of continuous improvement. It was emphasised that in order to carry this out we would need information on 'what' to measure, 'where' the measurement was to take place and 'when' we were going to do it. We could also add that we should know 'how' we were going to measure, and 'who' does the measuring.

The deployment flowchart we started in Chapter 2, shown in *Fig 2.8*, provides a simple example of how this can be done and how the emerging data provides the prompts for improvement.

Fig 3.1 shows *Fig 2.8* with some additional information. This highlights the 'process interfaces' and the various customer/supplier relationships.

It's so important to ensure requirements are clearly agreed and understood at the interface between customers and suppliers because it is here that things tend to go wrong.

So, Ann and Brian, Brian and Clare and Clare and Ann all have customer supplier relationships, but are their various requirements clear and how well are they being met?

And what is it that Brian needs from Ann? When and where does he need it? The requirements can be expressed simply. For example, I need 'this form', with boxes one to five correctly completed, in my office by 10.30 each working day.

Once these requirements have been agreed, measurement can help us identify performance and opportunities for improvement. We need to know whether the forms are arriving in the office by 10.30 each day and if boxes one to five are being correctly completed. The only effective way of doing this is by collecting the data and using a control chart.

Whatever you do, measure in order to help improvement. Don't measure for measurement's sake.

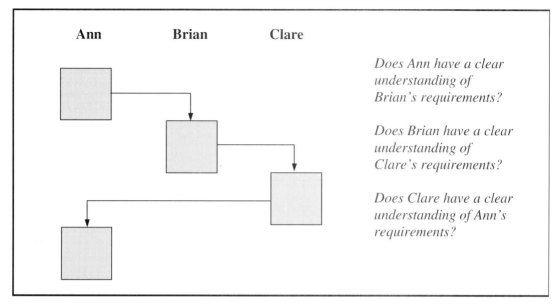

Ann   Brian   Clare

Does Ann have a clear understanding of Brian's requirements?

Does Brian have a clear understanding of Clare's requirements?

Does Clare have a clear understanding of Ann's requirements?

Fig 3.1 *A deployment flowchart showing customer-supplier relationships.*

And remember you're measuring to find out what has gone wrong with the process, not who caused the problem.

So, if the requirements are not being met each time, it would be sensible to find out what is going wrong by measuring the process in some way.

3.3 The check sheet

A complete chapter – Chapter 5 – is devoted to the detail involved with the measurement of a process and the statistical tools which are required. All we do here is to introduce the topic, and make the point that measurement is quite likely to be as simple as using a check sheet, recording 'five bar gate' style the number of times 'something' occurs over time. See also Section 5.3 in Chapter 5 for more information.

For example, one or more of the requirements specified in *Fig 3.1* may involve a document, and a measure of how the requirement is being satisfied is the level of errors of different types in the documents. The document may be an order form, a new business application, whatever.

Fig 3.2 (overleaf) shows how the error types are classified, and how many times these different errors occur.

Collecting and recording the data in this way helps us to begin to understand why the forms are incorrect. It provides the basis of a particularly useful type of control chart known as the multiple characteristics chart. The whole of Chapter 12 is allocated to this chart, and you can find all the detail you want there. However, there is benefit in bringing out some of the important features of the chart at this point.

For a start, by adding up the number of errors by type, we can construct a simple Pareto chart. Pareto was the Italian economist who observed the 80:20 rule i.e. in a general sense, 20% of the issues cause 80% of the effect.

This 80:20 relationship will not always be exact, and that is why it may be preferable to use the interpretation defined by Juran. He referred to "a vital few and a trivial many". In other words it's likely there will be a 'vital few' issues causing 'most' of the problem(s). In our example, we can see that 20% of the error types are causing not far short of 80% of the total errors.

No.	Characteristic	Week 1 M	T	W	T	F	Week 2 M	T	W	T	F	Total	%
		NO. OF ERRORS											
1	Form not signed	//	/			/		/	/				7	8.3
2	No part no.	/			//	/	/	//					7	8.3
3	Address missing	ЖНТ //		///	//	///	////	///	ЖНТ	///		///	33	39.4
4	No cheque	/			/	/	/		/	/	/		8	9.5
5	Wrong amount	///	/////	/	///	/	//	///	///	////	ЖНТ		29	34.5
	Total no. of errors	12	7	7	8	6	9	8	9	8	10	84	100
	Total no. of forms	24	20	21	18	18	24	16	20	14	22	197	
	Proportion	0.50	0.35	0.33	0.44	0.33	0.38	0.50	0.45	0.57	0.45	0.43	

Fig 3.2 Data collection sheet for recording errors in a document.

The Pareto diagram based on these error rates is shown in *Fig 3.3*.

The Pareto diagram presents and ranks data in order, showing those factors which occur most frequently. In this example, using the data from the check sheet we can easily see the two main errors that need to be addressed.

A second advantage to be gained from the layout of *Fig 3.2* is the variation in the proportion figures. A control chart can be created to track this information, and the multiple characteristics chart incorporates this in the layout.

3.4 Measuring the detail

Measurement can also help us identify other improvement opportunities in the process, particularly in terms of 'unit' and 'cycle' time. It is probably helpful to start by looking at how long each part of the process takes. It isn't necessary to use a stop watch to do this, certainly in the early stages, nor is it necessary to pretend that 'Billy Whiz' is doing the work. We simply need a reasonable picture of how long these activities usually take to complete.

This is where we revert to our deployment flow chart, using the basic layout provided in *Fig 2.8*.

In *Fig 3.4* the unit times for each stage of the process have been recorded.

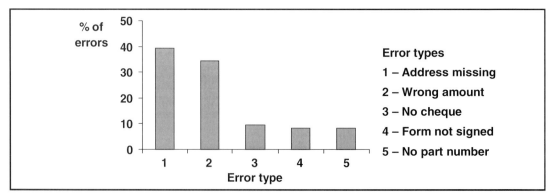

Fig 3.3 Pareto diagram for errors in a document.

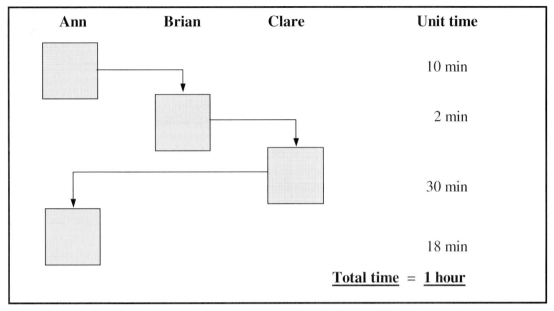

Fig 3.4 Deployment flowchart showing unit times.

This information could be very helpful in determining staffing requirements and might also prompt a number of questions about how long each step takes and "Why?" But our understanding of the process will increase significantly by building in the 'cycle time', i.e. the cumulative time required to achieve each stage of the process. This can help us identify bottlenecks and 'dead time'.

Fig 3.5 shows the cycle times added to the deployment flow chart.

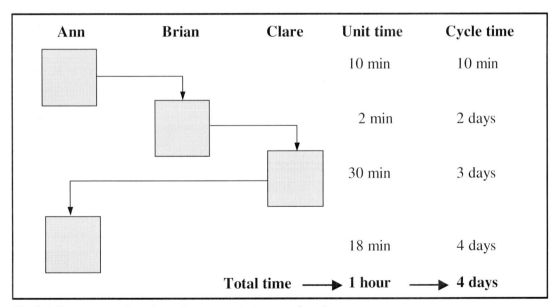

Fig 3.5 Deployment flowchart showing unit times and cycle times.

Quite simply, the difference between the unit and cycle times is dead time as far as the customer is concerned. Dead times reflect the bottlenecks in the process that need to be removed or at least reduced. It could well be, however, that you can do nothing about them. They might simply be the consequence of overnight computer batch runs, for example, and the implementation of an on-line system may not be practical.

At the beginning of this section we stated that in the early stage of process analysis it is adequate to provide a reasonable estimate of the unit time i.e. there is no need to be considering stop watches. Nevertheless, as we become more scientific in our approach to measurement, then we will need to get more accurate readings based on a series of documents. This is the step to using a control chart. As we get into the detail of the process, then there is no alternative but to use SPC to measure it. Some excellent examples are available showing how organisations have analysed cycle times for the successive parts of an ordering process.

Returning to our example, as things stand at present the cycle time could be halved if Brian's work could be actioned immediately in some way. The deployment flow chart has led to the use of data which in turn prompts some questions.

3.5 Asking the right questions

In Chapter 2, we looked at the importance of questions. How can we take Brian out of the process? Could Ann or Clare do that work? Is it possible to sequence the steps differently and find savings that way?

In particular there is a need to keep asking "Why?" In our example involving Ann, Brian and Clare, we might ask, "Why is Brian involved in the process?" The answer might be "Because only Brian is authorised by the Board to do this work".

That may well be so, and it could be you accept that as a reason not to change the process. But "Why is Brian the only person authorised by the Board to do this work?" Perhaps the Board have not been asked to approve the addition of other people. Perhaps the Board no longer need to be involved in granting the authority. Perhaps the step itself is no longer necessary, especially if it adds no value.

Asking the right question and measuring the right things go together as part of the improvement process.

Our deployment flowchart provides some examples of what might be measured. It really is worth considering what should be measured; and worth reflecting on the broadly true statement that "You get what you measure". Perhaps the step itself is no longer necessary, especially if it adds no value.

So, for example, if you measure how quickly something is produced and sent out to the customer, it's likely that speed or 'turn-round time' will be seen as the important thing, possibly at the expense of quality and getting it right. You will probably need to measure both these things. Deciding what to

CSF	KPI	CONTROL CHART
Produce policy documents that are 100% accurate	No. or % of documents containing errors	No. or % of documents in error
		No. or % of errors in documents
		Error types
Issue policy documents to the customer within 5 days	No. or % of documents issued within 5 days	Time taken for document to be processed
		No or % of documents issued within 5 days
		Reasons why documents are delayed
Ensure customers understand policy documents	No. or % of customers complaining that they do not understand their policy documents	No. or proportion of customers complaining
		No. or proportion of customer complaints
		Types of complaint
Ensure the monthly premiums are collected on time	No. or % of premiums collected on time	Time taken for premium to be paid
		No. or proportion of premiums late

Fig 3.6 Table showing the relationship between CSFs, KPIs and control chart measures.

measure becomes easier if we return to the starting point for a process.

What is the objective of the process and what are the customer's requirements?

The answers to these questions can help us determine the Critical Success Factors referred to in Chapter 2.

3.6 CSFs and KPIs

As we said, CSFs are simply the things that need to be done well in order to meet the objectives of the process and the requirements of the customer. There are no rules for how many there should be, but typically there are not likely to be more than five or six.

For each CSF there should be a measure, or Key Performance Indicator (KPI). So what are the things we need to do well, and how will we know how well we are doing them? How do control charts relate to CSFs and KPIs?

Fig 3.6 makes use of examples from a new business process of an insurance company. It shows some CSFs, possible KPIs that go with them, and the associated control charts that should follow.

More and more organisations are recognising the benefits of using business models, such as the EFQM's Excellence Model described in Chapter 2. They are increasingly using metrics and key performance indicators. However, few seem to have made the vital link with the control chart.

3.7 The Balanced Business Scorecard

In many ways the range of measures highlighted by the Excellence Model form the basis for an organisation's 'Balanced Business Scorecard'.

This concept, developed by Robert Kaplan and David Norton, looks to supplement traditional financial measures with criteria measuring performance from three additional perspectives. These cover those of the customers, the internal business processes, and learning and growth. *Fig 3.7* sets out the four quadrants, demonstrating the fit with the Excellence Model.

It's outside the scope of this book to go into any more detail on the Balanced Business Scorecard, but it is essential to be aware of the need for the right balance of measures in any organisation. It is also

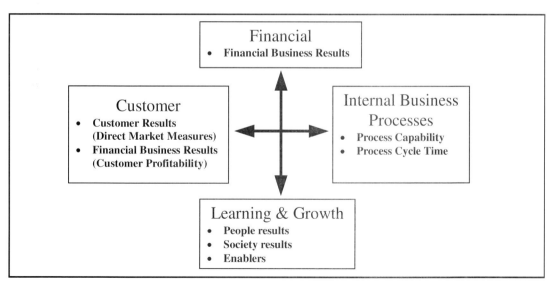

Fig 3.7 Getting the right balance – a view of the Balanced Business Scorecard.

worth noting that whatever the business model there is a repeated reference to the importance of measuring the process and assessing the customer's demands.

We have allocated a fair amount of space to discussing processes and systems based on them. We have rightly emphasised that in any situation we need to assess the process first before we can adequately decide how we can satisfy any customer requirements. However, the customer does have requirements which we are expected to meet.

The detail of customer requirements has not yet been discussed, and it is appropriate to do so now.

How are various customer requirements specified? Generally, by using service level agreements and targets.

3.8 Customer requirements

3.8.1 Service level agreements

Service level agreements of one form or another provide a typical operational target for suppliers, both internal and external. *Fig 3.8* shows a listing of typical service level agreements (SLAs) which are commonly seen.

SLAs are typically department or team based. The customer specifies a numerical figure that must be satisfied by the supplier. In office-based areas the SLA is typically measured in terms of time.

Most SLAs are one sided. For example, there is an upper limit on the time taken to respond to a customer. Alternatively, there may be a lower limit on the number of documents dealt with each day. Take care, though, because we can have two-sided SLAs, as in the last example in *Fig 3.8.*

3.8.2 Targets

Targets are also widely used. In a sense they are the same as SLAs except that whereas SLAs are group based, targets often relate more to individuals.

Fig 3.9 shows a list of typical targets that have been imposed on operational staff in office areas.

The same principle holds as for SLAs. Targets may involve a lower minimum value that has to be achieved, or a maximum upper level that should not be exceeded.

PROCESS	SERVICE LEVEL AGREEMENT
Putting orders through the system	Within 1 day
Time to deliver new PC's	Within 30 days
Provide a quotation	Within 3 days
Handle items of correspondence	No less than 35 a week
Ship to customer	Within 3 days on either side of target delivery date
Provide a Board report	By the 1st Thursday of each month
Deliver stationery	Within 28 days
Handle customer telephone enquiries	No less than 20 an hour
Provide a quotation	Within 2 days
Reply to correspondence	Within 15 days of receipt
Ship to customer	Within 3 days on either side of target delivery date

Fig 3.8 Some typical Service Level Agreements.

PROCESS	TARGET
Answer a telephone	Within 3 rings
Call on customers	At least 6 a day
Deal with items of correspondence	At least 25 a week
Provide a quotation	Within 3 days
Repair an electrical item	Within 5 days
Carry out research	Publish 5 papers a year

Fig 3.9 *Some typical individual targets.*

3.8.3 Choice of SLA and target

How do you think these numerical values, whether SLAs or targets, were determined? Was previous experience of the process involved used to specify the figure?

Very unlikely, because few organisations are anywhere near using process measures, based on control charts, as a valid means of determining how they can perform against customer requirements.

Are there laid down standards that can be referred to?

No, not in the main in the service field. Even if there were national and/or international standards on SLAs and targets, the basis on how these figures were obtained could be questioned.

Does the organisation concerned have a pool of highly qualified staff, whose responsibility it is to use scientific approaches to determine appropriate numerical values for SLAs and targets?

Highly unlikely.

So how are these various numerical values for SLAs and targets determined?

A caustic answer would be – "You tell me."

It is difficult to see how these numerical targets have been set other than by a combination of some sixth sense, a gut feel for what the figure should be and a knowledge of what other companies are doing.

Without an adequate knowledge of how our processes are performing, based on a proven scientific approach such as a control chart, there is no way we can respond to targets set by our customers without resorting to fire-fighting. Deming's response to any target was: "Ask by what method?" – highlighting his distaste of arbitrary targets.

NO	PROCESS	SERVICE LEVEL AGREEMENT	MEAN PERFORMANCE MEASURE
1	Putting orders through the system	Within 1 day	2 days
2	Time to deliver new PC's	Within 30 days	21.3 days
3	Provide a quotation	Within 3 days	1.5 days
4	Handle items of correspondence	No less than 35 a week	22 items
5	Enter bill of contract	Within 1 day	3 hours
6	Provide a Board report	By the 1st Thursday of each month	Achieved
7	Deliver stationery	Within 28 days	20 days
8	Handle customer telephone enquiries	No less than 20 an hour	15 an hour
9	Provide a quotation	Within 2 days	1 day
10	Reply to correspondence	Within 15 days of receipt	17 days

Fig 3.10 *A comparison of customer requirements and process measures.*

NO.	PROCESS	COMMENT
1	Putting orders through the system	Deep trouble, because the mean is above the SLA
2	Time to deliver new PC's	Could be O.K. but cannot be certain
3	Provide a quotation	Could be O.K. but cannot be certain
4	Handle items of correspondence	No chance of satisfying the SLA
5	Enter bill of contract	Possibly O.K. but need to investigate further
6	Provide a Board report	Acceptable, because all reports were done by 1st of month
7	Deliver stationery	Doubtful if SLA can be consistently achieved
8	Handle customer telephone enquiries	Unlikely to satisfy SLA
9	Provide a quotation	May be O.K. but needs more data
10	Reply to correspondence	No hope of satisfying the SLA

Fig 3.11 *Summary of comments on how processes are satisfying customer requirements.*

Of course, where the external customer has clearly described their prioritised requirements, you have to meet them. It's a question of comparing the voice of the customer to the voice of the process, finding the gap, and finding a way to fill it. Chapters 15 and 16 should help you here.

3.9 Comparison with reality

The problem of setting up arbitrary SLAs and targets without knowledge of process performance is highlighted by looking at the figures shown in *Fig 3.10.*

In this case we have used figures based on service level agreements, but we could equally well have used similar figures based on targets.

Let's look at some of these figures in a bit more detail because they are at the heart of what we are trying to do in this book.

First of all, what do we understand by a 'mean performance measure'?

A mean value is a type of average – a single figure which can be taken as representative of the process. It is based on actual readings from the process, unlike the service level agreement. Detail on how to calculate the mean appears in Section 5.7.2

Fig 3.11 provides a summary of relevant comments relating to the various processes identified in *Fig 3.10.*

As can be seen, there is often little agreement between the SLA and a typical representative figure from the process. This should come as no surprise, bearing in mind how the vast majority of SLAs have been determined.

In some cases it is not difficult to see that there is a problem. For example there is an immediate problem with processes 1,4, 8 and 10 because in each case the process mean is outside the SLA. In the remaining cases, apart from process 6, the process mean satisfies the SLA, but that does not necessarily suggest that all is well. It is quite possible for items to exceed the SLA. We don't know until we have developed a control chart and obtained the value of the upper control limit UCL. What's more, the mean may be disguising wide variation in the individual cases.

Understanding what is meant by a control limit is vital to SPC. This is covered in much detail in Chapter 6, and referred to at different times in other chapters.

The ability of our processes to match our customer's requirement is defined in terms of the capability of the process.

For example, we specify to our supplier that deliveries must be made within 21 working days of the receipt of order. If the natural variation of the delivery times results in a UCL of 25 days, then there is

---

ISO9001 AND SPC

4.20 Statistical techniques

4.20.1   *Identification of need*

The supplier shall establish the need for statistical techniques required for establishing, controlling and verifying process capability and product characteristics

4.20.2   *Procedures*

The supplier shall establish and maintain documented procedures to implement and control the application of the statistical techniques identified in 4.20.1

Fig 3.12 *Section of ISO 9001 which refers indirectly to SPC.*

no chance that we can satisfy the customer's requirement.

It is possible to define numerical indices to represent capability, i.e. how we are performing against our customer requirements. Detail on this appears in Chapter 14 where you will be taken through how to calculate capability indices.

3.10 Other issues

It is right that in this book we make references as appropriate to quality/Business Excellence systems and models, particularly those that emphasise the relationship between processes, customers and measurement.

But keep things in perspective. Watch that you don't get sidetracked into developing comprehensive documents that become a bureaucratic nightmare.

Some standards are very weak on processes and statistical measurement. For example, *Fig 3.12* shows what ISO 9001 currently has to say about the subject.

It isn't much. It's sad that a major international standard on quality devotes only some five lines to a topic that has been crucial to the development of Japanese trade since the last war. Is it any wonder that there has been a lot of debate regarding the real benefit of acquiring ISO 9000 recognition?

Thankfully, it now appears that future ISO requirements in the quality improvement field are changing. Documentation alone is not the best approach, and in future there is to be a much greater emphasis on processes, and all that implies.

3.11 Summary of symbols and formulae

80/20 Numerical interpretation of the Pareto principle.

3.12 Key points and summary

- Use a deployment flowchart to highlight process interfaces.
- Make sure customer/supplier relationships are clearly defined.
- Don't measure for the sake of measuring.
- The check sheet provides a simple method of recording data.
- A multiple characteristics chart is an extended form of check sheet.
- The Pareto principle can be used in conjunction with a check sheet.

- Keep the measurement simple to start with.
- Use a deployment flowchart to record unit times and cycle times and hence determine dead time.
- At a later stage you may need to measure each element of the process.
- Ask the right questions.
- CSFs and KPIs should naturally be associated with appropriate control charts.
- The Balanced Business Scorecard supplements financial measures with performance measures in non-financial areas.
- SLAs and targets are no substitute for actual process measures.
- The origins of typical SLAs are very much open to question.
- Control charts related to SLAs and targets enable a true assessment of process performance to be made.
- Capability is concerned with the ability of a process to satisfy customer requirements.

Various graphical representations have been used in this chapter to illustrate different aspects of process performance.

Sources of data, and the way we represent them, form a topic in itself. In Chapter 4 some of the existing methods of representing the many varied types of data are described. This leads to the need to look at preferred methods based on the use of a control chart.

GETTING THE MEASURE OF PROCESSES

4.1 Introduction

This chapter deals with the measurement of processes as it is generally understood i.e. the analysis of tables, bar charts and other representations which are intended to help us in making decisions.

Section 4.2 provides a short reminder on how we should approach the issue of measurement. Some established sources of measurement are discussed in Section 4.3, and in Section 4.4 we consider some of the traditional methods of representing this information. There are arrays of these, some useful, some less so.

Section 4.5 discusses some of the limitations of these approaches, and highlights the problem of using control charts in an environment that does not understand them.

4.2 Measurement

As with so many things, "begin with the end in mind". So, before you begin measuring this, that and the other, consider these simple questions:

1. What's the purpose of this measurement?'
2. What do you plan to do with the data?
3. How will you present it?
4. How will you interpret the data and take decisions?

Questions 1 to 3 seem straightforward enough, but your ability to interpret the data properly will be determined by how you present it. And if your ability to interpret the data is impaired or undermined, then your answers to the first three questions seem irrelevant!

4.3 Traditional sources of information

Traditionally, data has been kept on paper-based systems. Records of different types have been retained over the months, providing a potentially rich source for making effective decisions on process performance. Let's be honest, that's not what usually happens. Data has often been stored for purely defensive reasons, associated with a mixture of inspection, validation and traceability.

The growing availability and use of computers of different types has provided a better means of handling data. A simplistic, possibly naïve view suggests that we can now make better decisions because we have the ability to generate more data, more quickly. This may not be the case.

4.3.1 Manual records

Manual records of different types abound, hidden in files, ring binders and wallets. Folders crammed with figures. There is no shortage of data, even though it may not be information. Typically this data is in purely numerical form. We are all familiar with it. Hand-written records of customer complaints, tables of weekly error rates in documents, possibly some data on the number of deliveries early or late.

SPC training courses should prompt attendees to develop their newly-learned technique by applying it to their own office processes. In doing so they often make use of the historical data that is available.

There is no problem with this. However, questions are asked regarding the validity and usefulness of the data. Why was all this data kept? What has been done with it? How accurate is it? Why have records been kept on features that are now seen to be unimportant, and yet relevant data is not available?

4.3.2 Computer-based records

Modern computers of all types provide us with the power to collect more data then ever before, handle it in different ways and present it in a variety of formats.

Unfortunately, too few organisations recognise that just generating masses of numbers is of no help. This is an on-going theme in this book, and a source of concern to those who are trying to get decisions made in a different way. More and more data blocks, either as paper copies or directly via the Internet, or Intranet, find their way onto the desks of decision-makers at all levels.

With an array of graphics packages available, why not at least try presenting the data in a more visual form? It might not be the final answer, but at least it's a start.

Let's first look at the ways that organisations typically represent data.

4.4 Traditional methods of representation

Most organisations present their data simply as a mass of numbers. The data is generally available in two formats.

In the first case, data is limited and typically involves the comparison of one number with another. A profit and loss statement, as a summary of the performance of a company, is a good example, shown typically in *Fig 4.1*.

How can you interpret data like this and take sound decisions? In reality you can't but there are plenty of managers who think they can. It's easy! Their trick is to look at 'this number' and compare it with 'that number', or the equivalent number from last year, or last quarter. In doing so they will demand to know why the numbers are different. What's causing the improvement or fall in performance? Why aren't we hitting the forecast figure? And so on.

Unfortunately, these questions will be answered with apparent conviction and confidence, and decisions will be made on the comparisons of two numbers. Decisions that take no account of variation. Actions, or reactions, that lead to tampering. Managers will mistake natural variation as

PROFIT AND LOSS					
REF. NO.	ITEM	PREVIOUS MONTH (June)		CURRENT MONTH (July)	
		FORECAST	ACTUAL	FORECAST	ACTUAL
001	Sales – Domestic	565	617	570	563
002	Sales – Export	125	103	130	129
003	Gross sales	690	720	700	692
004	Allowed discounts				
005	Net sales	690	720	700	692
006	Finished goods	270	280	270	265
007	Raw materials	35	34	35	35
008	Packaging	79	72	81	83
009	Wages and salaries	120	124	120	121

Fig 4.1 *Section from a typical profit and loss statement.*

Country	Forecast	1997		1998												1999		Year
		Nov	Dec	Jan	Feb	Mar	Apr	May	Jun	Jul	Aug	Sep	Oct	Nov	Dec	Jan	Feb	to date
Austria	2.10	2.13	2.20	1.93	2.21	2.28	2.28	1.97	1.93	2.02	2.31	2.45	2.40	2.19	1.96	2.18	2.22	2.18
Belgium	2.20	2.29	2.42	2.45	2.60	2.37	2.40	2.49	2.53	2.46	2.70	2.77	2.82	2.65	2.38	2.56	2.44	2.53
Denmark	2.10	1.76	1.77	1.87	1.92	1.86	1.97	1.93	2.00	2.38	2.15	1.85	1.75	1.86	1.97	1.85	1.95	1.93
East	1.50	2.41	1.55	1.44	1.50	1.82	2.72	2.09	1.93	1.92	1.54	1.46	1.85	1.65	1.54	1.60	1.72	1.85
Finland	2.50	2.26	2.33	2.17	2.27	2.15	2.54	2.40	2.57	3.22	2.81	2.41	2.34	2.56	2.87	2.65	2.54	2.46
France	2.60	2.48	2.41	2.38	2.33	2.39	2.45	2.59	2.68	2.65	3.08	3.21	2.95	2.76	2.64	2.87	2.81	2.63
Germany	2.40	2.39	2.54	2.39	2.44	2.37	2.51	2.43	2.71	2.84	2.96	2.91	2.63	2.44	2.64	2.57	2.64	2.59
Greece	3.00	2.73	2.92	2.98	3.25	2.83	2.99	2.84	3.14	3.53	4.08	3.34	2.67	2.87	2.94	2.85	2.88	3.11
Gulf	1.30	0.80	0.92	0.95	1.08	0.96	0.89	0.76	0.75	1.42	2.39	1.33	1.18	1.33	1.22	0.87	1.03	1.12
Ireland	3.10	2.83	3.36	3.12	3.23	2.96	3.24	3.34	3.42	3.03	2.80	2.68	2.61	2.76	2.88	2.56	2.89	3.05
Italy	2.90	2.85	2.86	2.81	2.82	2.72	2.74	2.66	2.68	2.64	3.30	3.61	3.36	3.22	3.16	3.18	3.32	2.92
Netherlands	2.40	2.19	2.32	2.16	2.38	2.31	2.49	2.47	2.43	2.84	2.95	2.54	2.04	2.32	2.17	2.21	2.39	2.43
Norway	2.70	2.44	2.53	2.35	2.39	2.47	2.58	2.73	2.79	3.32	2.85	2.80	2.33	2.17	2.38	2.65	2.56	2.63
Portugal	3.00	2.53	2.65	2.66	2.68	2.67	3.28	3.41	3.60	3.55	3.92	3.52	2.88	2.65	2.87	2.65	2.44	3.11
Spain	2.10	2.38	2.47	2.35	2.53	2.26	2.48	2.45	2.64	2.80	3.30	3.24	3.34	3.28	3.46	3.24	3.41	2.68
Sweden	2.30	1.93	1.81	1.82	1.98	2.19	2.32	2.21	2.18	2.62	2.60	2.57	2.31	2.44	2.39	2.28	2.19	2.21
Switzerland	2.50	2.15	2.24	2.01	2.33	2.17	2.16	2.11	2.26	2.46	2.79	2.72	2.68	2.54	2.85	2.46	2.55	2.34
Turkey	1.60	1.56	1.27	1.06	0.83	1.18	1.13	1.39	1.48	1.39	2.14	1.65	1.66	1.87	1.54	1.65	1.54	1.40
U.K.	2.40	2.44	2.46	2.48	2.82	2.45	2.32	2.20	2.32	2.45	2.56	2.52	2.33	2.56	2.33	2.45	2.49	2.45

Fig 4.2 Table of inventory figures for different plant locations.

special causes; indeed each and every data item will be seen as significant.

Providing more data in a similar column and row format is no help. A mass of numbers, as shown in *Fig 4.2*, makes it no easier to actually see what is happening.

In this case the data relates to inventory levels for a large multinational. Without knowledge of variation, the senior executive responsible for making decisions based on this data knows no better than to use either gut feel, or some sixth sense, in order to come to a conclusion.

Do you really believe that sense can be made of this numerical grid? Senior executives in too many organisations work on numbers in this format and then pronounce with authority what they believe the information is telling them. "Show me the figures" is too often the cry.

As a result, changes will be made on the run, people will be moved here and there and management will feel they're taking decisive and effective action. Unfortunately, the cause and effect implications in other parts of the process, or other areas of the organisation, won't be seen, as fire fighting creates its own smoke screen.

This will also happen when the data is presented pictorially. Charts of various kinds are available to assist in making better decisions. Whether they really do so is a matter of debate. Only a control chart can show you the actual variation involved.

At least a picture is better than rows and columns of numbers, so let's have a look at some of the standard graphical techniques which are available.

In doing so, it is relevant to comment on how effective is the method of representation in enabling the decision-maker to make the correct judgement on what is actually happening.

4.4.1 Bar charts

Bar charts of different forms are often used when there is data available over time. Typically, we have data indicating some types of performance over the days, weeks or months. Have a look around the

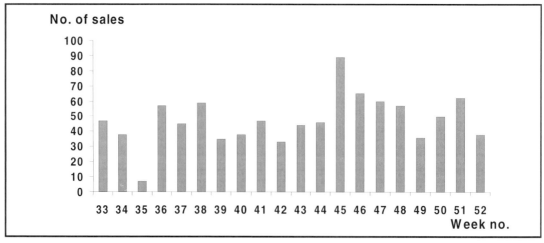

Fig 4.3 *Bar chart of sales figures over a period of weeks.*

office walls of almost any organisation and you will find some varieties of a bar chart. Do you understand them? Do people take action on what the bar charts seem to tell them? Are the bar charts continually updated?

Let's start with a simple example – the representation of sales over a period of months. Nowadays these results would typically be shown in the form of a bar chart as in *Fig 4.3*.

It is some consolation that this representation is a step up from a table of numbers, but does it really make it any easier to detect real changes? What about the sales for week no. 35? Are we sure that we had a really poor month? Would you be pleased about the performance for week no. 45?

Current software packages allow for much flexibility in representing data pictorially.

For example, *Fig 4.4* shows how bar charts can be used to compare the performance of two or more different areas, or organisations, in their performance in relation to three different products.

The figure shows a nice graphical representation, but what information can you really glean from

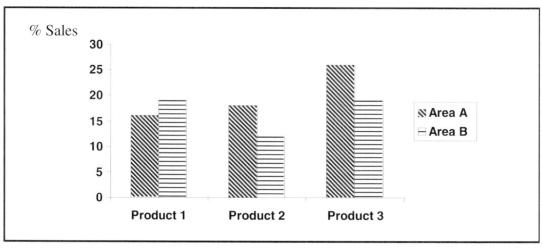

Fig 4.4 *Comparison of two different areas in producing three different products.*

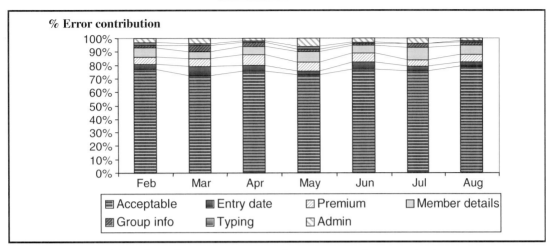

Fig. 4.5 Compound bar chart showing reasons, and percentages, for errors in documents.

this? Does the horizontal axis tell you anything about a time scale? Even if it did, are you convinced that Area A is improving, whilst Area B seems to be stagnant?

This is one of the problems with being presented with information on a short-term basis. Your view of what the data is telling you may be different to that of your colleague.

We also come across more complicated forms of bar charts, as shown in *Fig 4.5.*

This graph is based on error analysis in an insurance organisation.

Lines have also been added joining up the tops of each bar.

On the positive side, at least we have moved away from the familiar tabular format.

However, it is impossible to detect any real trends, or confirmation that any changes are due to special causes. Adding colours, as in the original, really doesn't help. A caustic SPC view would be that what we have is a nice work of art, suitable for framing and display.

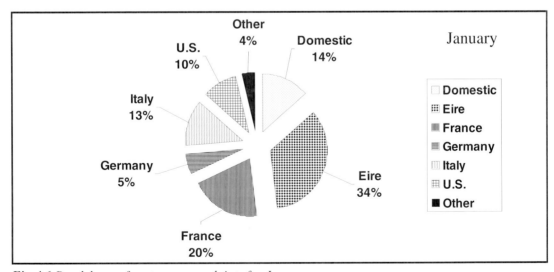

Fig 4.6 Breakdown of customer complaints for January.

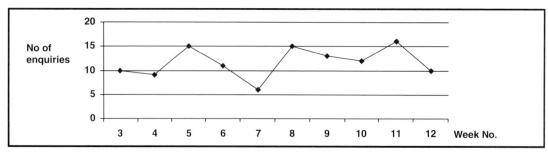

Fig 4.7 Line graph of number of customer enquiries.

4.4.2 Pie charts

Pie charts enable you to represent the breakdown of categories in a readily understandable form.

For example, *Fig 4.6* shows a pie chart used in representing the source of customer complaints for a multinational.

The difficulty with pie charts is that they are based on one set of readings. Sometimes an additional pie chart is provided for comparison, possibly using the annual figures for the previous year, or the figure for the same month the previous year. It still doesn't help. The message is the same. We need more readings and we need to use a control chart.

4.4.3 Line graphs or run charts

Fig 4.7 is a typical line graph. Here we are plotting the number of enquiries for a new product that has been introduced into the market place.

By implication, a line graph must be based on several readings, and hence there is at least a chance of picking up a pattern. But we should recognise the usual limitations in that, without control limits, we do not know when to take action on the process. The line graph is often called a run chart.

Variations on the simple line graph are available.

4.4.4 Rainbow charts

Rainbow charts are really a combination of several line graphs with the zones between the lines shaded in.

Fig. 4.8 shows how the method has been used to deal with the number of enquiries for five new products.

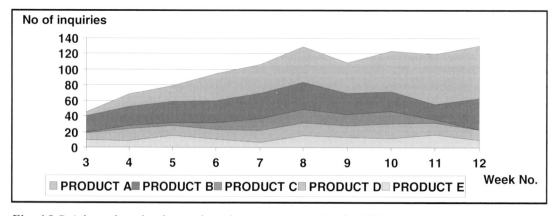

Fig. 4.8 Rainbow chart for the number of customer enquiries for different products.

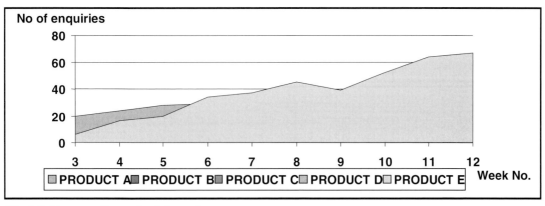

Fig 4.9 Alternate form of rainbow chart.

This type of rainbow chart records the accumulated results as well as the results for each product. Whilst we can see at a glance how one product compares directly with another, it is not easy to determine the actual number of enquiries.

Another version of the rainbow chart plots the actual numbers and shades in the area between the graphs. This can also cause problems in some cases. For example, *Fig 4.9* shows the same data as in *Fig 4.8* but this time represented in a different way.

This isn't much of an improvement. In fact, to be blunt, it is no improvement. The effectiveness of the graph will depend on the nature of the numbers involved and how different each plot is from another.

4.4.5 Glyph charts

A glyph chart, sometimes called a radar or spider chart, is particularly useful when there are several factors being compared, as *Fig 4.10* shows.

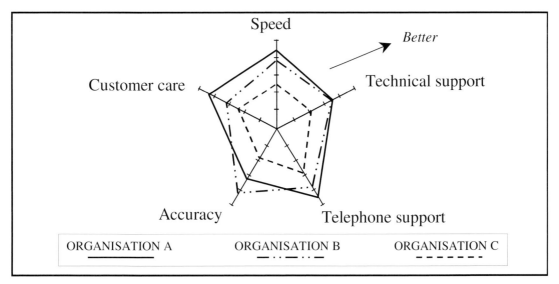

Fig. 4.10 Glyph chart comparing the performance of different organisations.

No.	Characteristic	No. of errors										Total	%
		Week 1					Week 2						
		M	T	W	T	F	M	T	W	T	F	Total	%
1	Form not signed	2	1	0	1	0	1	1	0	0	1	7	8.3
2	No part no.	1	0	2	1	1	2	0	0	0	0	7	8.3
3	Address missing	5	2	3	2	3	4	3	5	3	3	33	39.4
4	No cheque	1	0	1	1	1	0	1	1	1	1	8	9.5
5	Wrong amount	3	4	1	3	1	2	3	3	4	5	29	34.5
	Total no. of errors	12	7	7	8	6	9	8	9	8	10	84	100
	Total no. of forms	24	20	21	18	18	24	16	20	14	22	197	
	Proportion	0.50	0.35	0.33	0.44	0.33	0.38	0.50	0.45	0.57	0.45	0.43	

Fig 4.11 A record of error rates relating to a banking operation.

This looks at the performance of three organisations in the delivery of five different quality characteristics important to the customer (service, technical support, telephone support, speed and accuracy). A scale is provided on the arms, often measured on a scale of nought to a hundred, with the convention that moving outwards from the centre is equivalent to an improvement. As you can see, organisation C is unsatisfactory in all respects compared to A and B.

If more readings over time become available, then control charts come into their own. In the case of the characteristics used in *Fig 4.10*, five separate control charts would eventually be created for each of the three organisations.

4.4.6 Other charts

You might be attracted to other forms of representing data.

Nowadays, with the ready availability of computers, graphic packages allow for all sorts of options. Various impressive charts and diagrams can be generated, but often the problem is knowing which presentation is most effective.

With the same set of data, we can use different representations.

In *Fig 4.11*, for example, we have data that is similar in nature to that shown in *Fig 3.2*. The original used tally marks to represent the frequencies. Here we are using the actual totals.

Fig 4.12 represents the same information in two different ways.

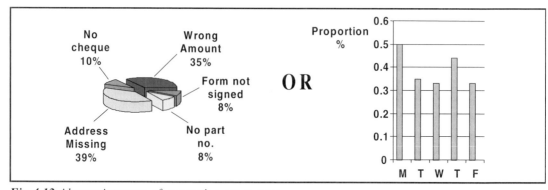

Fig 4.12 Alternative ways of expressing error rates.

PROFIT AND LOSS

REF. NO.	ITEM	PREVIOUS MONTH (June)		CURRENT MONTH (July)	
		FORECAST	ACTUAL	FORECAST	ACTUAL
001	Sales – Domestic	565	617	570	563
002	Sales – Export	125	103	130	129
003	Gross sales	690	720	700	692
004	Allowed discounts				
005	**NET sales**	690	**720**	700	**692**

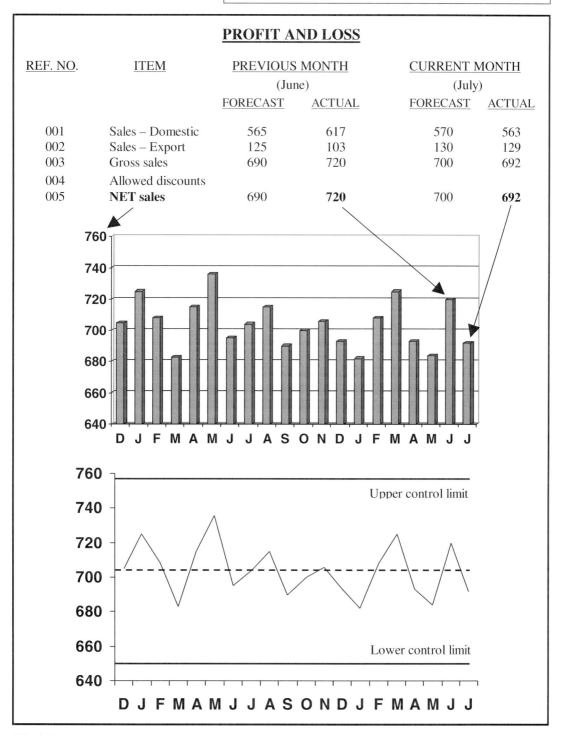

Fig 4.13 *From figures, through a bar chart, to a control chart.*

On the left hand side a pie chart is used to show the % of errors contributed by different causes. On the right hand side, a bar chart represents the number of errors in documents as a proportion of the number of the documents available. Results for the first week have been used.

There is no intention here to go into detail on the advantage or disadvantage of one standard graphical technique as opposed to another. We would rather concentrate on getting over the message that when it comes to understanding variation, the control chart is the answer.

4.5 Limitations of existing methods

Software packages provide access to a range of different techniques to enable us to present data in whatever way it suits us. In effect, all that can be said is that it makes the information a little easier to understand. Whether it helps in decision-making is another issue. Knowledge of SPC will tell you that bar charts, pie charts, doughnut charts, whatever you use and whatever you call them, cannot provide you with an effective method of reacting correctly to the information. Most conventional graphical techniques camouflage the true pattern of the process.

Edward Tufte, in an excellent book titled *The Visual Display of Quantitative Information*, writes:

"*Computers and their affiliated apparatus can do powerful things graphically, in part by turning out hundreds of plots necessary for good data analysis. But at least a few computer graphics only evoke the response 'Isn't it remarkable that the computer can be programmed to draw like that?' instead of 'My, what interesting data.'*"

Rather than get carried away with exotic software graphics, we should be using them with caution and as an intermediate step in the use of the control chart.

Fig 4.13 restates the point made in Section 1.5 in Chapter 1. It indicates that there are three stages involved in using a control chart to present information.

Typically we initially have a tabular format. In this case it is the profit and loss statement that was used in *Fig 4.1*. There are various characteristics that could be chosen to work on. We look at Net Sales for which we currently have on display the June and July figures only.

We get a truer picture of performance by taking more readings. The bar chart in *Fig 4.13* shows the results for the twenty months ending in the July in question, and is certainly preferable to the presentation using numbers. But it isn't good enough.

Instead of a bar chart, we should move on to a control chart, shown at the bottom of the diagram.

There is a communication problem if an organisation progresses directly from the first stage to the third. If there is a limited amount of SPC knowledge available, then control charts are probably of little more help than the original rows and columns approach. Certainly the chart will be confusing. So whilst there is a strong argument for using control charts, they cannot be used to communicate in a wider sense unless personnel understand them.

As the understanding spreads, then it may be appropriate to represent both a conventional format and a control chart together. Eventually the original display can be removed and only control charts put on display.

Making this transition to a new way of thinking is not easy. The following example, shown in *Fig 4.14*, illustrates the problem.

A graphic such as that shown in *Fig 4.14* appears in the display of a leading manufacturer of portable communication equipment. In marketing the model, the company has used sales figures and represented them in a form which is best suited to switch on those managers who need to interpret sales related data. The current way of making decisions is by bar charts, or their equivalent. Consistently in this book we are advocating the use of control charts, rather than bar charts. Before introducing control charts, it is important that people recognise how they work. Otherwise, control charts would either not

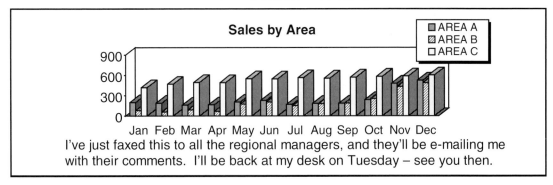

I've just faxed this to all the regional managers, and they'll be e-mailing me with their comments. I'll be back at my desk on Tuesday – see you then.

Fig 4.14 A typical display of sales data

be understood by the great majority of sales and marketing personnel, or if they are understood they would not be seen as relevant in a sales function. It will take some time before a control chart is seen as the natural way to represent the data shown in *Fig 4.14*.

4.6 Key points and summary

- Before measuring anything, reflect on what you are measuring, and what you intend to do with the data.
- Data abounds in various forms, but has tended not to be used to improve processes.
- Manual records provide an ideal resource for creating process control charts.
- Computer-based graphics packages are a step forward, but fall short of providing the complete answer.
- Existing data is often limited to the comparison of one number and another. It is impossible to make sensible judgements in this case.
- More data is required, but unless it is presented in the form of a control chart, it is not being used correctly.
- Far-reaching implications for an organisation are too often made on the basis of a very limited amount of data.
- Bar charts provide a good picture but cannot help in indicating an unusually high, or an unusually low figure.
- Similarly, line graphs are of little use unless the central line and the control limits are added, converting them into control charts.
- Rainbow charts and others look good, but do not provide the information required to indicate if the process is stable and predictable.
- Some charts, such as glyph charts, do have value, but they are not really part of an SPC toolkit.
- The same set of data can be represented in different ways, but these methods are limited unless they can discriminate between real changes and natural changes in the system.
- Changing the conventional view of how to present data and make the correct decision has other long-term training implications.

In this chapter we have looked at traditional ways of measuring processes and representing the associated data. Hopefully, it has indicated how dangerous these traditional methods can be.

A control chart is the correct technique to use. Understanding a control chart is only possible if we have an understanding of some of the basic statistical ideas that lie behind it. This material is covered in the next chapter.

MEASURING THE RIGHT THINGS

5.1 Introduction

We have talked about measurement in different ways in the previous chapter. We deal with it in detail in this chapter. Measuring a process ultimately means handling numbers in one way or another, and hence we need to acquire a level of confidence in dealing with quantities which specify a process in a very numerical format.

Section 5.2 covers the difference between items which are measured and items which are counted, an important difference in terms of control charts. Representing the data using frequency diagrams and histograms is covered in Section 5.3. Some discussion on the usefulness, or lack of it, of the histogram appears in Section 5.4, followed by sections giving detail on the mean, the range, and the standard deviation – essential building blocks which are needed to understand how to develop a control chart.

Finally, Section 5.10 covers material which is as important as any in the book – how to interpret a control chart for the presence of special causes.

5.2 Measuring or counting?

One of the first steps in assessing a process is to decide on the form of the metric to be used. For example, are we interested in the time taken to carry out a transaction, or are we more concerned about the level of errors in the document? Are we analysing the response time to a customer or are we assessing the number and nature of the complaints?

This sort of questioning leads to a classification of metrics based on whether the item is being measured or counted. We need to understand the difference between these two.

A measurable quantity is known as a variable. The scale used in measuring can, in theory, be subdivided indefinitely. For example, instead of recording turnaround times for a certain process as one, two, three etc days, we can get more useful information by measuring the times to the next decimal place, or, more practically in this case, in hours. As the process improves further, then times in minutes are required to detect the variation at the reduced level. *Fig 5.1* shows how better and better information can be achieved as we subdivide the scale further and further. Sometimes variable data is referred to as continuous data.

If we cannot measure it, then we can count it and items defined in this way are known as attributes. Hence the number of documents in error is an attribute, as is the number of errors in a document. For example, suppose we have batches of documents which we analyse for faults on a weekly basis. In week one we have two reject documents, week two we have one reject document, and so on. On this basis it is not possible to have a reading between one and two. A reading for any one week has to be recorded at exactly nought, one, two, three, on a scale.

If we record by tally marks the number of incorrect documents obtained over the first few weeks, then we get the result shown in *Fig 5.2*.

Attributes are therefore defined on a go/no-go, present/not present basis. The item is either there or

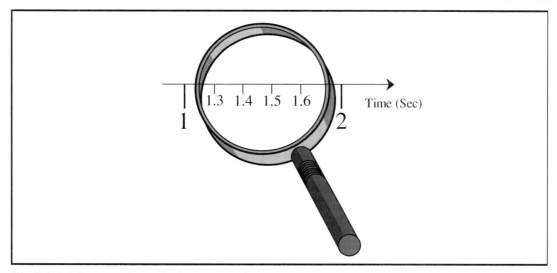

Fig 5.1 Subdivision of a scale for measured quantities.

not there. This means, for example, that we cannot have documents containing a fraction of an error. Unlike the variable scale, the zone on the attribute scale between one and two, two and three, etc, is free of any reading. Of course, we may wish to express an error rate as a %, and there are ways of allowing us to do that. But at this stage we restrict ourselves to a strict go/no-go definition.

In SPC terms, variables give us a lot more information than attributes. They tend to reflect the parameters of the process itself. Attributes are often associated with an analysis late in the process. For example error rates in documents, whilst being a useful guide, typically reflect the results of some inspection task after the document has been processed. By using a variable chart monitoring time as a key metric, and then controlling and reducing the processing time, there is less need for an attribute chart at a later stage in the process. However, this is a long term strategy, and in the early stages of introducing charts we will certainly need to introduce an attribute chart on errors in order to assess the fault level and prioritise on those errors which cause the biggest problems.

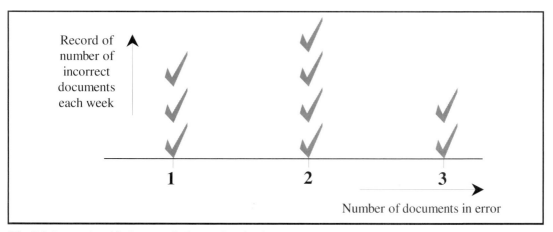

Fig 5.2 Items classified on a whole number basis.

5.3 Representing the data

In this and previous chapters there has been a strong emphasis on the process, and measuring the process. We have seen how key performance indicators and in-process measures provide us with readings that we can then use to set up an appropriate chart.

These readings will vary over time and will give different patterns. Control charts are the correct tools to use in understanding and interpreting these patterns.

However, in order to understand the basis on which a control chart works we need to become familiar with some statistical building blocks.

Recognising simple patterns of variation is the first step.

5.3.1 Representing the data

Suppose we are interested in monitoring how long it takes for a document to be processed. The actual time may comprise a series of sequential times, but we won't complicate the analysis unnecessarily at this stage. We will consider a certain specific operation, and simply monitor how long it takes, in hours, for the documents to be handled, one after the other, with no sampling involved.

Fig 5.3 shows how the times for the first five of a series of successive documents vary. The actual times for the first five documents are also recorded.

Note that the scale for recording the times is vertical. There is a reason for this that will become clear as we proceed through the explanation.

5.3.2 Building the picture

By the time we get to twenty documents, the pattern changes quite a bit, as shown in *Fig 5.4*. As further readings are taken again, then the pattern will tend to stabilise.

How many readings do we need before we have a good idea of how the final pattern should look?

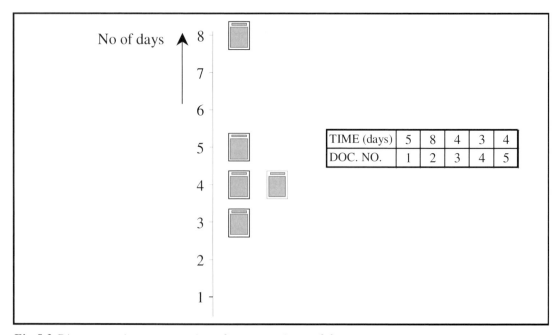

TIME (days)	5	8	4	3	4
DOC. NO.	1	2	3	4	5

Fig 5.3 *Diagrammatic representation of response times of documents.*

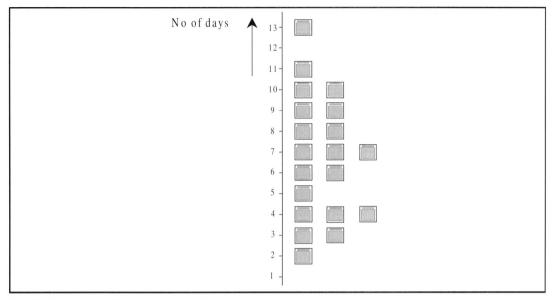

Fig 5.4 *Representation of response times for first twenty documents.*

It is suggested that one hundred readings, taken one after the other, give an adequate picture of the pattern of the distribution.

In developing the representations shown in *Fig 5.3* and *Fig 5.4*, we have used a schematic representation of a document. In a general sense, when accumulating data in this way, we typically use tally marks, grouping them in bundles of five to make it easier to count them as the numbers increase.

The final representation of the pattern of document response times can now be seen in *Fig 5.5.*

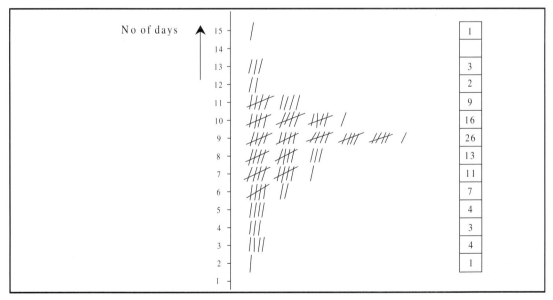

Fig 5.5 *Frequency diagram of response times for first hundred documents.*

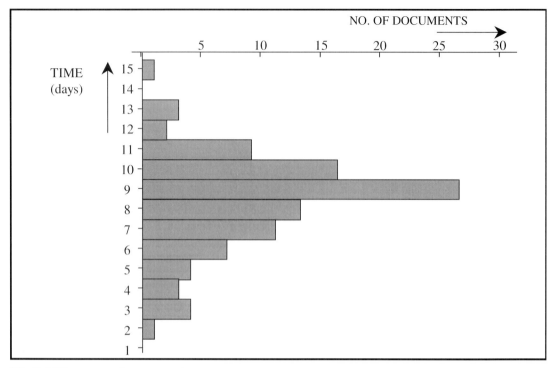

Fig 5.6 *Histogram of response times.*

The total number of documents corresponding to a particular time is shown on the right hand side of the figure. These values are known as frequencies, and the diagram as a frequency diagram.

We tend to carry out a further step in practice to make the representation a little neater. By constructing bars where the length of each bar corresponds to the frequency in a given interval, we finish up with the form shown in *Fig 5.6*. This is commonly known as a histogram.

Typically, when developing a histogram, a horizontal axis is introduced which makes it easier to determine the number of documents corresponding to a given response time.

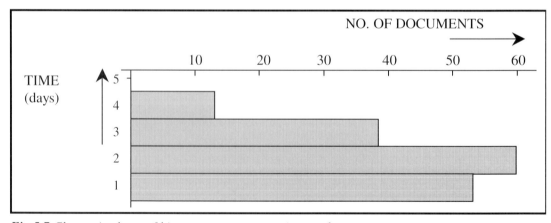

Fig 5.7 *Change in shape of histogram as response times reduce.*

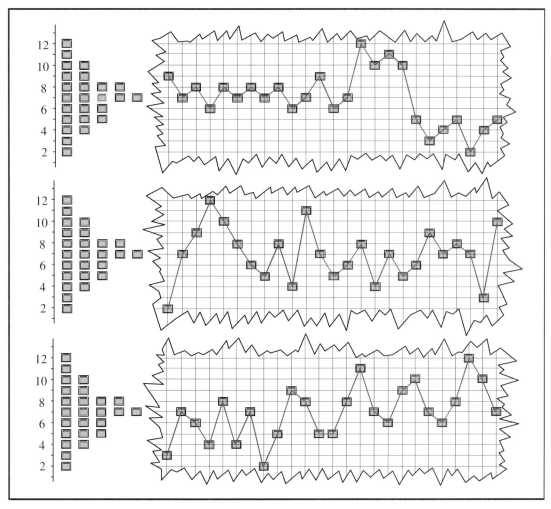

Fig 5.8 *One histogram – three run charts.*

5.4 What does the histogram tell us?

Well, it indicates that the response times seem to peak at nine days and that they range from two days to fifteen days. Note also that the pattern is not symmetrical. We are commonly led to believe that readings of this nature give us a symmetrical distribution. Real life usually suggests otherwise.

For example, as our process improves and we drive down the response times towards zero, then the pattern will get less and less symmetrical, as shown in *Fig. 5.7*.

There is an important issue here. There is a widely held view that the pattern has to be symmetrical in order to make use of SPC. This is not so. This over-emphasis on a symmetrical pattern, often called a Normal Distribution, can cause confusion and is unnecessary. There are related issues in terms of capability and these will be discussed in Chapter 14. Despite our reservations, the histogram can be useful in detecting when two processes have been treated as one. In these circumstances we will see two peaks rather than one.

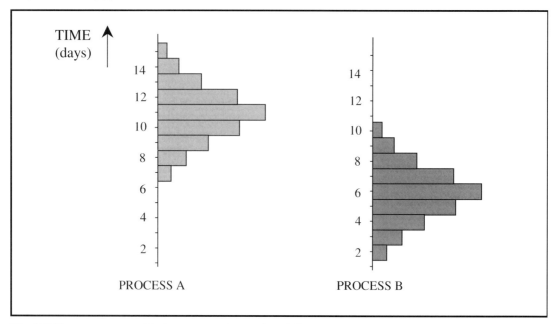

Fig 5.9 Two processes with the same variation but different settings.

5.5 What doesn't the histogram tell us?

The histogram reflects the pattern in a set of readings, but it does not reflect the time sequence in which the readings were taken. This can be seen in *Fig 5.8*.

The response times of twenty-five successive documents have been measured and the final pattern has been recorded in the usual way on the left-hand side of the diagram. There are various ways in which this pattern could have been built up, and *Fig 5.8* shows three possible sequences – a process running at different levels, a process reflecting natural variation and a process which moves consistently in one direction or another. The latter is often called a drifting process. All these processes, and others, can produce the same final pattern shown on the vertical scale. In other words, a histogram is of no use in detecting the order in which readings have been taken. It is vital that we use a control chart, which is based on the order in which readings have been taken, to monitor our process. The only way that we use a histogram is in checking on whether the process satisfies service level agreements that have been imposed by the customer, and this will be discussed further in Chapter 14 when discussing capability.

It is suggested that response times are plotted on a vertical scale. This will allow us to use the horizontal scale to record the sequence in which the times were recorded. The plot of the results over time is called a run chart.

5.6 Variations in patterns

What happens if we change the process? We can do this in various ways.

In the first case we can we can reduce the response time without changing the variation.

This is illustrated in *Fig 5.9* where an improvement in a process is reflected in a reduction in the average response time. For Process A, the average response time, as suggested by the peak of the histogram, is eleven days. For Process B the average has reduced to six days. Note that the variation has not changed. We have the same spread of readings in each case.

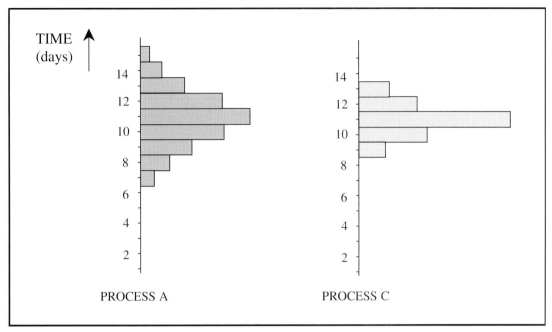

Fig 5.10 *Two processes with the same setting but different variation.*

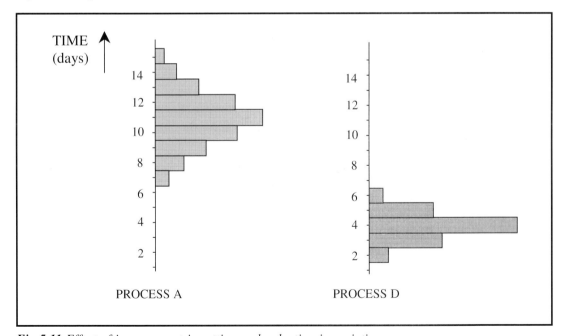

Fig 5.11 *Effect of improvement in setting and reduction in variation.*

Fig 5.10 shows an improvement in a process, but in a different way. In this case both processes have the same average response time of eleven days. Process C, however, has less variation than Process A.

The average response time has not changed, but the variation in the response times has reduced. The readings in Process C are much more consistent than those in Process A.

Ideally, we would like a combination of the two effects, i.e. a reduction in the average response time coupled with a reduction in the variation, as suggested in *Fig 5.11*.

Process D reflects this improvement – a reduced average response time of four days, and further reduction in the variation.

We have used the word 'average' in the last few lines in a general sense of representing a rough level at which the process is running. In the same way we have said that one set of readings is more consistent than another. Exactly what is an average value? What do we mean by consistency? Can these terms be specified in a technical sense?

The only real way to assess a process, given a set of numbers that relate to that process, is to make use of readily available statistical measures. These originate from classical statistics, and you may well have come across some of these, and in particular the ones to be introduced shortly, when studying statistics. Don't get worried at this point, thinking you might have a re-run of some unpleasant previous exposure to mathematical statistics. However, you do need to become confident in handling a couple of these classical ideas. They are widely used in general analysis of data, and they are of specific relevance in building up a tool kit that can be used to develop a control chart.

5.7 Measures of the position of a process

5.7.1 The mode

In a simplistic way this measure has already been introduced. For example, in Section 5.4 when discussing the information available in *Fig 5.6*, we said that the response times peaked at nine days. This is a crude measure of the level at which the process is operating. It is a particular type of average value, and referred to as the mode.

In our case the mode is simply telling us that more documents correspond to a response time of nine days than any other time. It has some visual relevance, being determined quickly by looking at the peak of the histogram, but mathematically it is very limited. In determining the mode no use was made of individual times other than twelve days. This has to be a limitation. There is a lot of numerical information that is being ignored in this way, and there must be a better type of average to use.

5.7.2 The mean

Unlike the mode, the mean takes into account each numerical value.

We will introduce it by making use of figures we have been working with. Have a look at the distribution of the twenty individual responses represented in *Fig 5.4*. The twenty values that produced this figure are shown in *Fig 5.12*.

To calculate the mean value we simply add up the twenty readings and divide by twenty (the number of readings).

TIME (days)	5	8	4	3	4	11	7	6	3	7	9	8	13	7	10	2	4	9	10	6
DOC. NO.	1	2	3	4	5	6	7	8	9	10	11	12	13	14	15	16	17	18	19	20

Fig 5.12 *Twenty successive document processing times.*

The mean value, sometimes called the arithmetic mean, is therefore given by: -

$$\frac{5+8+4+3+....+9+10+6}{20} \quad = \quad \frac{136}{20} \quad = \quad 6.80$$

We typically use X to denote the item being analysed, in this case the document response time, and the mean value is denoted by $\overline{X}$, pronounced 'x bar'.

In general, therefore, the mean $\overline{X}$ is

$$\frac{X_1 + X_2 + X_3 + ... + X_n}{n}$$

where n is the number of readings, in our case 20, but not always so.

Writing down 5 + 8 + 4 + 3 ... etc can be somewhat tedious. For this reason we make use of the Greek letter capital sigma, denoted by Σ, where Σ is a shorthand way of representing the fact that we are adding the various X values.

Our formula for obtaining a mean value is therefore:

$$\overline{X} \quad = \quad \frac{\Sigma X}{n}$$

This mean value corresponds to the central line on the control chart, and is typically represented by a broken line.

We have chosen twenty readings for the basis of this example. There is a reason for this.

Twenty is a guideline figure for the number of readings to be used when first setting up a control chart. In other words, every time we develop a control chart, of whatever type, we carry out a calculation similar to that above.

Don't get too hung up on this figure of twenty readings. It is a suggested figure, representative of the span over which the process is acting in a natural way without any adjustments. As far as possible we should follow the guidelines, but there will be occasions when we use less than twenty readings. A typical example will be when analysing monthly sales figures. If we are starting with no past records to work on, then we really cannot wait almost two years to get our readings. There is no real problem in calculating $\overline{X}$ using fewer than twenty, but probably not less than ten readings. As more readings become available, then we can upgrade the value of the central line.

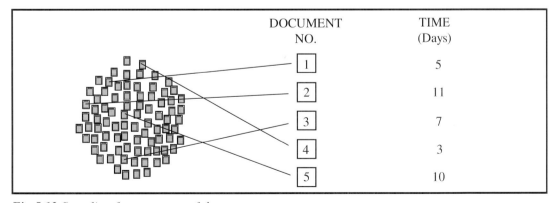

Fig 5.13 Sampling from a group of documents.

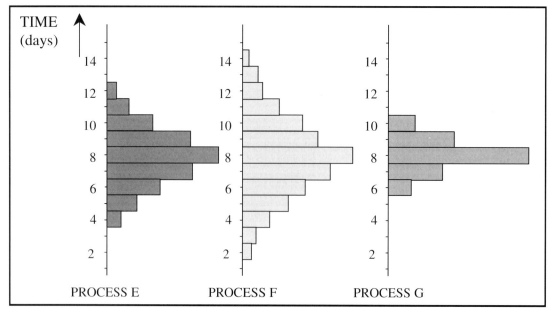

Fig 5.14 *Limitation of the mean as an indicator of variation.*

In the above analysis we have been using single readings as the basis for plotting. This is not always the case.

One form of control chart, which we shall be developing in Chapter 10, makes use of samples. Typically, five readings are taken in sequence, and are used to provide a snapshot of the process at that time, as suggested in *Fig 5.13*. We apply this method when there are a large number of readings available and resource reasons, as much as any other, force us to take samples. In such a case we need to calculate the mean of the five readings.

As an example, suppose that in a particular organisation, on June 20th, 75 documents were available for assessment that day. Five documents are to be used as a monitor of the process, and *Fig 5.13* shows the times for these five documents to be processed.

In a strict SPC sense, these five readings should be taken one after the other, reflecting the time sequence of the process. This may not always be possible.

For this sample, the mean value is given by: -

$$\overline{X} = \frac{\Sigma X}{n}$$

$$= \frac{5+11+7+3+10}{5}$$

$$= \underline{7.2 \text{ days}}$$

When setting up the control chart for monitoring $\overline{X}$, we need twenty $\overline{X}$ values in order to work out the mean value. In other words we need twenty samples of five.

The central line of the $\overline{X}$ chart is then given by: -

$$\overline{\overline{X}} = \frac{\Sigma \overline{X}}{20}$$

$\overline{\overline{X}}$ is known as 'X double bar', and sometimes referred to rather regally as 'the grand mean'.

$\overline{\overline{X}}$ is an indicator of the position of the process. It is a measure of location, sometimes referred to as the setting of the process.

The mean is the value we shall use whenever we are relating to the position of a distribution on a certain scale. It is the best indicator we have in telling us the level of a process. Useful as it is, however, it tells us nothing about the variation of the process. *Fig 5.14* suggests why.

The figure shows the pattern for three processes – E, F and G. All three processes have the same average response time. To avoid making the analysis too detailed at this stage, we shall use the mode as an indication of the average response time, i.e. eight days. Whilst the processes are all set at the same level, each of the three distributions shows different variation. Knowing that the average response time is eight days is of no help in assessing the variation involved. We would not know if the process has deteriorated, as in Process F, or improved, as in Process G. We therefore need other measures for assessing the variation in a set of readings.

5.8 Measures of variation

There are two measures that we make use of when considering the variation in a set of readings.

5.8.1 The range

The range of a set of numbers is just the numerical difference between the largest number and the smallest number. It is denoted by R.

We will use the data previously shown in *Fig 5.13*.

The greatest value in the set is eleven days and the least value is three days. R is therefore the difference between eleven and three i.e. eight days.

Generally, the range is easy to calculate. The only possible difficulty lies in recognising that the range is always a positive quantity, or zero. Hence if the least value is minus seven and the greatest value is minus three, then the range is four. Similarly, a least value of minus two and a greatest value of six gives a range of eight.

Simplicity of calculation of a range makes it one of its main attractions. However, it is limited because its value depends only on the two extremes in the sample. For example, in using the data for the sample shown in *Fig 5.15* we have ignored the three other values of five, seven and ten.

With a small sample of size five, this does not turn out to be a problem. Using the range as an indicator of variation is not an issue. In some respects it may be a benefit. A large R, resulting from either or both of the extreme values being positioned some way from the central three items, gives a quick signal that something untoward is happening. The range in this sense is being used purely as a reflection of the process itself, and helps to highlight variations disguised by the mean.

If we are looking at using the range as a representation of the variation of the process, then that is a different issue. We would not have too much confidence in a measure that ignores three readings out of

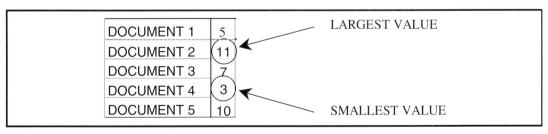

Fig 5.15 Least and greatest readings in a sample of five.

five. As the sample size increases then the problem gets worse. For example, with a sample size of twenty-five, the range will only make use of the extreme two in the group, leaving twenty three numerical values which are not being used in the calculation. Is there a better measure of variation we can make use of? As expected, classical statistics has provided us with an excellent measure – the standard deviation.

5.8.2 The standard deviation

Don't be put off by the name. It sounds rather technical and suggests we could be going into involved mathematics.

True, there is a formula for calculating the standard deviation. The bad news is that it is somewhat mathematical. The good news is that we don't use it.

There is an important point to be made here. Classical approaches to the use of mathematical statistics provide us with many formulae that are available to be used. The vast majority of these formulae bear no relationship to process control, and hence are not relevant. The classical formula for the standard deviation falls into this category. There is no point in introducing it – it only represents an unnecessary diversion from reality.

However, at some stage in developing the control chart, we will need to calculate a standard deviation. The detail will be covered when we look at the two types of charts to be discussed later – the (X, Moving R) chart in Chapter 8 and the ($\overline{X}$, R) chart in Chapter 10. We will see that there are neat formulae available that make use of tables of constants, combined with values calculated when setting up the control charts, to give us an appropriate standard deviation. Just accept at this stage that the standard deviation can be calculated quite painlessly.

A more important point is to understand what it means when we have worked it out.

5.8.3 Interpreting the standard deviation

The best way of explaining what we mean by a standard deviation is to relate it to the control chart and how Walter Shewhart developed the latter in the 1920's.

Shewhart was working on a series of experiments which involved time-based readings. It is not appropriate to enlarge on the detail here. There are several references that can be used. One or two are in the appendix, and for some the sources will make interesting reading.

Shewhart recognised that with a series of points available he needed some rules to help him to make decisions. Without these rules he could make the wrong ones. On the one hand, he could react to a point, believing it was unusual against the pattern of the other points. In fact he should have left the process alone because the point in question was just part of the natural ups and downs of the process – sometimes referred to as the noise in the process. On the other hand, he could judge not to react, believing that the point in question was just part of the natural variation in the process. In this case he might have again made the wrong decision because the point in question was genuinely unusual and he should have taken action.

Shewhart recognised that he needed rules to tell him when to react to a point and when not to.

His first step was to plot the results on a graph. Bearing in mind that this was some seventy-five years ago, it seems we haven't learnt a great deal. How much of the data in your organisation is presented in a graphical/pictorial format? In most companies, possibly not much.

With the values plotted, a central line was drawn in corresponding to the mean of the first twenty readings. This mean line provided a natural reference level from which to measure the variation.

Fig 5.16 represents a typical pattern of points, including two that were some way from the rest.

Shewhart then introduced what he initially called decision lines – lines which would enable him to

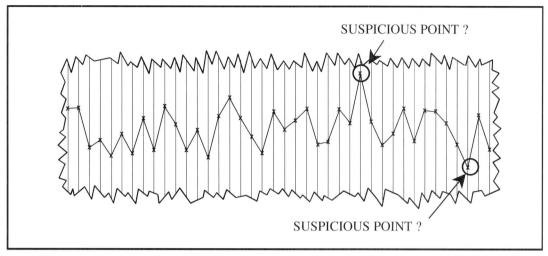

Fig 5.16 *Run chart, showing two possibly unusual points.*

decide on the status of any unusual points. These lines were to be placed symmetrically about the central line and measured outwards in units of standard deviation from the central line. His problem now was to decide on where to position these lines to make sensible judgements. If he placed the lines at, say six standard deviation distance outwards, then the lines would not be sensitive enough. The chance of getting a point six standard deviation away from the central line is extremely small. If he placed the lines at, say, one standard deviation distance outwards, then the lines would be too sensitive. He would react to far too many points, judging them to be unusual when in fact they were part of the system.

Shewhart chose to fix these lines at a distance of three standard deviations out from the central line. These decision lines were then subsequently defined as the control limits. The upper control limit is denoted by UCL and the lower control limit by LCL. Control limits were set at three standard deviations to minimise the risk between reacting when he should not and not reacting when he should. This has

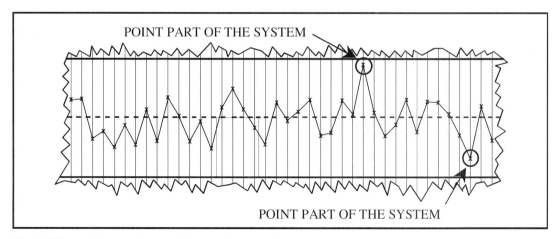

Fig 5.17 *Run chart with central line and control limits added.*

been the basis on which the control charts have operated successfully since Shewhart's time. Control charts that operate on a different system, e.g. using control limits set at four standard deviations, or one and a half standard deviations, for example, simply do not work.

So this is a tangible interpretation of what we mean by a standard deviation. Three standard deviations on either side of the mean represents the limits of natural variation in a set of sequential readings. This variation is said to represent the system, and all control charts operate essentially on this principle.

Improving the process means reducing the variation by reducing the value of the standard deviation. This is primarily a management issue because it relates to the materials being used in the process, the working environment in the office, the equipment, such as computers, that operational staff are provided with, and so on.

Fig 5.17 shows our set of readings with the control limits added. We now see that the possibly suspicious points are within the control limits and are therefore part of the system. Without the use of the control chart, we would not have been able to make this judgement.

5.9 From run chart to control chart

A run chart, as shown in *Fig 5.16,* is simply a graph of some characteristic, a response time, a type of customer enquiry, etc plotted in time sequence.

Some suggest that a run chart is a useful tool to apply. At least a run chart shows a variation over time, and so in that respect it is better than the histogram in seeing a variation in the process. But that's all that can be said for it. Plotting a run chart without adding the central line and the control limits is almost a waste of effort. Without the additions we are not able to discriminate between items which are part of the natural variation and those which are really unusual.

The natural variation in the process is due to what are called common causes and controlling and reducing the common cause variation is a system issue.

Any unusual features resulting in points outside the control limits are known as special causes. These special causes need to be identified and appropriate action taken. The control chart is the only technique that identifies unusual features in this way by providing a clear picture of the variation in a process.

Interpreting the chart for stability requires us to be very familiar with specific rules for detecting the presence of something unusual.

5.10 Rules for special causes

There are four of these that are generally adopted.

5.10.1 RULE 1. Point outside the control limit

This is the rule that Shewhart developed and is the main rule to be applied when checking the stability of a process.

Fig 5.18 shows the presence of a special cause based on *Rule 1*

Of the four rules, *Rule 1* is the most important one to use. It tells us that if a point falls outside the control limit, then almost certainly a special cause is present. There is a small element of uncertainty, however, based on the way the control limits were devised. The limits were set up to minimise the risks involved in taking action. They do not eliminate the risks. In other words, every now and again a point will fall outside the control limits and we cannot find a reason for the special cause. In this case the point will be assumed to be part of the system. Equally, we sometimes find a point inside the control limit, and near to it, and we can find a reason why this point is different to the other values i.e. it actually is a special cause. In this case, appropriate action is taken.

Control charts in administrative areas require different action to those in manufacturing areas, and

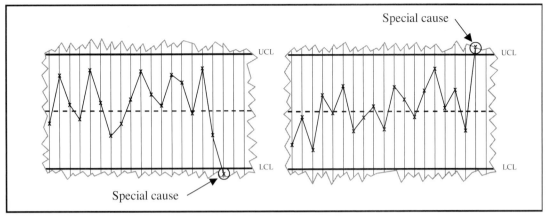

Fig 5.18 *Rule 1 applied to a process.*

responding to a point outside the limits is a good example. Control charts in office areas are typically used to assess processing times. Hence an out-of-control signal corresponding to a reading of say, eleven days, means that the reason for the out-of-control signal may have taken place some eleven days earlier. There is therefore a time lag involved in using the chart. We cannot stop the process in real time as we might do in a manufacturing process.

Rule 1 is the rule that takes priority in interpreting a chart for special causes. Other rules are available as follows. Whilst there is no priority as such, experience has shown that it makes sense to apply the three rules which follow in the order given.

5.10.2 RULE 2. Run of seven

Rule 2 looks for a sequence of seven points in succession, all above or all below the central line, or all increasing or all decreasing.

Fig 5.19 shows how the rule applies when looking at the occurrence of seven points in succession above, or below, the central line.

In *Fig 5.20 (overleaf)* we have the alternative – a sequence of seven points all moving in the same direction, either up or down. Note that in this latter case the points may, or may not cut the central line. Reference to the central line is not an issue in this interpretation of the rule.

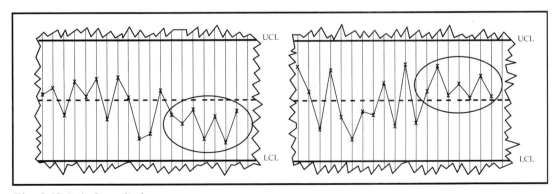

Fig. 5.19 *Rule 2 applied to a process.*

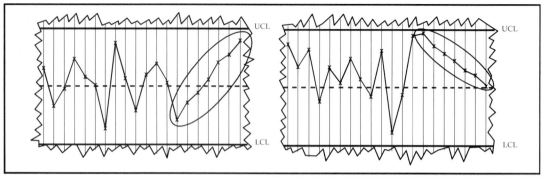

Fig 5.20 *Second version of Rule 2 applied to a process.*

The run of seven is based on mathematical rules of probability. It can be shown that the chance of obtaining a run of seven points in succession is 1 in 128. Therefore whilst a run of seven could signal a special cause, it could also occur by chance. Hence the response to a *Rule 2* signal is not as definitive as in the case of a *Rule 1* signal. The guidance is to use the experience of the chart owner in investigating the process in case there is the possibility of an early warning of deterioration in the process performance, or a possible indicator of improvement.

Sometimes you will come across this rule expressed in terms of seven intervals, i.e. eight points. This is just another variation on the theme. To avoid confusion, in this text we will stick with the convention of seven points, rather than intervals.

5.10.3 RULE 3. Unusual pattern

All four rules are there to provide the earliest possible indication of the presence of a special cause, i.e. a change from a natural random pattern based only on common cause variation.

A typical example of natural variation is shown in *Fig 5.21*.

The process shows ideal natural variation – no points outside the control limits, no runs of seven, points mainly clustered around the central line, as we would expect, and the odd one near the control limit, again as we would expect. It could be argued that the control limits are set too far apart, and that progress needs to be made in reducing the variation and hence pulling the control limits in. However, as it stands, the pattern of variation within the control limits is one we should be looking for.

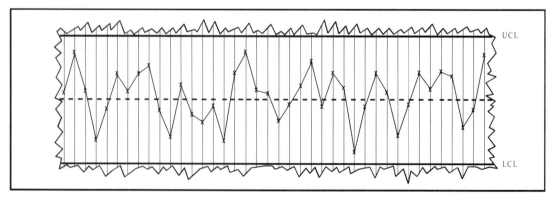

Fig 5.21 *Representation of a process showing typical natural variation.*

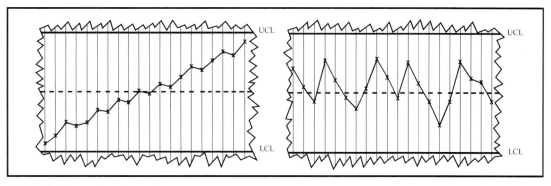

Fig 5.22 *Unusual patterns in a process.*

Any change from this natural pattern is a possible indication of a special cause.

Several unusual patterns can emerge. Fig 5.22 shows two typically unusual figures – a process that shows a drift and a process that shows a cyclic pattern. Rule 2 – a run of seven – could have given us an even earlier warning. Dealing with these unusual patterns is covered in a section in Chapter 17.

We need to be careful in interpreting the unusual pattern. Is it something we have not expected, i.e. is it a change from the natural expected pattern, or is the unusual pattern really the natural pattern for the process. The action to be taken will differ depending on what we find.

A fourth rule is available, completing the tool kit we can use to detect the presence of special causes.

5.10.4 RULE 4. Middle third rule

The rule states that the number of points within the middle third of the region within the control limits should not differ markedly from two-thirds of the total number of points.

The rule seems a bit technical. Let's look at it in a bit more detail.

We know that the principle of the control chart is that the control limits are set at a distance of three standard deviations outwards from the central line. The distance between the control limits is therefore six standard deviations. If we now add an extra pair of lines that are set at one standard deviation out from the central line, then the distance between these lines is two standard deviations. Another way of looking at it is to say that the distance between these new lines is the middle third zone of the distance between the control limits.

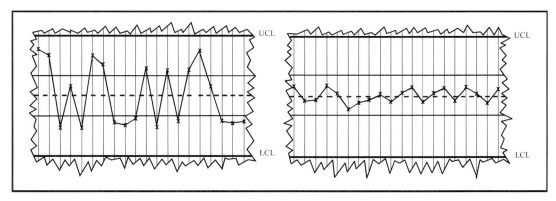

Fig 5.23 *Typical non-random patterns in a process.*

When applying this rule we simply count the number of points on the chart for the sequence we are interested in. We then count the number of points in the middle third zone. This second result should be about two-thirds of the first result. For example, if we have thirty points in total, we should expect to get about twenty in the middle-third zone.

This relationship is based on a statistical property and we needn't worry about where it comes from. Use the rule with some caution. There is obviously room for different interpretations. How do we interpret 'about two-thirds', for example? In this book we use the rule very simplistically.

For example, *Fig 5.23* shows two processes that indicate clear-cut examples of the application of the middle third rule.

The example on the left-hand side of the diagram shows a process where very few points fall in the middle third zone. There are twenty points in total, and so we should expect about six or seven points in the zone and in fact we have only two. This figure is so low that it suggests an unusual feature is present. The chart pattern hints that we really have two processes giving a control chart for the combination of the two.

On the right hand side of *Fig 5.23* we have a case where all the points fall within the middle third zone. On the basis that the control limits shown have been calculated earlier, then it is not possible for this to happen unless a change in the process has occurred which has resulted in reduced variation. In practice, we should now check back in the process to find the reason. This would then be integrated into the system as a permanent improvement and the control limits recalculated.

There is a specific use of the charts in telling us when we are justified in recalculating. Chapter 17 gives the detail we need.

These four rules for identifying special causes are vital, and here is a summary of them. We shall refer to them again in further chapters.

RULE 1	Any point outside one of the control limits.
RULE 2	A run of seven points, all above or all below the centre line, or all increasing or all decreasing.
RULE 3	Any unusual patterns or trends within the control limits.
RULE 4	The number of points within the middle third of the region between the control limits differing markedly from two-thirds of the total number of points.

5.11 Other issues

Be careful when handling special causes in that not all of them are associated with things going wrong. For example, a change in a software programme on a trial basis might result in quicker response times to the customer. The associated control chart has provided an out-of-control signal that can clearly be associated with the change of software. Here we have a message that is associated with an improvement in the process and the procedure is to integrate the reason for the change as part of the system.

5.12 Summary of symbols and formulae

Symbols

X Item being analysed

n Number of items in the sample

$\overline{X}$ Mean of X values

$\overline{\overline{X}}$ Mean of $\overline{X}$ values

R Range of a sample

UCL   Upper control limit
LCL   Lower control limit

Formulae

$$\overline{X} = \frac{\Sigma X}{n}$$ When calculating the central line, n is typically 20. When calculating a sample mean, n is typically 5

$$\overline{\overline{X}} = \frac{\Sigma \overline{X}}{20}$$ This formula applies to the ($\overline{X}$, R) chart

5.13 Key points and summary

- A variable is a quantity that can be measured.
- An attribute is a quantity that is counted.
- Frequency is the number of items corresponding to a particular value on a variable scale.
- A frequency diagram shows the accumulation of tick marks corresponding to given scale readings.
- A histogram uses bars to represent the number of readings corresponding to given readings on a continuous scale.
- Patterns of readings do not have to be symmetrical to use SPC.
- The histogram provides no detail on the time sequence of readings from a process.
- An average value is a single representative value of a set of readings.
- The mode is the most frequently occurring value in the set and corresponds to the peak of the histogram.
- The mean is the better value to use when setting up a control chart.
- Control charts are typically set up using the first twenty readings.
- Control charts based on samples typically use a sample size of five.
- The mean gives an indication of how the setting in the process is changing.
- The range is the simplest method of measuring variation.
- A better measure of variation, used in setting up a control chart, is a standard deviation.
- Never use the standard deviation keys on a calculator in setting up control charts.
- Each control chart has its own formula for calculating the control limits.
- Run charts have minimal use because they do not have any decision lines.
- Control limits represent the system, i.e. the natural variation in the process.
- Four rules are used to detect special causes.
- Apply the rules in the order of priority suggested.
- Special causes can be due to good reasons as well as unacceptable ones.
- Occasionally something that we think is a special cause is part of the system.

This chapter has included a lot of detail on the building blocks used to develop a control chart. It has also covered the four rules that we use to interpret a control chart.

In the next chapter we start to put this together in taking you through the sequence of actually setting up a control chart.

HOW TO MEASURE. THE CONTROL CHART – A STEP-BY-STEP GUIDE

6.1 Introduction

This chapter is probably the most important one in the book because it takes you through the sequence of setting up a control chart. The sequence is basically the same whatever type of chart is used, and will therefore be adapted to the specific control charts when they are discussed in detail in Chapters 8, 10 and 12.

After a brief reference to the need to define the process, Section 6.3 covers the important issue of collecting the data. Section 6.4 provides comprehensive detail on the various calculations involved in setting up a control chart. These relate to the sample, the central line and the control limits. Section 6.5 concentrates on the practical issue of plotting and recording, and is followed in Section 6.6 by considerable detail on the four rules associated with the occurrence of a special cause. Also included in this section are some useful flowcharts that can be made use of when setting up a control chart.

6.2 Defining the process

In Chapter 2, in particular, you were introduced to the definition of a process. In setting up a control chart we must first be quite clear that we understand the process that is to be measured, and that we have determined the key characteristic that is to be measured.

It is likely that you will need a balance of measures to assess inputs, activity within the process itself and outputs. Start with the output measures, the dependent variables. These measures must focus on the customers requirements. The measures needed to assess the inputs and in-process performance are the upstream independent variables that influence the output results to the customer. We're talking cause and effect, or Xs and Ys, as you will see when you come to the scatter diagram, described in Chapter 16, Section 16.10.

Once it is clear what we are going to measure, then data needs to be collected.

Fig 6.1 Typical sources of existing data.

Process - *Batch*				Chartkeeper- *Jane*		
Sample No	Batch Ref. no.	Date commenced	Time commenced	Date completed	Time completed	Time taken (hours)
1	BG/387	Jun-03	8:35	Jun-03	16:36	7
2	BT/776	Jun-04	8:47	Jun-04	12:45	4
3	H/2391	Jun-04	14:17	Jun-05	09:56	3
4	CG/65	Jun-05	10:37	Jun-05	16:49	5
5	AVY/54	Jun-06	8:48	Jun-06	10:46	2
6	CG/65	Jun-06	11:19	Jun-07	10:38	8
7	PJ/56	Jun-07	11:46	Jun-07	15:37	4
8	CDW/19	Jun-07	16:07	Jun-10	09:37	2
9	VK/65	Jun-10	10:14	Jun-10	14:54	3
10	BF/2128	Jun-11	15:45	Jun-12	10:56	4
11	GHY/9	Jun-12	11:36	Jun-12	15-25	3
12	DD/43	Jun-12	15:48	Jun-13	11:38	5
13	PP/444	Jun-13	12:50	Jun-14	10:37	5
14	GHT/332	Jun-14	11:31	Jun-17	09:05	6
15	GHT/54	Jun-17	9:23	Jun-17	11:20	2
16	P/498	Jun-17	12:08	Jun-17	16:26	3
17	FT/443	Jun-18	9:05	Jun-18	12:34	3
18	BF/554	Jun-18	14:00	Jun-19	11:38	7
19	CDW/665	Jun-19	12:36	Jun-19	15:04	2
20	PJ/543	Jun-19	16:28	Jun-20	12:05	5
21	BV/559	Jun-20	13-34	Jun-21	09:45	5
22	CS/3	Jun-21	10:23	Jun-21	16:25	5
23	GT/87	Jun-24	8:45	Jun-24	11:34	3
24	CDW/5	Jun-24	12:20	Jun-24	14:50	2

Fig 6.2 Completed data collection sheet for document processing times.

6.3 Collecting the data

How we proceed at this stage will depend on the availability or otherwise of data.

We may have data available in one form or another, typically manual records and files or computer printouts, as suggested in *Fig 6.1*. We can make use of this in setting up a control chart.

It is very possible that we are starting from scratch in that there is no existing data. It needs to be collected, and in order to do this a simple data sheet is required. In some cases it may be sensible to use a blank control chart as the data collection sheet, particularly in the case of multiple characteristics, but in general there is a lot to be said for designing a very simple sheet which satisfies our particular requirements.

Suppose, for example, we are interested in the response time to an internal customer. We have set up a service level agreement (SLA), measured in hours, for the processing of a set of documents in batches, and we now need to collect data.

A typical completed data collection sheet for this sort of process is shown in *Fig 6.2*.

Because the sheet has been designed for use in an on-going mode, it can accommodate more than twenty readings. In line with the usual convention, the first twenty readings on the data sheet are used to set up the chart.

Note that the times are such that the final processing time for each batch is in hours. Initial data gathering exercises of this nature often use readings based on days. This is fine if the values are, for example, into double figures. However, if the response times are typically single figures, such as two, one, five days, then the readings may not be sensitive enough to pick up the variation. Case Study 21 in Section 17.9 provides a good example of this problem.

Note also that the form of the data collection sheet will be different when dealing with other types of control charts. Chapter 7 gives a lot of detail on this.

It is important that this initial stage of collecting data and recording it is kept as simple and straight-forward as possible. It is easy to make a mistake, resulting in data that is suspect and conclusions that could be invalid.

Remember that data collection is itself a process and needs managing and on-going improvement. Try to ensure the data collection process doesn't contribute to the variation in the data.

6.4 Calculating results

Having collected the data, appropriate calculations can be made. It is necessary to carry these out before setting up scales for the charts and doing any plotting. The values of the control limits will provide a guide as to what scale to use. It makes sense to choose one that will utilise as much of the allowed space on the vertical axis as possible.

Fig 6.3 shows a schematic diagram of a typical control chart and we will use this to illustrate the various stages in carrying out the calculations required.

All control charts essentially follow this common layout.

The major section of the sheet allows for the actual numerical values. These are recorded in time sequence, together with a central line and control limits. It may be that the section is split and includes

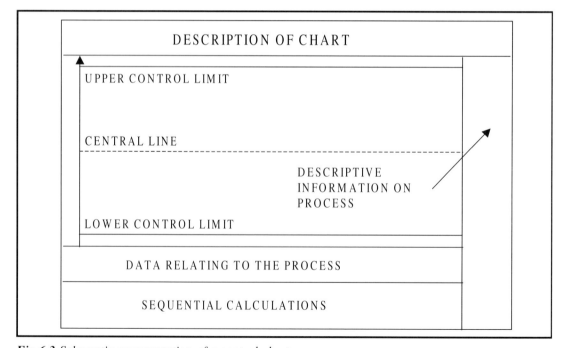

Fig 6.3 Schematic representation of a control chart.

two control charts monitoring two features, one that tracks the location of the process and the other the variation in the process. Data relating to the process is also recorded, and a further section allows for the recording of calculated values referring to the successive readings as they appear. Finally, there is a section where descriptive data can be logged – data such as the name of the customer, the characteristic being studied, etc.

After the data has been collected, there is no reason why it could not be transferred directly onto the appropriate section of the chart. At the same time data boxes providing descriptive/technical information on the process itself could be completed.

The various calculations then follow.

6.4.1 Sample calculations

These depend on the chart being used. For the ($\overline{X}$, R) chart, the mean, $\overline{X}$, of the values in each sample is calculated, together with the range R, as we did in the previous chapter. For the (X, Moving R) chart we need to calculate a moving range (R), and specific detail on this appears in Chapter 8.

6.4.2 Calculation of central lines

Whatever the type of chart, central lines need to be determined. These lines are based on the mean of the first twenty readings. Twenty has been chosen as an adequate figure that covers the time over which the natural variation of the process will be represented. Whilst this is the suggested figure, it is by no means sacrosanct, and can vary depending on the type of data being considered. For example, in handling sales data, based on monthly readings, there is no harm done in setting up a chart based on, typically, ten sets of readings. Fine-tuning of the results is then suggested as more readings become available. It is satisfying to know that the control limits based on, for example, ten readings are reasonably close to those obtained when using the full complement of twenty.

6.4.3 Calculation of control limits

The control limits are based on the general principle of being 3 standard deviations away from the central line. In Chapter 5 we referred to the fact that the relevant calculation for the standard deviation depends on the type of chart being looked at. The calculations are based on making use of some simple constants that are available in standard reference tables, a copy of which appears in Appendix 2.

It is extremely important that the calculation of the standard deviation is based on these constants and not the standard classical approach making use of other more complicated formulae. The increased availability and use of scientific calculators tends only to confuse, and not to help, and some explanation is appropriate.

Many hand-held calculators, more particularly the scientific ones, now include statistical routines. You may well have come across keys that are identified with a standard deviation. You might be attracted to making use of one or other of these keys in working out a standard deviation and then using it to determine a control limit. The advice is not to. Without going into the detail, the usual formulae for calculating a standard deviation, the ones that most of us are introduced to in the educational system, are not applicable when calculating control limits. Any calculations done in this way are inherently invalid, and in some cases can lead to results that are considerably in error. Refer to the article by Don Wheeler – *Charts done right* - noted in Appendix 4, for more detail on this.

6.5 Plotting and recording

The various results for the central lines and control limits can now be recorded in appropriate reference boxes on the control chart. The values of the control limits are then used to decide appropriate scales for the vertical axis, and the sample results can then be plotted on the vertical line through the centre of the sample value box. The central lines are drawn, using the generally adopted convention of a broken line. Because we need to get the process under control before using the chart to monitor future readings, the central line is drawn only as far as the last of the first twenty points.

Finally, the control limits are drawn corresponding to the values of UCL and LCL, and again spanning only the first twenty points. The convention for a control limit is to use a solid line. Some organisations use the reverse convention – bold lines for the central line and broken lines for the control limits. These differences tend only to reflect the different approaches adopted by various countries.

On a practical note, sometimes different colours are used for the control limits as opposed to the central lines.

6.6 Interpreting the chart

How the chart is interpreted depends on the stage we are at. Are we setting up the control chart in the first place, using the typically first twenty readings to generate the various lines? Or has the chart been set up, and we are using it in an on-going sense to monitor and improve the process?

6.6.1 Interpretation based on setting up the chart

The chart is now checked for stability by using the four rules that were introduced in the previous chapter, i.e: -

RULE 1	Any point outside one of the control limits.
RULE 2	A run of seven points, all above or all below the central line, or all increasing or all decreasing.
RULE 3	Any unusual patterns or trends within the control limits.
RULE 4	The number of points within the middle third of the region between the control limits differing markedly from two-thirds of the total number of points.

For example, *Fig 6.4* shows the sequence, which follows the use of RULE 1. A special cause is identified, the reading concerned is deleted and new control limits, and a new central line, determined using the remaining nineteen values. This has the effect of pulling the control lines inwards towards the central line.

Sometimes there may be a special cause present in the first twenty points which is attributable to a

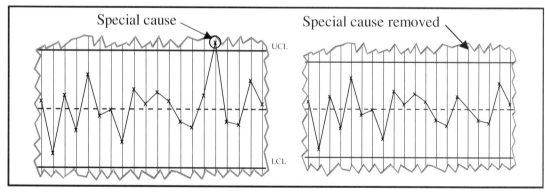

Fig 6.4 *Recalculation of control limits after removing a special cause.*

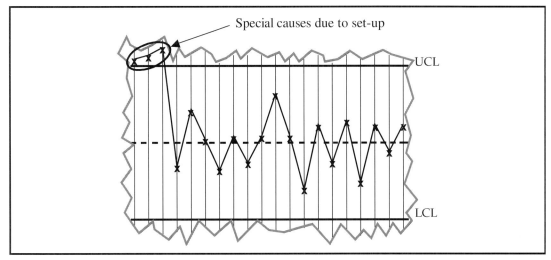

Fig 6.5 *Special cause identification in the first few points of a control chart.*

start up procedure – equivalent to the introduction of a new form. *Fig 6.5* shows such a situation. It transpired that a minor adjustment had been made to the design of the form at sample no 4. The control chart had already indicated that something unusual was taking place in the first few readings.

It is unlikely that RULES 2, 3 and 4 will apply in detecting an out of control signal in the first twenty points. If RULE 2 applies, then the result will be a run of 7, but it would rare for you to be able to detect the reason for this. It must be a chance occurrence and therefore part of the system.

RULE 3 may be present. For example we may have bunching of results, indicating the presence of two groups in the data. This problem should not have arisen because we should have been careful when taking the data that it was related to only one process, and not a combination of two or more processes. It would be extremely rare for RULE 4 to operate, and even more so to find a reason for it.

An interesting unusual feature is shown in *Fig 6.6*.

With more points outside the control limits than there are inside, a first response is that the process is without doubt highly unstable, with many special causes present. We could be side-tracked into

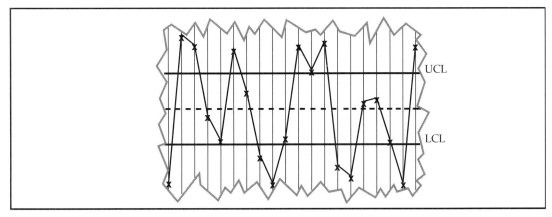

Fig 6.6 *Unusual pattern caused by use of wrong control chart.*

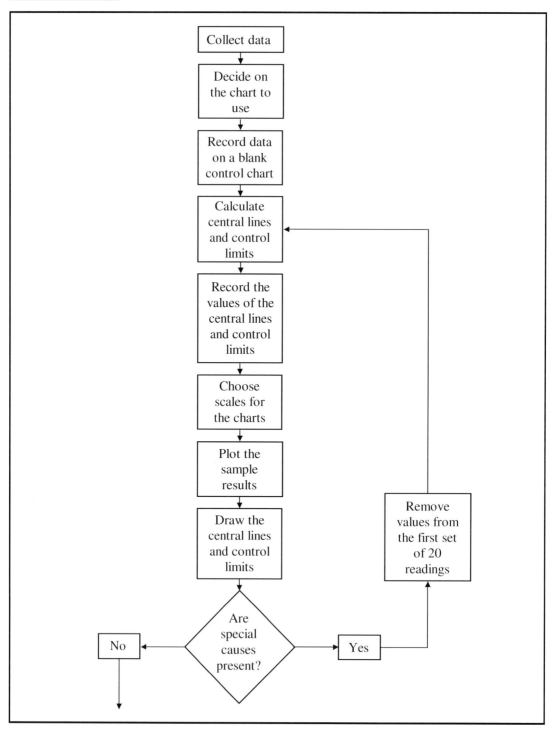

Fig 6.7 *Flow-chart for setting up a control chart and interpreting it.*

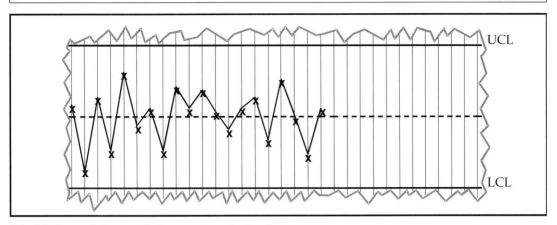

Fig 6.8 *Control chart with lines projected ahead.*

chasing the reasons for the occurrence of these special causes when it is very likely that all the points in question are actually part of the system. In fact, the problem is due to the wrong type of control chart being used. In practice, if the correct chart is being used, it is impossible to have a situation shown in Fig. 6.6. Choosing the correct chart to use is therefore crucial. More on this appears in Chapter 7.

To summarise, any special causes in the first twenty points result in recalculation of the control limits to more adequately represent the common cause variation. *Fig 6.7* shows a flowchart for the sequence of setting up a control chart and then checking on stability in the first twenty points.

6.6.2 Interpretation when using the chart in an ongoing situation

After the special causes in the first twenty readings have been eliminated, then the lines are drawn onwards as a basis for continually monitoring the process, as indicated in *Fig 6.8*.

The process is then continually monitored for stability by using the conventional four rules as each point, and subsequent points, are exposed. However, the rules are used in a slightly different way in an ongoing mode than they were in the initial stage of setting up the chart using the first twenty points.

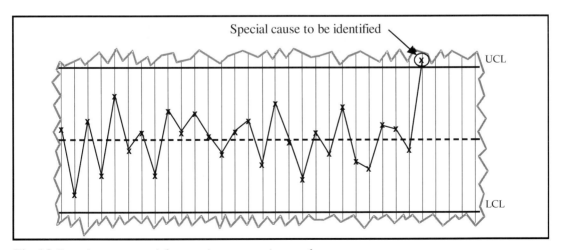

Fig 6.9 *Reaction to a special cause in an on-going mode.*

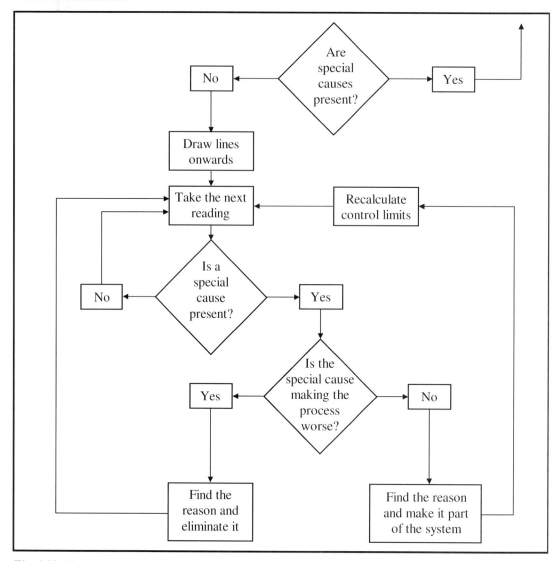

Fig 6.10 *Flow-chart for handling special causes in an on-going sense.*

For example, if an out of control signal is subsequently detected, then action is taken on that point. If the signal shows that it is related to RULE 1, then the action depends on whether the point being considered indicates a problem, or an opportunity. If the point suggests that there is deterioration then, ideally, the process is stopped and the reason for the special cause is investigated, as shown in *Fig 6.9*. In administrative processes, where the typical measure is time based, the occurrence of a special cause is due to an event that has happened in the past. We cannot stop the process as such, as we would do in a manufacturing environment. However, we need to identify the reason for the special cause. Once we are satisfied, then the recording process is continued. Certainly no recalculation of the limits is in order.

Depending on the type of chart being used, if the special cause is associated with improvement, then recalculation of the central line and control limits could be a possibility. However, it is essential that

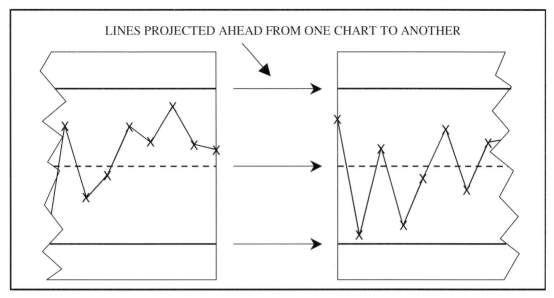

LINES PROJECTED AHEAD FROM ONE CHART TO ANOTHER

Fig.6.11 *Moving from one control chart sheet to the next.*

the cause of the improvement is substantiated, and that further calculations are based on enough points to justify the recalculations. More on this appears in Chapter 17.

Fig 6.10 shows a flowchart for handling a special cause in an ongoing sense.

6.6.3 Moving from sheet to sheet

With the central line and the control limits drawn ahead to the end of the first control chart in use, and data collected and results plotted, then a second blank control chart sheet is used.

The central line and the control limits are drawn in the same position on this second sheet. *Fig 6.11* shows how one chart leads on to the next.

This step may seem obvious and almost trite. In practice, this is not at all so. Incorrect procedures often follow at this stage. For example, in too many cases a new central line and new control limits are determined by accumulating all the readings that were available on the first completed chart, and using these as the basis of the calculation. This is inherently incorrect. Providing that the first twenty points taken were an adequate representation of the variation in the process, then the only way that we can justify any recalculation is when the chart signals that an improvement has taken place. Somehow or another, for all sorts of reasons, personnel make a connection between a control chart sheet and the process, i.e. a new sheet is a new process. This is a very dangerous practice. The only reason we use a new sheet is that it is impractical to have a control chart a mile long.

Another related issue is associated with carrying out a recalculation when a visual picture of the process at any stage suggests a set of twenty points which 'look good to work with'. Unfortunately, the flexibility of some of the current software packages that are available makes this an attractive option. Again, this is a very dangerous in SPC terms. Chapter 17 will give you some guidelines on when you are justified in recalculating control limits.

It is important to emphasise at this stage that the main function of a control chart is to improve the process. Controlling it at an established level is not improvement. The statistical guidelines for improvement are specific and need to be adhered to, and the detail appears in Chapter 17.

In this chapter, a sequence for data collection, recording, plotting and analysing has been introduced, shown in flow chart format in *Fig 6.7* and *Fig 6.10*.

This will be used in the chapters that follow when considering the three key control charts which will be concentrated on in this book.

The flow chart suggests that when a signal for improvement has been determined, then the control limits should be recalculated, and new scales for the control chart adopted. There is an interim step, which it is advisable to adopt. If the reason for improvement is known, which can result in the determination of new control limits, then it is advisable to keep the same scales for the sheet corresponding to the improvement to the process. There is a psychological benefit in using the same scales in the short term to show the effect of a change in process. After a common scale has been used spanning the improvement stage, then it is definitely worthwhile changing the scale to relate more sensibly to improved values of the control limits.

6.7 Summary of symbols and formulae

SLA	Service Level Agreement
$\overline{X}$	Sample mean
R	Range
$(\overline{X}, R)$	Chart for use with samples
Moving R	Moving Range
(X, Moving R)	Chart for use with single readings

6.8 Key points and summary

- Data is potentially available in a whole variety of forms.
- Keep the initial stage of collecting data as simple as possible.
- Do not carry out any plotting until the necessary calculations have been completed.
- Make sure that the unit is measured to a sufficient level of detail, e.g. hours rather than days.
- Control limits and central lines are conventionally based on the first twenty readings.
- Do not use the standard deviation key on a calculator to calculate control limits.
- Use the first twenty readings to check for stability.
- Remember the convention for drawing the various lines.
- Use the four rules to check that the first twenty points are under control
- A special cause in the first twenty points is removed from the calculations.
- An unusual pattern in the first twenty points could be due to the use of the wrong control chart.
- With the first twenty points under control, the central line and control limits can be drawn ahead.
- The reasons for out-of-control signals relating to a problem should be identified and eliminated.
- The reasons for out-of-control signals resulting in improvement should be integrated into the system.
- Remember to draw the lines onward from sheet to sheet.
- Never recalculate the control limits on what seems to be 'a good set of points'.
- Be careful when acquiring software packages.
- Control charts are used to improve a process, not just control it.
- A control chart provides good visual information on process improvement.

Now that we have developed a sequence for setting up a control chart we can use it in particular situations. The type of chart depends on the nature of the data we have available. The next chapter covers the important area of matching the data to the chart to be used.

WHICH CHART TO USE?

7.1 Introduction

There's no doubt that people often tend to be confused as to which type of control chart to use. It may be less of a problem for those involved in the operational function, dealing with data that will always be of the same type. Only one type of control chart will be required, and so the decision on chart type is straightforward. The choice will have been made for them, and they will be trained in an appropriate way in how to use the chart, interpret it and make decisions on what it tells them. It is the view of the authors that those using the chart should also be shown how the central lines and control limits are obtained. Others may not agree.

The problem of chart choice is likely to arise for those who have attended a more in-depth training course. They will have been exposed to a variety of terms and charts – charts dealing with samples, individuals, items which are measured, items which are counted, varying sample sizes, constant sample sizes, errors which are counted, faults which are analysed. The course might also have introduced flow-charts, and discussion examples, to make sure that people are confident in being able to apply the correct control chart. Even so, back in the work place, the choice may not be so obvious, particularly if there is a delay in applying the techniques practised on the training course.

It is no wonder that SPC causes so many difficulties.

One of the aims of this book is to make the choice as simple as possible. Hence the emphasis is on providing an understanding of three key charts. These three types provide adequate armoury for dealing with the great majority of data that you are likely to come across. In putting this book together, it was felt that there was more to be gained by pruning the choice than in trying to cover almost every option. Experience in providing many training courses and working closely with those who are using control charts has suggested that this would be a sensible attraction. For those who need more detail, reference will be made to other choices, and particularly so when considering attribute charts.

Basically, there are three choices.
1. Do we have single readings from the process?
2. Are we using samples rather than individual readings?
3. Do we have data that can be classified into different categories?

Throughout this book we will return to these three questions in one way or another, and the three charts we shall cover in further chapters provide the answers to these questions.

7.2 Chart based on individual readings

When dealing with individual readings, the chart to be used is known as the (X, Moving R) chart. The specific detail on the chart appears in Chapter 8, but it will help if we explain at this stage what a 'Moving Range' means.

Fig 7.1 (overleaf) shows a section from an (X, Moving R) chart, and the calculations involved.

	X	12	15	13	17	11
Moving R			3	2	4	6

Fig 7.1 Data recording section of an (X, Moving R) chart.

X could typically represent a monthly sales figure, an error rate, a processing time, and so on. In carrying out the necessary calculations, the X values are paired, e.g. twelve and fifteen, then fifteen and thirteen, thirteen and seventeen, etc. The range of the two numbers is the difference between them and is always treated as a positive quantity. The range could also be zero. The value of the moving range is then recorded in the 'Moving R' box. Note that the first Moving R box is blanked out because we must have two X values to start with in order to calculate a Moving R. By pairing the values in this way, we develop a series of moving ranges.

MR is often used to denote the moving range, although the general symbol R is also used.

This chart is likely to be the one for you. There is far more data about in administrative and service areas which allows us to use this particular chart, rather than the one to be covered in Section 7.3. It is also used as an acceptable alternative to the traditional approach when considering the chart to be covered in Section 7.4.

This is the chart we shall use when faced with the first question asked in the previous section, i.e. Do we have single readings from the process?

There are going to be many situations where this is going to be the case. Some specific examples follow.

These examples can be grouped into two main categories. In the first case data is available. It may either be limited to typically one or two sets, or we may have much more data available, often at least twenty sets – enough to create a control chart. In the second case we have no existing data for our process and we have to start collecting it.

7.2.1 Data available

Data limited in volume

We often have data in a form which lends itself naturally to be represented on a control chart, but is limited in the number of readings available. *Fig 7.2* shows a typical example.

PRODUCT	MAY 1995 - JULY 1995			AUGUST 1994 - JULY 1995		
	UNITS SOLD	MARKET SHARE	INDEX	UNITS SOLD	MARKET SHARE	INDEX
A	12,222	23.5%	180	48,755	23.9%	173
B	18,846	35.5%	105	74,746	36.6%	104
C	4,944	9.3%	69	19,721	9.7%	70
D	5.045	9.5%	68	17,489	8.6%	66
E	6,766	12.5%	88	25,018	12.2%	87
F	2,182	4.1%	99	8,342	4.1%	98

Fig 7.2 Section from a typical sales analysis sheet.

Location	Reportable accidents			Non-reportable accidents			Lost days		
	Quarters ending			Quarters ending			Quarters ending		
	March 1996	June 1995	June 1996	March 1996	June 1995	June 1996	March 1996	June 1995	June 1996
A	1	0	1	2	5	2	13	1	7
B	0	1	0	1	7	2	1	1	3
C	0	0	0	5	2	6	1	1	3
D	1	0	0	6	5	5	3	17	5
E	0	0	1	2	5	3	3	8	5
F	1	2	0	3	7	3	24	3	17
G	0	1	1	2	0	2	2	21	13
	3	4	3	21	31	23	47	52	53

Fig 7.3 *Tabular report on accidents.*

The data is a section from a regional sales analysis. Other data may also often be included, e.g. data that relates to market share by area and territory. It provides a typical basis for conventional decision making – compare the reading in one column for a particular product with the average result for the previous year. In other words, it takes no account of variation.

Note also that it compares a year with a quarter, which makes any analysis even less credible.

Taking more readings for the same product can make far better conclusions. For example, we could concentrate on Product B, and take 20 successive quarterly readings, and then use these to set up a control chart. But this takes too long. Why not create a control chart looking at daily, weekly or monthly results? Quarterly readings are not good enough. Sales figures provide excellent material for SPC analysis, as illustrated by one of the case studies to be discussed in Chapter 9.

Accident figures should also be represented in SPC format, but unfortunately this is not the norm. Typically, accident analysis is represented by *Fig 7.3*, a tabular layout similar in format to that shown in *Fig 7.2*.

Comparisons between this quarter and last quarter, this quarter and the same quarter last year are then carried out. In one organisation analysing accident patterns in this way, the person responsible for preparing summary reports came to the following conclusion based on a certain set of results: -

"*The results for this quarter are disappointing. Not only are they a complete reversal of recent trends for this quarter over recent years but they are also significantly worse than the last quarter, which in turn was a reversal over previous years.*"

Statements such as this are almost certain to follow if it is someone's responsibility to produce monthly/quarterly reports on data and they have not been exposed to SPC thinking.

So, if you have available any single reading data based on a one-to-one comparison, your first step is to collect more data, i.e. twenty sample points, and then use the (X, Moving R) chart.

Data not limited in volume

Sometimes we already have available a large amount of data which is sufficient to set up a control chart. *Fig 4.2,* in Chapter 4, showing inventory figures, was a typical example.

Fig 7.4 (overleaf) shows another typical sheet.

The figures in this example relate to numbers of forms at various stages of processing in an insurance company. They are part of a larger display, the sheet being accompanied by other similarly detailed information in the familiar row and column format. Again, this type of data is ideal for an (X, Moving R) chart. Twenty sets of data are already available for use. The only issue is to decide the relative importance of each set of figures so as to know the priority areas for setting up control charts.

	During the week			At end of week				Correspondence		
				Total	Number	Work			Outstanding	
Period	Proposals		Cases	in	not	in	Pending			Not
ending	Estimated	Received	Compl'ed	Dept.	started	progress	reply	Rec'd	Matched	matched
17-Jan	288	88	133	534	104	116	314	68	31	2
24-Jan	312	135	109	639	118	110	411	76	22	0
31-Jan	336	65	119	503	48	72	383	35	0	0
7-Feb	426	180	125	494	51	53	390	53	1	3
14-Feb	532	181	114	501	11	128	362	74	5	1
21-Feb	585	115	141	478	14	37	425	79	9	3
28-Feb	585	267	111	565	75	133	357	52	13	1
7-Mar	617	178	179	688	59	235	394	57	40	0
14-Mar	1152	181	81	902	62	221	619	52	23	0
21-Mar	1049	204	261	731	79	134	518	100	38	10
28-Mar	1296	235	239	764	108	158	498	105	32	1
4-Apr	1344	437	113	954	205	158	591	63	15	1
11-Apr	1393	883	425	1429	834	270	325	118	60	3
18-Apr	552	385	232	1577	895	335	347	98	47	2
25-Apr	518	859	410	1876	1228	269	379	124	63	23
2-May	497	669	1115	1782	1221	378	283	234	97	50
9-May	497	346	712	1565	1072	187	306	92	78	156
16-May	497	262	207	1606	902	365	339	135	101	56
23-May	497	137	384	1268	721	206	341	144	72	62
30-May	497	144	172	1306	752	196	358	109	110	80

Fig 7.4 Summary of status of documents being processed in an insurance office.

Many more examples similar to those shown in *Fig 7.3* and *Fig 7.4* could be shown. Almost certainly you will have come across computerised data sheets in your own organisation. What do you do with them?

If you are starting a new process, then you will need to collect data, and a data collection sheet is therefore required.

7.2.2 Data not currently available and has to be collected

We already had an example of this in *Fig 6.2* in Chapter 6. A more complete section of the same data collection sheet is shown in *Fig 7.6*.

Typical data collection sheets used in practice follow this general format.

For example, *Fig 7.5* shows a section of a data collection sheet used by a bank.

ANALYSIS OF PROCESSED PAYMENTS				
Date	Number of payments received	Number of files held over	Total number of files	Proportion of files held over
04-Jan	233	33	266	0.124
05-Jan	240	70	310	0.226
06-Jan	199	64	263	0.243
07-Jan	272	70	342	0.205
08-Jan	257	69	326	0.212
11-Jan	238	52	290	0.179

Fig 7.5 Section of a data collection sheet used in processing payments in a bank

Process - *Batch completion times*				Chartkeeper- *Jane*		
Sample No	Batch . Ref.No.	Date commenced	Time	Date completed	Time	Time taken (hours)
1	BG /387	Jun-03	8:35	Jun-03	16:36	7
2	BT /776	Jun-04	8:47	Jun-04	12:45	4
3	H /2391	Jun-04	14:17	Jun-05	09:56	3
4	CG /65	Jun-05	10:37	Jun-05	16:49	5
5	A VY /54	Jun-06	8:48	Jun-06	10:46	2
6	CG /65	Jun-06	11:19	Jun-07	10:38	8
7	PJ/56	Jun-07	11:46	Jun-07	15:37	4
8	CDW /19	Jun-07	16:07	Jun-10	09:37	2
9	VK /65	Jun-10	10:14	Jun-10	14:54	3
10	BF /2128	Jun-11	15:45	Jun-12	10:56	4
11	GHY /9	Jun-12	11:36	Jun-12	15-25	3
12	DD /43	Jun-12	15:48	Jun-13	11:38	5
13	PP /444	Jun-13	12:50	Jun-14	10:37	5
14	GHT /332	Jun-14	11:31	Jun-17	09:05	6
15	GHT /54	Jun-17	9:23	Jun-17	11:20	2
16	P /498	Jun-17	12:08	Jun-17	16:26	3
17	FT /443	Jun-18	9:05	Jun-18	12:34	3
18	BF /554	Jun-18	14:00	Jun-19	11:38	7
19	CDW /665	Jun-19	12:36	Jun-19	15:04	2
20	PJ/543	Jun-19	16:28	Jun-20	12:05	5
21	BV /559	Jun-20	13-34	Jun-21	09:45	5
22	CS /3	Jun-21	10:23	Jun-21	16:25	5
23	GT /87	Jun-24	8:45	Jun-24	11:34	3
24	CDW /5	Jun-24	12:20	Jun-24	14:50	2

Fig 7.6 Data collection sheet for recording times to process documents

In this example it is 'proportions' that will be plotted on an (X, Moving R) control chart, each proportion being treated as a single reading.

To summarise, all the examples of data covered in Sections 7.2.1 and 7.2.2 relate to a single reading. It may be a variable or an attribute – it doesn't matter. We simply call the variable an X value and use it in an (X, moving R) chart.

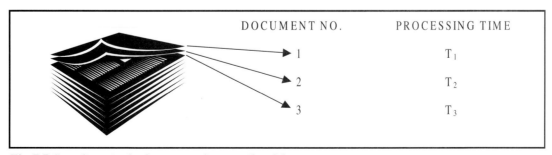

	DOCUMENT NO.	PROCESSING TIME
	1	T_1
	2	T_2
	3	T_3

Fig 7.7 Sampling single documents from a pile of documents.

CHAPTER 7

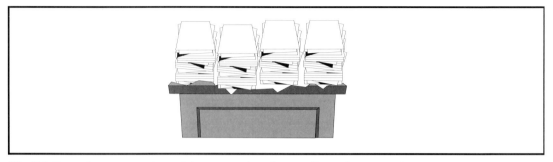

Fig 7.8 *Typical representation of documents in a large office where sampling is a necessity*

7.3 Chart based on samples

When taking samples, we use an ($\overline{X}$, R) chart. Some explanation is required as to why we need a different chart.

In the previous section, we had a situation represented by *Fig 7.7*, i.e. documents being analysed, and it is possible to measure the time taken for each document to be processed.

For the larger organisations, dealing with more and more documents, it may be physically impossible to measure the response time for each document. There are situations where there are so many documents available that there is not enough resource available to handle the requirements necessary to look at each document, as shown in *Fig 7.8*.

Measurement shouldn't become a hassle. So if it's not practical to measure every item using an (X, Moving R) chart, we take samples, as indicated schematically in *Fig 7.9*.

Because we are now using samples, and not individuals, then we use a new chart – the ($\overline{X}$, R) chart. In Sections 5.7 and 5.8 we explained how to calculate a sample mean $\overline{X}$ and a sample range R.

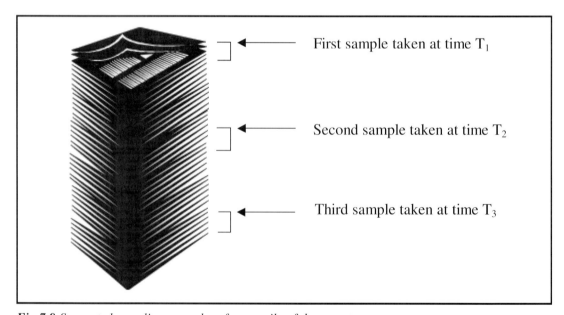

First sample taken at time T_1

Second sample taken at time T_2

Third sample taken at time T_3

Fig 7.9 *Suggested sampling procedure from a pile of documents*

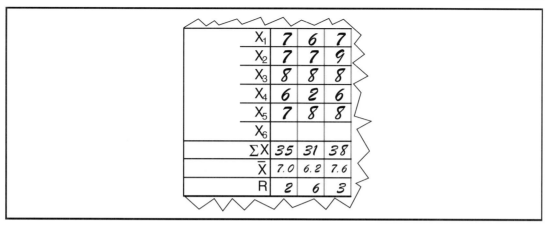

Fig 7.10 Data recording section of an ($\overline{X}$, R) chart.

SUPPLIER	REF. NO.	DATE RECEIVED	DATE COMPLETED
A.R.Watkins	ARW/2459	May-14	May-23
Selco	SE/12239	May-14	May-29
W. Bristoe	WB/98	May-14	Jun-02
H. Johnston	HJ/25673	May-14	May-26
Selco	SE/12240	May-14	May-29
B.P. Armitage	BPA/398	May-14	Jun-12
R.Gillespie	RG/45	May-14	May-25
A.R.Watkins	ARW/2460	May-14	May-29
D. Peters	DP/223	May-14	May-26
H.O. Trust	HO/978	May-14	May-29
H. Johnston	HJ/25674	May-14	May-25
Parkers	P/447	May-14	May-26
Jim Churchill	JC/76	May-14	May-31
D. Peters	DP/224	May-14	May-29
A. Smythe	AS/67	May-14	May-30
H. Johnston	HJ/2565	May-14	May-26
R. Wilson	RW/982	May-14	May-28
Tedder & Son	T/655	May-14	Jun-08
A.R. Watkins	ARW/2461	May-14	Jun-01
Sungold	S/9973	May-14	Jun-05
A.R. Watkins	ARW/2462	May-14	May-29
Peter Roberts	PR/4432	May-14	May-23
H.L.R. Butcher	HLRB/33	May-14	May-31
H. Johnston	HJ/25675	May-14	Jun-05
R. Wilson	RW/983	May-15	Jun-01
Sungold	S/9974	May-15	May-31
H. Johnston	HJ/25676	May-15	Jun-05

Fig 7.11 Section from a data sheet indicating response times from suppliers.

In practice the results are recorded on a control chart. A section of a chart showing the results for the first three samples is shown in *Fig 7.10*. More detail on this appears in Section 10.7.1 in Chapter 10.

In this case we have been using a typical sample size of 5 documents. Consideration of sample size, etc. will be discussed in Chapter 10.

So, when we are using samples rather than individual readings, we use the ($\overline{X}$, R) chart.

7.3.1 Data available

A typical set of data which lends itself to the ($\overline{X}$, R) chart is shown in *Fig 7.11*. It represents a section from a table that relates to the time taken to respond to documents coming from different suppliers.

Traditionally, the data has been collected more as part of a checking procedure, rather than being used to measure the process itself.

Sometimes the actual response times may be used to develop response tables, such as that shown in *Fig 7.12*.

Tables of this form are commonly on display at railway stations. Do you feel any better regarding performance times when you read them?

With new processes, there is probably no data available, and so we need to design a data collection sheet.

7.3.2 Data not currently available and has to be collected

A typical data collection sheet is shown in *Fig 7.13*. It is based on the data sheet shown in *Fig. 7.11*. Extra columns are added to allow for the fact that we are going to take samples of five from the many readings available each day rather than consider all the readings which may be available.

It is important that we take samples in a way which best reflects what the process is doing. This issue is covered in detail in a case study that appears in Chapter 17.

In summary, whenever the data involves a measurable feature such as time, and we are taking samples from the process at regular intervals and not looking at each item, then we use the ($\overline{X}$, R) chart.

7.4 Data which is classified into different categories

When handling data of this type, we make use of what we call a multiple characteristics chart.

The data is usually recognisable in that it refers to faults, omissions, errors, etc. Unlike the data used in the previous section, which refers to items which are measured, multiple characteristic data refers to counts – how many documents are rejected, how many customers are complaining, for what reason, etc. More detail on the nature of the data, and how we develop the chart, appears in Chapter 12.

Suffice to say that the chart used for recording and plotting this data has a different layout to the two previous charts.

Fig 7.14 shows a section from typical multiple characteristics chart. In this case we have been

% OF DELIVERIES ARRIVING WITHIN GIVEN TIMES					
< 2 DAYS EARLY	2 - 1 DAYS EARLY	1 - 0 DAYS EARLY	0-1 DAYS LATE	1-2 DAYS LATE	> 2 DAYS LATE
6	11	66	12	3	2
9	14	67	4	4	2
7	8	73	6	3	3
6	9	72	3	6	4
9	5	65	9	9	3

Fig 7.12 *Section from a table indicating response times against performance standard.*

SAMPLE NO.	SUPPLIER	REF. NO.	DATE RECEIVED	DATE COMPLETED	TIME (DAYS)
1	A.R.Watkins	ARW/2459	May-14	May-23	7
	Selco	SE/12239	May-14	May-29	11
	W. Bristoe	WB/98	May-14	Jun-06	17
	H. Johnston	HJ/25673	May-14	May-25	9
	Selco	SE/12240	May-14	May-29	11
	B.P. Armitage	BPA/398	May-14	Jun-07	18
	R. Gillespie	RG/45	May-14	May-25	9
	A.R.Watkins	ARW/2460	May-14	May-29	11
	A R.W atkins	ARW /2462	M ay-14	M ay-29	11
	PeterRoberts	PR /4432	M ay-14	M ay-23	7
	H L R .Butcher	HLRB /33	M ay-14	M ay-31	13
	H .Johnston	HJ/25675	M ay-14	Jun-05	16
2	R.W ilson	RW /983	M ay-15	Jun-01	13
	Sungold	S /9974	M ay-15	M ay-31	12
	H .Johnston	HJ/25676	M ay-15	Jun-05	15
	A R.W atkins	ARW /2463	M ay-15	M ay-29	10
	B PA rm itage	BPA /399	M ay-15	M ay-28	9
	Tedder& Son	T /656	M ay-15	M ay-23	6
	PeterRoberts	PR /4433	M ay-15	M ay-29	10
	Sungold	S /9975	M ay-15	M ay-24	7

Fig 7.13 *Data collection sheet for recording sample times for a process involving many documents.*

PROCESS CONTROL CHART

No	Class / Characteristic				
1	Post code	1	3	2	
2	Area code			3	2
3	Payment type		1	3	2
4	Customer reference	2		2	2
5	M/c data		2		
6	List price		4		2
7	Unauthorised discount	4	2	1	3
8	Bank details	9	8	11	4
9	No official order				3
10	No trade code			4	3
11	Other	2	3	2	5

Fig 7.14 *Section from a multiple characteristics chart.*

COMPLAINTS ANALYSIS - September		
TYPE OF COMPLAINT	NUMBER	%
Communication	2	8
Clerical error	3	12
Fleet	1	4
Picking error	7	27
Packaging/labelling	2	8
Carrier	8	31
Loading	3	12
	26	100

Fig 7.15 *Section from a monthly report relating to customer complaints.*

recording data on the different types of errors in a sales form. The type of error is noted in the class/characteristic column, and the columns that follow allow us to record how many errors of a certain type occurred over the weeks as more and more forms are scrutinised.

As with item 11, you might use a 'miscellaneous' or 'other' category. If you do, make sure it is not the biggest one.

Similarly, there are boxes available to record the total number of errors occurring in a given week, as well as the number of documents examined. When we come to plotting the data available we again make use of the (X, Moving R) chart, as shown in detail in Chapter 12.

The third question asked at the beginning of this chapter was: Do we have data that can be classified into different categories?

If the answer is yes, then we go straight to the multiple characteristics chart.

7.4.1 Data available

Multiple characteristic data is frequently available, although we may not recognise it for what it is.

The data might be limited, as shown in *Fig 7.15*.

Here we have a section from details of customer complaints for the month of September. The complaints relate to delivery problems.

Data is very often available in a less limited form, as shown in *Fig 7.16*.

The data in this case tabulates errors in processing documents in an insurance organisation. It represents a section from a large amount of data that is available for analysis.

There must be so much historical data of this type hidden away in various locations. It is ideal for representing in the form of a control chart.

7.4.2 Data not currently available and has to be collected

An appropriate data sheet needs to be designed for collecting data, which can be used in a multiple characteristic sense.

We are fortunate in the case of this type of data because the layout of the multiple characteristic control chart enables it to be used as a data collection sheet. For example, *Fig 7.17* shows a section of a data collection sheet used by a bank.

The category codes refer to the type of errors.

Fig 7.18 (overleaf) shows how the error type, and a record of the frequencies involved, can be entered directly into a multiple characteristics sheet.

FILE NO	DATE DEALT	WHAT FAILED	WHY FAILED - MUST BE COMPLETED	PROCESS OWNER	TOTAL NO. OF RECORDS ON FILE
6273	Aug-02	UCDx2	Tidy duplicated	J.I.	
		UCDx2	Wrong policy number	J.M.C.	
		CCA	Wrong policy number	U.L.S.	
		RPAx9	Fdate policy instead of due date	D.B.	
		UCDx6	Tidy duplicated	T.C.	
		UCD	Wrong member no.	A.M.	
		UCD	No apparent reasons	Keytapes??	
					523
6279	Aug-05	UCDx2	Wrong date paid	L.W.	
		UCD	Wrong policy no.	D.S.	
		CCA	Wrong member no.	S.J.	
		RPA	Wrong member no.	S.J.	
		UCD	Wrong policy no.	D.P.	
		UCD	Wrong date paid	D.P.	
		UCD	Wrong due date	L.W.	
		UCD	Wrong policy no.	L.W.	
		UCD	Already cleared	D.P.	
					253
6286	Aug-06	UCD	Wrong policy no.	D.B.	
		CCA	Wrong policy no.	D.B.	
		TCA	Tidy duplicated	W.H.	
		UCD	Tidy duplicated	W.H.	

Fig 7.16 Section from a log sheet recording errors in a document.

There is nothing to be gained by designing a check sheet when there is a ready-made sheet provided as part of the multiple characteristics chart. The data is now neatly recorded and ready to be used in setting up a control chart. This will be covered fully in Chapter 10.

The only limitation on using the data collection part of the control chart sheet directly is that an intermediate step may be required. When there is a large amount of data, the total for each box

Week commencing	Day	Category Code								Daily total
		A	B	C	D	S	E	FF	N/A	
Jan-06	1	7	10	24	0	0	3	2	4	50
	2	20	9	21	3	1	1	2	12	69
	3	23	5	28	3	0	5	3	16	73
	4	17	10	20	2	1	4	2	13	69
	5	19	18	24	0	0	2	2	12	77
TOTAL		86	52	117	8	2	15	11	47	338
Jan-13	1	16	9	28	0	0	5	3	6	67
	2	19	5	23	1	6	1	2	8	65
	3	21	9	29	2	0	3	4	6	74

Fig 7.17 Section from a typical data collection sheet used for recording errors.

PROCESS CONTROL CHART - MULT

No	Class / Characteristic						
1	A = Agent	7	20	23	17	19	16
2	B = Branch	10	9	5	10	18	9
3	C = Customer	24	21	28	20	24	28
4	D = department	0	3	3	2	0	0
5	S = system	0	1	0	1	0	0
6	E = re-open	3	1	5	4	2	5
7	FF = Fate	2	2	3	3	2	3
8	N/A = Non-applicable	4	12	6	13	12	6

Fig 7.18 Preferred method of collecting multiple characteristic data.

corresponding to the number of occurrences may not be easily obtained without using tally marks when first accumulating the information. A first sheet is then used, and the totals recorded in the second chart as suggested in *Fig. 7.19 (a)*. Alternatively, and more appropriately for smaller items of information, both the frequencies and the totals can be recorded in the same box, as shown in *Fig 7.19 (b)*.

In this chapter we have covered the three different data types which can be plotted on a control chart, i.e. the (X, Moving R) chart, the ($\overline{X}$, R) chart, and the multiple characteristics chart. How do we know which chart to use?

7.5 Making the choice

Fig 7.20 provides a flow chart for deciding on the right chart.

The flow-chart provides answers to the three questions that were asked in Section 7.1: -

1. Do we have single readings from the process?
2. Are we using samples rather than individual readings?
3. Do we have data that can be classified into different categories?

The flow chart should make the choice straightforward. However, there is nothing better than practice in order to become confident in which chart to apply.

In the following three chapters, the three charts to be covered will be looked at in detail, and a series of case studies are provided showing how the particular chart has been applied in practice by various organisations.7.6 Summary of symbols and formulae

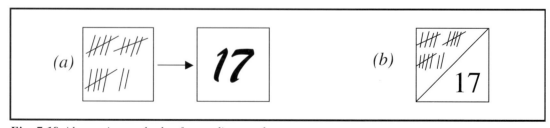

Fig. 7.19 Alternative methods of recording totals.

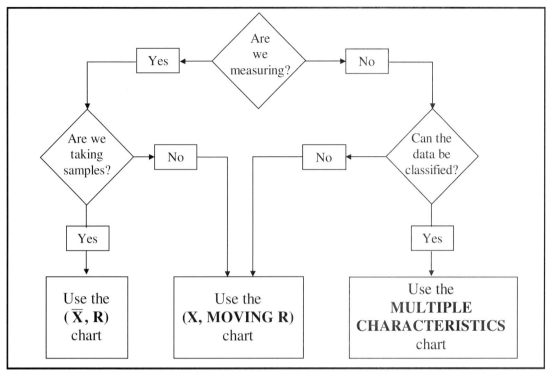

Fig 7.20 *Flow-chart for deciding on type of chart to use.*

R   Moving Range or Sample Range
MR   Alternate symbol for Moving Range
$\overline{X}$ Mean of X values

7.7 Key points and summary

- Three control charts are available which cover the majority of data sets.
- Historical data is often used for setting up control charts.
- If no data is available, then data collection sheets need to be designed and utilised.
- If single readings are available, either as a variable or an attribute, then use an (X, Moving R) chart.
- If we are dealing with variables, then use the ($\overline{X}$, R) chart.
- If we are using attributes, and the data can be classified in one way or another, then use the multiple characteristics chart.
- Choose the time period for the chart to match the availability of the data.
- A multiple characteristic sheet can be used to collect the data directly.
- Use a flow chart in helping you to make the right choice.

Having introduced the three charts, we now look at each one in detail.

Chapter 8 covers the (X, Moving R) chart. In doing so it makes use of typical data which is available in an office – sales figures.

THE (X,MOVING R) CHART

8.1 Introduction

In Chapter 7, various data formats were displayed which are ideal to be plotted on a control chart. By far the most common form of chart which can be applied to data in general is the (X, Moving R) chart, sometimes referred to as the individual, or single reading, chart. Sales figures, response times of all types, absenteeism – these are typical examples which provide data that is being plotted on an (X, Moving R) chart in an increasing number of organisations.

The bulk of the chapter takes you through the calculations that are required in setting up the control chart. These calculations are not arduous. By following a logical sequence, and making use of indices which are available from standard tables, the central lines and control limits can be obtained in a relatively painless way.

Many interesting applications of the use of this chart are becoming available, and these will be referred to in a general sense in the chapter. The next chapter will provide specific detail on eight case studies, which in various ways highlight the potential for using this chart in process improvement.

8.2 Some typical figures to work on

In Chapter 7, in Section 7.2, a variety of different sets of data was shown which could be used for plotting on an (X, Moving R) chart.

Fig 8.1 provides a list of some further general applications.

Abandoned telephone calls	Lost man-hours
Regional manpower numbers	Authorisation response times
Analysis of customer service times	Analysis of sales staff
Settlement of benefits	Organising shipping instructions
Response times	Overtime analysis
School attendance level	Budget preparation
Analysis of self-certification forms	Accounts overdue
Payment of expense claims	Revenue control
Gas consumption	Implementing suggestions
Analysis of petty cash	Stock analysis

Fig 8.1 *Typical applications of the (X, Moving R) chart in office areas.*

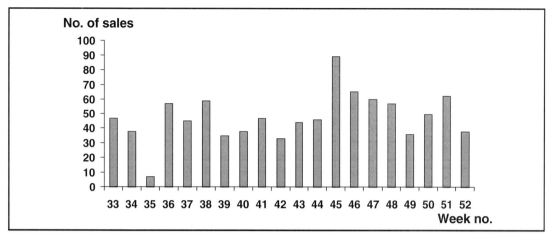

Fig 8.2 *Bar chart of sales figure over a period of weeks.*

These are a representative selection of typical SPC projects that are being progressed in administrative areas in different organisations.

In developing the (X, Moving R) chart, we shall follow the generic sequence laid down in Chapter 6. The first requirement is to define the process.

8.3 Defining the process

A sales process is common to most organisations, and Chapter 2 considered it in some detail.

How can we measure the sales process? Well, it seems natural to make use of the number of sales made in a given time, or alternatively, the value of these sales. Other measures might include the number of calls made per week, the times involved at different stages in the sales process, and so on.

A specific example of data representation shown in *Fig 4.3* in Chapter 4 was the bar chart used to represent sales figures. The chart is shown again in *Fig 8.2*.

We will use the actual sales values as the working figures in developing the (X, Moving R) chart.

In progressing through the sequence, the guidelines shown in the flowchart in *Fig 6.7* in Chapter 6 will be adopted. The flowchart is shown in reduced form as a guide in each of the relevant sections that follow.

The first step is to collect the data.

8.4 Collecting the data

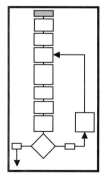

Collect data

The bar chart shown previously was produced from raw data, which in all probability had been collected by means of a data collection sheet. The figures that were used are shown in the table in *Fig 8.3 (overleaf)*.

| No. of sales | 47 | 38 | 7 | 57 | 45 | 59 | 35 | 38 | 47 | 33 | 44 | 46 | 89 | 65 | 60 | 57 | 36 | 50 | 62 | 38 |
| Week no. | 33 | 34 | 35 | 36 | 37 | 38 | 39 | 40 | 41 | 42 | 43 | 44 | 45 | 46 | 47 | 48 | 49 | 50 | 51 | 52 |

Fig 8.3 *Table of sales figures over a period of weeks.*

8.5 The control chart format to be used

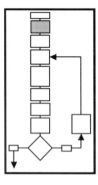

> **Decide on the chart to use**

Reference to the various examples dealt with in Chapter 7 indicates that it is the (X, Moving R) chart that is used with single readings such as sales figures. Use of the flow chart shown in *Fig 7.20* confirms this.

Each type of control chart varies slightly in its layout. The basic format is the same, represented schematically in *Fig 6.3* in Chapter 6. Because the various calculations required are slightly different, then we can expect that the control

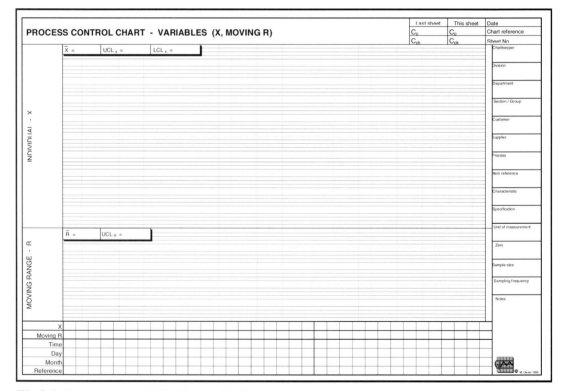

Fig 8.4 *Master version of (X, Moving R) chart.*

chart to be used reflects this, and hence the design of each chart is modified slightly to allow for the type of calculation required.

For each chart, it is the section for recording the data to be used that causes the difference. It may be helpful here to show you the blank chart we shall be working on. *Fig 8.4* is the version of the (X, Moving R) chart we shall use.

At some stage we need to record the descriptive information relating to the process, and it is just as well to do this at the beginning of the control chart procedure.

Fig 8.5 shows some of the completed boxes relating to the sales process.

In addition to completing the data boxes shown in *Fig 8.5*, at this stage we should also complete the boxes at the bottom of the sheet, which identify the time, sample no. etc.

Fig 8.6 shows the completed section of the chart.

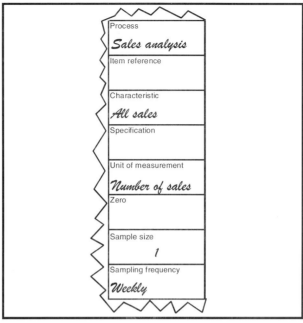

Fig 8.5 Section showing some of the completed process information boxes.

It is very important that we complete the various boxes. They provide necessary reference data that identifies with the process.

8.6 Recording data on chart

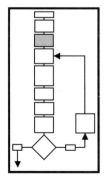

Record data on a blank control chart

Fig 8.7 shows part of the data recording section for the (X, Moving R) chart.

The X figures refer to the values to be plotted, in our case the sales values. The Moving R value needs to be explained.

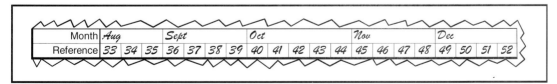

Fig 8.6 Section of chart showing completed 'month' and 'reference' boxes.

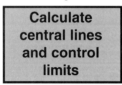

| X | 47 | 38 | 7 | 57 | 45 | 59 | 35 | 38 | 47 | 33 | 44 | 46 | 89 | 65 | 60 | 57 | 36 | 50 | 62 | 38 |
| Moving R | | | | | | | | | | | | | | | | | | | | |

Fig 8.7 Data recording section of an (X, Moving R) chart with the X boxes filled in.

8.7 Carrying out the required calculations

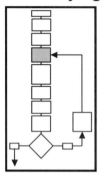

Calculate central lines and control limits

Before we can calculate the central line and the control limits, we need to calculate the moving ranges.

8.7.1 Sample calculations

A moving range was introduced in *Fig 7.1* in Chapter 7. It is a value that represents the variation from one reading to the next.

We will use the first six values of the sales readings, as shown in *Fig 8.8*, to show how to calculate the moving ranges for our figures.

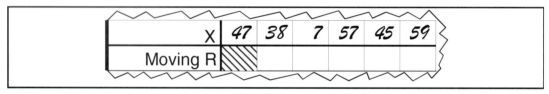

Fig 8.8 Data section showing the first six sales readings.

The moving range R is determined by calculating the difference between each two successive X values, the R value being taken as positive irrespective of the order of the two numbers concerned.

For the first two readings, the moving range is $47 - 38 = 9$.

This value is recorded in the second box in the Moving R row. We can block out the first Moving R box as it is not used.

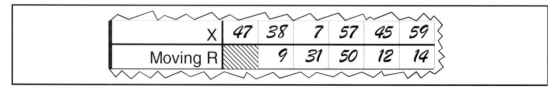

Fig 8.9 Completed data boxes for the first six X values of an (X, Moving R) chart for sales.

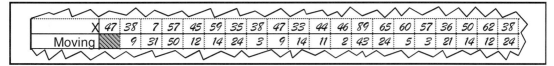

Fig 8.10 *Completed data boxes for the first twenty X values of an (X, Moving R) chart for sales.*

The first reading, 47, is now dropped, and we have a new pair, involving the second and third values for X. This gives a new moving range of 38 – 7 = 31.

The next pair, 7 and 57, give a moving range of 50, and so on giving completed boxes for the first six readings as shown in *Fig 8.9.*

This procedure is continued for the twenty X values provided, and we then have a set of X and Moving R values shown in *Fig 8.10.*

Now that we have calculated the 19 moving ranges, we are in a position to determine the central lines for both the X section and the Moving R section of the control chart.

8.7.2 Calculation of central lines

For the X section of the chart: -

$$\overline{X} = \frac{\Sigma X}{20} = \frac{953}{20} = 47.65$$

For the Moving R section of the chart: -

$$\overline{R} = \frac{\Sigma R}{19} = \frac{325}{19} = 17.11$$

8.7.3 Calculation of control limits

Control limits for the X section of the chart

We use the notation UCL_X and LCL_X for the upper and lower control limits respectively.

For the X section of the chart, we know that UCL_X and LCL_X are to be positioned at a distance of 3 standard deviations out from the central line $\overline{X}$.

How are we going to obtain the standard deviation $\hat{\sigma}$?

Certainly not by using any of the conventional formulae which have been referred to earlier. If we do so, then we will finish up with incorrect results. There is some further explanation on this later in Section 8.15.1.

What we do is make use of an index d_2 that can be obtained from tables.

We then calculate our standard deviation from the formula $\hat{\sigma} = \dfrac{\overline{R}}{d_2}$.

The complete tables appear in Appendix 2 and a sub-section of them is shown in *Fig 8.11.*

The row corresponding to the sample size 2 has been highlighted because we have been using paired values as the basis of working out our moving ranges.

From the tables we see that or required value of d_2 is 1.128.

We have already calculated $\overline{R}$ as 17.11

$$\therefore \hat{\sigma} = \frac{17.11}{1.128} = 15.17$$

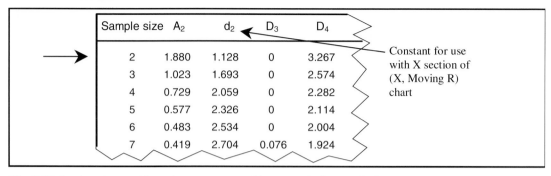

Sample size	A₂	d₂	D₃	D₄
2	1.880	1.128	0	3.267
3	1.023	1.693	0	2.574
4	0.729	2.059	0	2.282
5	0.577	2.326	0	2.114
6	0.483	2.534	0	2.004
7	0.419	2.704	0.076	1.924

Constant for use with X section of (X, Moving R) chart

***Fig 8.11** Section from tables of constants used in control chart calculations*

The control limits can then be calculated as follows: -

$$UCL_X = \overline{X} + 3\hat{\sigma}$$
$$= 47.65 + (3 \times 15.17)$$
$$= 47.65 + 45.51$$
$$= 93.16$$

Similarly,

$$LCL_X = \overline{X} - 3\hat{\sigma}$$
$$= 47.65 - 45.51$$
$$= 2.14$$

Now that you know how to work out the values of UCL_X and LCL_X, we can make things a little simpler.

In determining the values of UCL_X and LCL_X , we used the expression $3 \times \dfrac{\overline{R}}{d_2}$.

If we keep the sample size fixed at two, then d_2 is always 1.128, and $\dfrac{3}{d_2}$ is 2.66.

Hence: -

$$UCL_X = \overline{X} + (2.66 \times \overline{R})$$
$$LCL_X = \overline{X} - (2.66 \times \overline{R})$$

Control limits for the R section of the chart

We use the notation UCL_R and LCL_R for the upper and lower control limits respectively for R.

For the X section of the chart, we positioned the control limits 3 standard deviations about $\overline{X}$.

We cannot use this approach when deaing with the control limits for R. The reason for this is tied up with the statistical theory behind the various indices that are available. Basically, the distribution of R does not give a symmetrical pattern about $\overline{R}$. We need not worry, however, because other indices have been obtained, denoted by D_3 and D_4 , to help us get over the problem. *Fig 8.12* shows the same section of the table of constants, but this time highlighting the D_3 and D_4 constants.

UCL_R is then obtained by multiplying D_4 by $\overline{R}$ and LCL_R similarly obtained from D_3 multiplied by $\overline{R}$. From the tables, with a sample size 2, D_4 is 3.267

$$\therefore UCL_R = D_4 \overline{R}$$
$$= 3.267 \times 17.11$$
$$= 55.90$$

With a sample size 2, D_3 is 0 and hence LCL_R is zero.

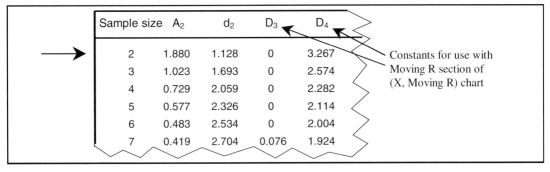

Sample size	A₂	d₂	D₃	D₄	
2	1.880	1.128	0	3.267	
3	1.023	1.693	0	2.574	Constants for use with
4	0.729	2.059	0	2.282	Moving R section of
5	0.577	2.326	0	2.114	(X, Moving R) chart
6	0.483	2.534	0	2.004	
7	0.419	2.704	0.076	1.924	

Fig 8.12 *Section from tables of constants used in control chart calculations.*

8.8 Recording numerical values on chart

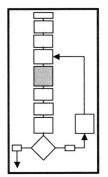

> **Record the values of the central lines and control limits**

Now that the central lines and control limits have been calculated, the results can be recorded in the data boxes on the two sections of the chart.

Fig 8.13 shows the completed boxes.

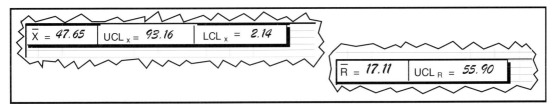

$\bar{X} = 47.65$ $UCL_x = 93.16$ $LCL_x = 2.14$

$\bar{R} = 17.11$ $UCL_R = 55.90$

Fig 8.13 *Data boxes showing values of central lines and control limits.*

8.9 Choosing scales for the charts

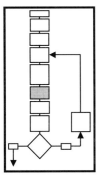

> **Choose scales for the charts**

With the control limits calculated, we can use them to determine suitable scales for the X and Moving R sections of the control chart.

We know that UCL_x is 93.16 and LCL_x is 2.14. The blank control chart has ten major gridlines for the X section. By recording 10, 20, 30 etc. at the tick marks corresponding to the major grid lines, we end up with a suitable scale to use. There is no need to have a scale that allows us to record the numerical

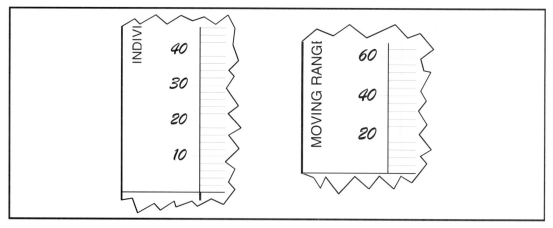

Fig 8.14 Sections of scales to be used when plotting the X and moving R values.

values of potential special causes. Data will either be inside, and plotted, or outside and not plotted. A section of the axis for plotting the X values appears in *Fig 8.14.*

Similarly for the Moving R values. We know that UCL_R is 55.90 and LCL_R is 0. The blank chart has 5 major gridlines. Hence a suitable scale is to record 20, 40, 60 at the tick marks corresponding to the major grid lines. A section of the axis for plotting the Moving R values also appears in *Fig 8.14.*

8.10 Plotting the sample results

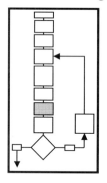

Plot the sample results

With the scales completed, the X and Moving R values can be plotted in the usual way, and the points then joined up. A section of the control chart showing the two graphs, essentially run charts, now appears in *Fig 8.15.*

If, in our sequence of readings, we have a value which falls beyond the scale, then the usual convention is to put a cross as far out as possible and write the numerical value alongside it.

8.11 Drawing the central lines and control limits

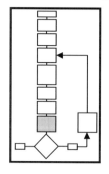

Draw the central lines and control limits

The final step is to draw the lines corresponding to the central line and control limits for the two sections of the chart.

The final control chart is now shown in *Fig 8.16 (on Page 98).*

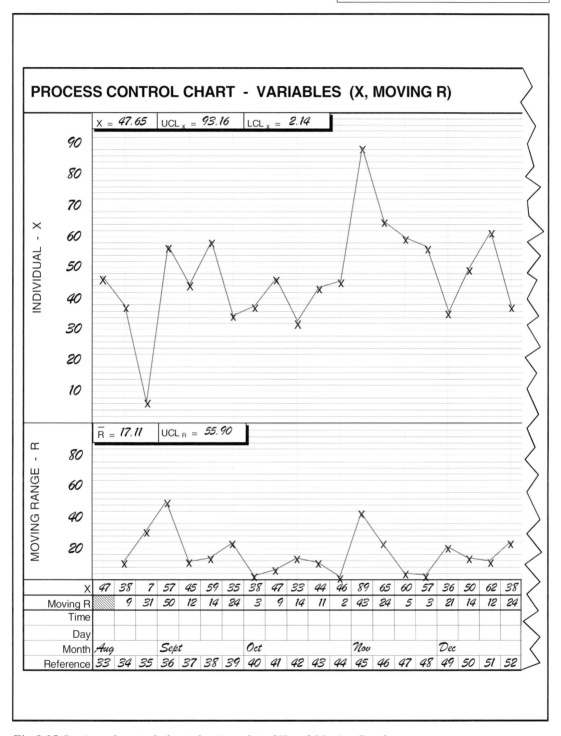

PROCESS CONTROL CHART - VARIABLES (X, MOVING R)

| X = 47.65 | UCL_x = 93.16 | LCL_x = 2.14 |

R̄ = 17.11 | UCL_R = 55.90

X	47	38	7	57	45	59	35	38	47	33	44	46	89	65	60	57	36	50	62	38
Moving R		9	31	50	12	14	24	3	9	14	11	2	43	24	5	3	21	14	12	24
Time																					
Day																					
Month	Aug			Sept				Oct						Nov				Dec			
Reference	33	34	35	36	37	38	39	40	41	42	43	44	45	46	47	48	49	50	51	52

Fig 8.15 *Section of control chart showing plot of X and Moving R values.*

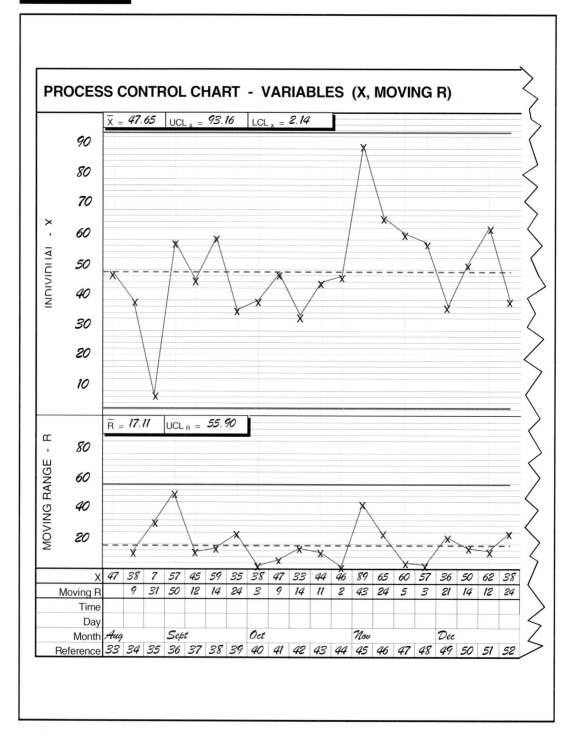

Fig 8.16 *Section showing completed control chart for the first 20 points.*

8.12 Interpreting the chart

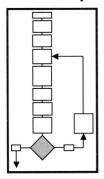

Are special causes present?

The chart is now interpreted to see if there are any special causes present. We use the four rules introduced earlier in the book and shown again below.

RULE 1	Any point outside one of the control limits.
RULE 2	A run of seven points, all above or all below the central line, or all increasing or all decreasing.
RULE 3	Any unusual patterns or trends within the control limits.
RULE 4	The number of points within the middle third of the region between the control limits differing markedly from two-thirds of the total number of points.

RULE 2 has to be used with care when applied to the Moving R section of the chart. Further explanation appears in Section 8.15.2.

As we understand them at present, none of the rules apply and hence the process is under control.

Having said that, there is a point on the Moving R section which is very close to the control limit. This is associated with the low X value of 7 corresponding to week no. 35 and a higher X value of 57 corresponding to week no. 36.

It is not unusual for the Moving R section of the control chart to flag up what seems to be a possible special cause. The Moving R graph is simply reflecting the fact that there is a large movement from one X value to the next. It is worthwhile looking to see if there is a reason for this, although it is much more likely that the jump is part of the natural variation of the process.

Having drawn the control chart, we are now in a much stronger position to assess the true sales performance. The chart warns us against reacting to the low figure of 7 for week 35 and the high figure of 89 for week no. 45.

Now that the process is stable and predictable, the next step is to use the control chart to continue to monitor the process and then find ways of improving it.

Fig 6.10 in Chapter 6 provided a flow chart for doing this. As before we shall use a reduced form of this as a guide.

8.13 Projecting lines ahead

The central lines and control limits are now extended to the end of the first control chart sheet. The results are shown in *Fig 8.17 (overleaf)*.

Because our process is predictable, then we can expect our sales figures to fall within the control limits. This might be re-assuring, but in a sales sense it would be worrying. If our sales figures remain at the same overall level, then we are not improving our business. Usually, sales figures need to increase linearly over time.

More technical detail on this appears in Chapter 17. A case study shows how 3M Healthcare have tackled the problem of applying SPC to what is sometimes called a drifting process.

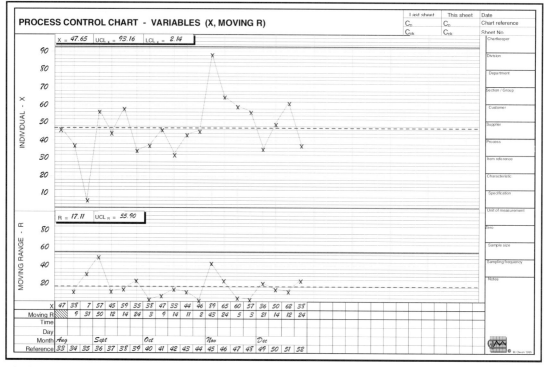

Fig 8.17 *Final control chart to be used for monitoring ongoing sales*

8.14 Continue monitoring the process

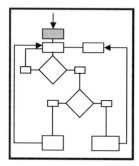

> **Draw lines onwards**

The next reading is taken and the situation assessed using the flow diagram shown symbolically here.

Depending on the status of the point, various actions will result. Throughout, however, the aim is to use the chart to detect a signal. For example, responding to a continued drop in sales, or detecting an increase in sales, finding the reason, and building it into the system.

8.15 Other issues relating to the (X, Moving R) chart

8.15.1 Choice of correct formula for evaluating the standard deviation

In Section 8.7.3 you were warned of the dangers of using the wrong formulae when calculating the standard deviation for the X section of the chart. The advice was to make use of the formula: -

$$\hat{\sigma} = \frac{\overline{R}}{d_2}$$

and not any other. Some explanation is necessary.

No. of sales	47	38	7	57	45	59	35	38	47	33	44	46	89	65	60	57	36	50	62	38
Week no.	33	34	35	36	37	38	39	40	41	42	43	44	45	46	47	48	49	50	51	52

Fig 8.18 *Table of sales figures over a period of weeks.*

In *Fig 8.18* we have the set of numbers we have been using in developing the control chart, shown originally in *Fig 8.3*.

Without knowledge of control charts, we are likely to make use of conventional calculator routines to work out the standard deviation of this set. Two classical forms of standard deviation are available. They are generally denoted by $\hat{\sigma}_{n-1}$ and $\hat{\sigma}_n$, and you will typically see calculator keys marked in this way.

If we feed in the nineteen R values into a calculator, we find that $\hat{\sigma}_{n-1} = 16.45$ and $\hat{\sigma}_n = 16.04$. There is nothing to be gained by going into any detail on these results. If you want to know more then other more detailed SPC books can provide it. What is important is that these results differ and that they are not the same as the result we had when using the formula $\hat{\sigma} = \dfrac{\overline{R}}{d_2}$. This gave us a value of 15.17, which is considerably different.

The problem with using either $\hat{\sigma}_{n-1}$ or $\hat{\sigma}_n$ is that the final result is independent of the order of the X values. If we could change the sequence of the X readings in *Fig 8.18*, then it would not change the standard deviation results.

That is not the case when using $\dfrac{\overline{R}}{d_2}$. If the sequence of X values is changed, then the corresponding Moving R values change. If the Moving R values change, then by definition $\overline{R}$ changes, and if $\overline{R}$ changes then it follows that the standard deviation $\hat{\sigma}$ also changes. We must make use of the right tool in calculating the standard deviation and the correct one here is $\hat{\sigma} = \dfrac{\overline{R}}{d_2}$.

8.15.2 Limitation of the Moving R section of the chart

In Section 8.12 it was pointed out that in reflecting changes in successive X values, the Moving R section may suggest changes that are actually due to common causes rather than special causes.

Another problem with the Moving R chart is that the 'run of 7' rule does not apply.

To explain why, suppose we take the first three values for X shown in *Fig 8.18*, i.e. 47, 38 and 7. The value of 38 is used in calculating the first moving range of 9 and the second moving range of 31. Hence the R values of 9 and 31 are not independent because they are linked by a common X value of 38. A similar result holds for the X values 38 and 7, 7 and 57, 57 and 45 and so on. As a result, if we are to apply the 'run of 7' rule, then we need 7 independent Moving R values, which in effect means 14 successive R values. You will often find that organisations tend not to plot the moving R values, and concentrate instead on the X values.

8.16 Summary of symbols and formulae

Symbols

R	Moving Range
MR	Alternate symbol for Moving Range
$\overline{X}$	Mean of X values

$\overline{R}$ Mean of moving range values

$\hat{\sigma}$ Symbol for standard deviation

UCL_X Upper control limit for X

LCL_X Lower control limit for X

UCL_R Upper control limit for R

LCL_R Lower control limit for R

D_4 Constant used in determining UCL_R

D_3 Constant used in determining LCL_R

$\hat{\sigma}_{n-1}$ and $\hat{\sigma}_n$ Standard deviation formulae – not used in developing control charts

Formulae

$$\overline{X} = \frac{\Sigma X}{20}$$

$$\overline{R} = \frac{\Sigma R}{19}$$

$$\hat{\sigma} = \frac{\overline{R}}{d_2}$$

$$UCL_X = \overline{X} + 3\hat{\sigma} = \overline{X} + (2.66\overline{R})$$
$$LCL_X = \overline{X} - 3\hat{\sigma} = \overline{X} - (2.66\overline{R})$$

$$UCL_R = D_4\overline{R}$$
$$LCL_R = D_3\overline{R}$$

8.17 Key points and summary

- Make sure the process is well defined.
- Choose a suitable measure for the process.
- Use a flow chart to decide that the (X, Moving R) chart is the appropriate one.
- When calculating a moving range, keep the options to a minimum by always using a sample size of 2.
- Remember to divide MR by nineteen, not twenty, when calculating $\overline{R}$.

- Make sure that $\hat{\sigma}$ is calculated using the expression $\dfrac{\overline{R}}{d_2}$.
- Always choose suitable scales for the axes.
- The Moving R section of the chart can sometimes provide misleading messages.
- Because a process is stable, it does not necessarily mean that the process is satisfactory.
- Sales figures should increase over time, and not remain stationary.
- If sales figures do drift, then there is a way of applying SPC to deal with it.
- Never use $\hat{\sigma}_{n-1}$ or $\hat{\sigma}_n$ when calculating the control limits.
- The 'run of 7' rule is invalid for the Moving R section of the chart. It is replaced by a 'run of 14' rule.

This chapter has shown you how to develop an (X, Moving R) chart.

The possibilities for applying this chart are almost endless, and some ideas on extending its use are provided in the next chapter.

Perhaps this is the real benefit of the (X, Moving R) chart. It has been the catalyst in opening up SPC into different, newer areas. It has helped to dispel the myth that SPC and the better known $(\bar{X}, R)$ chart are synonymous. There are still many useful applications of the latter chart, as the case studies in Chapter 11 will show. Nevertheless, it is the (X, Moving R) chart that is now proving to be a real bonus.

Now that the detail of the (X, Moving R) chart has been covered, we are better able to appreciate the applications. The case studies that follow in the next chapter show you how some leading organisations have been making use of the (X, Moving R) chart in improving their business activities.

THE (X, MOVING R) CHART – CASE STUDIES

9.1 Introduction

The sequence for setting up an (X, Moving R) chart, and the key points associated with the chart, were set out in Chapter 8.

In the pages that follow you will find some interesting and relevant examples of how some leading organisations have made use of this chart in office or office-related areas. The examples come from a range of interests and from various departments. They could have been added to many times. It is not an overstatement to say that the scope for the use of the (X, Moving R chart) is enormous.

As far as possible, and depending on the ability to reproduce the relevant charts that go with the case studies, a copy of the original control chart has been included. This helps to supply the authenticity associated with the projects. It also shows the diversity of format of the actual control chart, reflecting how an organisation can, and should, modify a basic chart if necessary to make it suitable for its own specific use.

There is no significance in the order of the projects or the order in which the organisations are represented. Some of the case studies are more involved than others, but that is not the point. In their own way each project shows how powerful this chart can be.

The first case study looks at water consumption – not normally an area associated with control charts.

9.2 CASE STUDY 1 Kerry Milling

WATER CONSUMPTION

9.2.1 Background to the company

Kerry Milling operates as the flour milling arm of Kerry Ingredients (UK) limited, producing in the region of 100,000 tonnes of flour per annum from blends of home-grown and imported wheats. The Gainsborough mill employs 'Fred the flour grader' and produces all the consumer packed flour sold under the Homepride brand as well as baker's grade flours for several plant bakers and soft flours for large cake manufacturers. In addition, the flour mill is a major internal supplier of flour to other operating companies within Kerry Ingredients (UK) limited which has grown to become one of the largest and most technological manufacturers in the world.

9.2.2 The project

The Kerry Milling operation based at Gainsborough, Lincolnshire, occupied a shared site with Dalgety Agriculture Limited (DAL) and Morton Foods. Water consumption had been static for the previous two years, running at a level of approximately 3500 cubic metres, but there were some underlying events that needed reconciling.

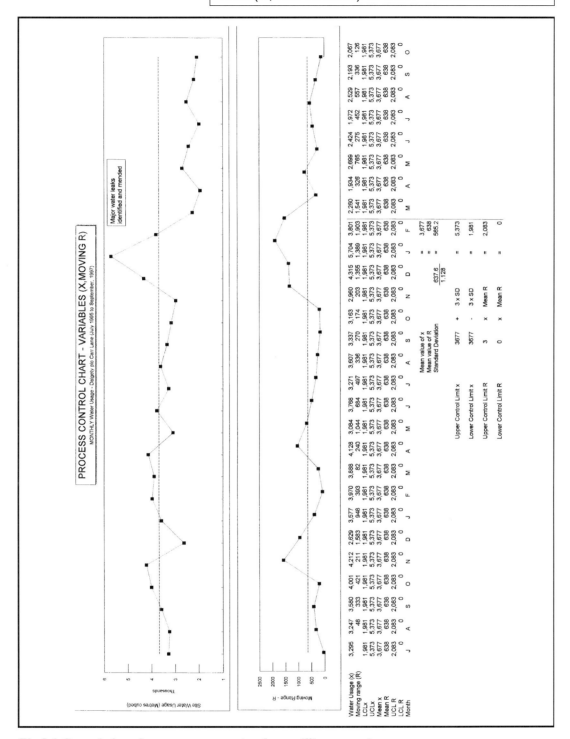

Fig 9.1 Control chart for water consumption for a milling operation.

In June 1995 there was a review of the recharges to Dalgety Agriculture Ltd. In November 1996, DAL installed water meters on feed mill processes and challenged the basis of Kerry Milling recharges.

In January 1997 site water consumption increased to 5704 cubic metres. This led to a more detailed analysis of water consumption charges, making use of an SPC chart.

9.2.3 The control chart

Fig 9.1 shows a control chart for monthly water consumption, ranging over a series of months spanning the time interval in question.

The chart shows some interesting results. For example, for the period spanning the first eighteen months until the November of the second year, water consumption was under control and running at a mean level of 3700 cubic metres.

A special cause showed up in the following January. Water consumption had risen to a high of 5704 cubic metres.

The local water authority, Anglian Water, was called in and an investigation of the water distribution on site was carried out. It was found that the special cause was due to a major water leak. In tracing and rectifying this problem, other minor leaks were located. As a result, when water consumption figures were subsequently recorded on the control chart, they reflected a consumption level that was below that which was recorded before the occurrence of the out-of-control signal.

In May 1997, following the tracking and repairing of the leaks, Anglian Water made a one-off ex-gratia payment of £2000.

Following this, discussion took place on-site between the three operating organisations involved. The operating company installed ten new water meters to monitor consumption. Kerry Milling, for its part, would continue to monitor water consumption using SPC methods.

Quite apart from detecting special causes, the control chart indicated a change of process level to which expenditure could be attached. Knowing the cost of water usage, it would be possible to indicate savings following the detection of the water leaks. These would be useful. Tracking down costs in administrative/service areas is possibly not as easy as in production areas. Any initiative such as that described in this case study can only help in this respect.

Case Study 2 comes from the defence industry. It provides a relatively simple, yet at the same time an excellent visual example of how a control chart can be used very effectively in showing how some new factor has influenced a process.

9.3 CASE STUDY 2 GEC-MARCONI Avionics

RESPONSE TIMES TO TASK AUTHORISATION

9.3.1 Background to the company

Since this project was set up, GEC-Avionics has become part of BAE SYSTEMS. Its Customer Support Group provides a comprehensive service of life cycle support to a wide variety of customers world-wide in the field of military and civilian avionics. The company supports the customer in terms of the provision of spares repairs and on-going development for equipment of both GEC manufacture and that of other companies during the time in service. Typically, the contracts provide a comprehensive support package for any equipment.

The company undertakes to provide the support of all documentation, drawings, specifications and spares, and the provision of query answering and tasking services. The tasking service enables the customer to place requirements on the company to advise on, and resolve all sorts of technical issues relating to the performance of the equipment.

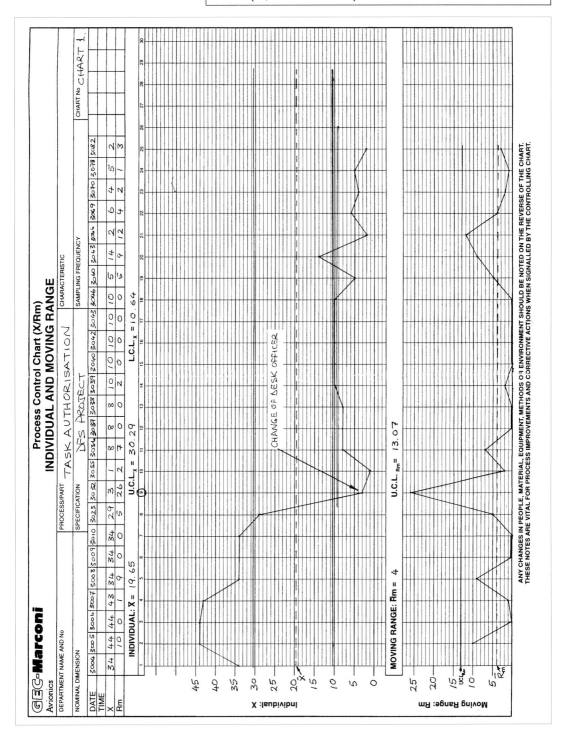

Fig 9.2 Control chart for time taken for the customer to achieve tasks.

9.3.2 GEC-Marconi and SPC

The company was introducing SPC on a project basis as an essential part of its continuous improvement programme. At the same time there was a requirement from one of its major customers to apply SPC in key administrative processes.

This particular case study was based on the relationship between GEC-Marconi and a customer in the control and monitoring of certain tasks.

The task process involved three stages – the authorisation, the task activity and the sale. SPC was being applied in order to: -

1. Improve the forecasting of point of order and sale.
2. Improve long-term forecasting and budgeting.
3. Reduce cost and turn-round time.

In so doing it would help to identify and resolve delays and problems in the process.

9.3.3 The project

The part of the case study described here concentrated on the task authorisation process. This involved submitting a document to the customer for approval, after which the document would be returned to GEC-Marconi so that an order could be raised. A control chart was to be used to monitor the time taken, in days, for the customer to respond to the company.

9.3.4 The control chart

The control chart is shown in *Fig 9.2*.

The first twenty documents were used to obtain the central line and the control limits.

The chart indicated a very obvious change at sample point 9. An investigation into the cause revealed that a new manager had taken over the task authorisation function during the time period involved. This new member of staff quickly put in place a more efficient way of dealing with the authorisation process, resulting in a significant reduction in turn-round time.

9.3.5 Conclusion

The result of a change in a process was demonstrated very effectively in this example. Other charts were developed, highlighting various trends and changes. Control charts clearly demonstrated success and failure and their use was to be extended in the future.

The next case study shows how a control chart has been used in a recruitment process.

9.4 CASE STUDY 3 Ronaldsway Aircraft Company

RECRUITMENT SELECTION TOOLS

9.4.1 Background to the company

The company was founded in the Isle of Man in 1955. The objective of the company was to be a dedicated sub-contractor to Martin Baker, a company set up and owned by Sir James Martin. Sir James was the inventor of the Martin Baker ejection seat and an uncle of the present chairman of Ronaldsway Aircraft.

The company diversified in 1989 to become a supplier to the aerospace industry. As part of its commitment to a continuous improvement programme it embarked on a company-wide SPC programme in 1996 and the benefits of this are beginning to show through. Administration applications of SPC are evident, as well as those based in the traditional production areas, and the case study described here shows how the technique can be applied in recruiting personnel.

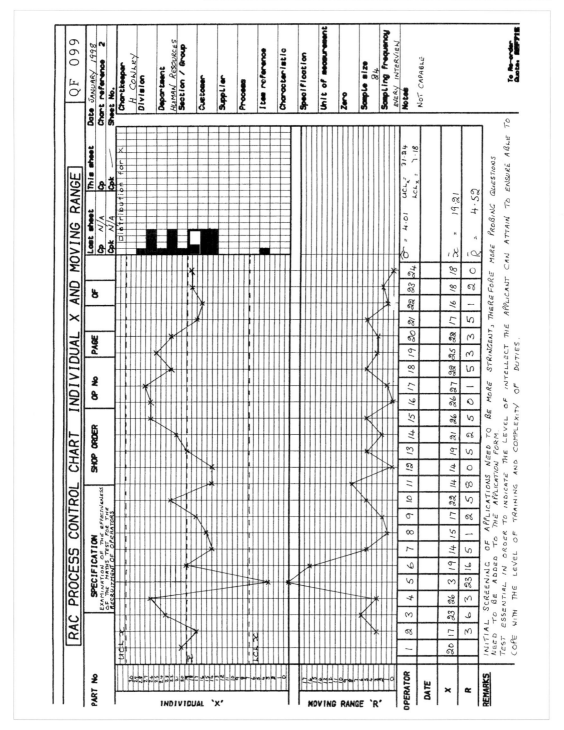

Fig 9.3 Control chart of scores obtained in a maths test as part of a selection procedure.

9.4.2 Purpose of the application

The project was set up to ascertain the effectiveness of the current mathematics test as a selection tool in recruiting unskilled and semiskilled operators for the company.

9.4.3 Introduction

In September 1997 Ronaldsway commenced a large recruitment campaign for the purpose of increasing the direct labour force within the company so as to double shift the key work centres. Due to the current low unemployment figures on the Island, it was realised that many of the new employees would have little or no experience of working on CNC machines. The recruitment process therefore had to ensure that candidates were able to illustrate at interview that they were able to attain a common, minimum standard.

9.4.4 Current selection process

After initial screening of applications, a short-list is produced for interview of candidates who have attained the selection criteria for the position.

At the interview stage the candidates are interviewed, taken on a site tour and given a twenty-minute maths test.

The test is designed to assess the individual's knowledge of basic arithmetic and mechanics. A few more challenging questions are asked on trigonometry to test those candidates who state they have had some previous experience. The purpose of the test is to ensure that candidates selected for employment attain the standard acceptable by the company so that they can be developed and trained to become competent operators. The current requirement is that a minimum score of 16 is attained in the test and that the candidate attains a pass against the interview criteria.

9.4.5 Data collection and the SPC chart

The data was readily available, as it was the sequential score attained by each person interviewed.

Because the data was single reading then the (X, Moving R) chart applied, and the result is shown in *Fig 9.3*. The chart was out of control in that there was one score outside the control limits. This candidate, who attained only 3/30, was an acquaintance of an existing employee. Normally this candidate would not have been selected for interview, but as it is the policy of the Company to interview such recommendations, then he was given an opportunity.

The rules applying to control charts require special causes to be removed when the control chart is being first set up and therefore new control limits were worked out using the remaining points. This resulted in a new set of values as follows: -

$$\overline{X} = 19.91$$
$$UCL_X = 30.10$$
$$LCL_X = 9.73$$

Using this new set we could then make a decision regarding capability.

Capability, in the context of test scores, could be interpreted in a different ways. Do we require all students to achieve a minimum score of 16 in order to be accepted? Can we accept a given percent to fall below the LSL of 16? Perhaps of more relevance, is the figure of 16 appropriate?

9.4.6 Conclusions

The chart proved useful in confirming that a personal recommendation from a colleague does not necessarily mean that the person concerned is of the required standard, and that any test procedure must be applicable to everyone.

The control chart opened up various possible avenues for further analysis regarding the setting of a minimum standard. In addition it highlighted the need for the initial screening to be more stringent. For example, more probing questions could be added to the application form so that it would eliminate unsuitable candidates at a much earlier stage.

Sales figures provide excellent material for applying SPC. Case Study 4 shows how charts can be used to assess sales performance of staff.

9.5 CASE STUDY 4 Spillers Milling

DAILY CALL RATES FOR SALES PERSONNEL

9.5.1 Background to the company

Spillers Milling are a £150M p.a. turnover, UK-wide manufacturer and distributor of wheat flour with a strong presence in all major end users ranging from bread, cake, biscuits to soups, coatings and thickeners for the food processing industry with overall market leadership within the non-vertically integrated food manufacturing sector. Of special note is that the company has brand leadership in the UK Asian population flour sector and in the technical and specialist flour market where the flour undergoes secondary processing, such as steam or heat treatment, agglomeration or drying, before onward sale to food manufacturers.

9.5.2 Spillers Milling and SPC

The inherent variability of wheat characteristics, which as an organic raw material will be influenced by not only the variety sown but weather, geography and farming practices at source, places particular demands upon Spillers Milling for the manufacture of consistent, quality performing flours for the food processing industry. In addition, increasing customer expectations place the associated challenges of managing and containing the potential for variability introduced throughout the manufacturing and distribution supply chain, typical of any short order lead-time FMCG.

Statistical Process Control, as a tool for measuring and understanding system variability, has been pivotal to Spillers Milling in identifying, prioritising and addressing process, logistical and administrative inconsistencies within their supply chain, all of which have historically added cost to their business, coupled with sometimes causing delay and annoyance to their customers.

In a top-down integrated approach, to ensure complete ownership and cascade accountability throughout the organisation, seventy-five managers, of all functional disciplines, were trained over a four-month period in the use and implementation of SPC. This was followed by a formal review process to ensure demonstrable understanding of the tool, requiring participants to present a particular application to illustrate appropriate use, with accompanying analysis and relevant improvement plans. This process was supported using a network of mentors/local experts to ensure that every participant was encouraged and assisted according to their individual requirements.

On-line SPC has been extensively adopted throughout the organisation to track the performance of repeating activities and events ranging from Product and Process specification monitoring, distribution, Key Performance Indicators across a range of product and customer categories, sales volume and margin contribution variations for particular classifications of products and customer categories, attribute measurement of invoice content to assess percentage accurately despatched, etc. In all such applications, SPC has propagated an understanding of system variation and the need to investigate or stop a process or activity if this variation becomes statistically unacceptable. In this way substandard production, wasteful rework and unnecessary and costly mistakes are being managed out of the business and a culture of sustained incremental improvement is becoming institutionalised.

SPC has also been extensively adopted as a project analysis tool such as for assessing the historical and ongoing performance of specific equipment as a means of determining process capability against existing or envisaged requirements and therefore, in some instances, supporting capital expenditure proposals.

SPC has been of great benefit to Spillers Milling and is now becoming an integral element of managing and improving business operations in a demonstrable fashion

9.5.3 The project

As a result of the SPC programme, a series of highly relevant SPC projects were developed, several of which relate specifically to office areas, and three of which appear in this book.

Sales figures, in particular, provided a good opportunity to use control charts.

9.5.4 The sales operation

Each salesperson was expected to make daily call rates on customers. There was a long-standing perceived target of twelve calls per day, but this figure is dependent on the territory involved.

Four sales sites were operating, each with a different number of sales personnel. Three staff were based at Newcastle, five at Tilbury, five at Avonmouth and four at Liverpool.

The initial object of the SPC project was to monitor the average call rate over the weeks for each salesperson. This would provide accurate feedback to the sales mangers so that they, in turn can monitor their own teams.

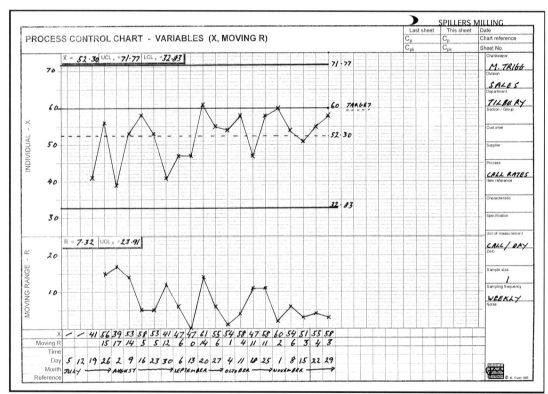

Fig 9.4 *Control chart for call rates for salesman A.*

9.5.5 The control charts

For the purpose of this case study, figures for the Tilbury location were used.

The daily call rate for salesman A was recorded for the first twenty weeks and the results are shown in *Fig 9.4*. Twenty-two weeks were actually used, allowing for two weeks holiday.

The process is under control, with a mean call rate per week of 52 customers.

The chart shows that the target of 60 customers per week cannot be met.

A similar approach was adopted with the other four sales staff based at Tilbury. Control charts were set up with the results shown in *Fig 9.5*.

The only out-of-control signal appeared on the chart for salesman D. A low call rate of 38 customers occurred for the week commencing August 16th. This was due to the fact that the salesman concerned took two days holiday that week.

The inability to achieve target was a more worrying feature. In this respect salesman D performed best in that the mean for the process matched the target of 60 customers. That still meant that, on average, 50% of his weekly call rate figures would be less than 60.

Charts for the other regions were developed in the same way and provided very similar results.

9.5.6 The next step

The control charts created in this way provided the natural measure for assessing the performance of different sales staff.

An immediate concern was the target of 60 customers a week. It was clear that this figure was unrealistic and could not be achieved. A short-term approach was to recognise that if targets were to

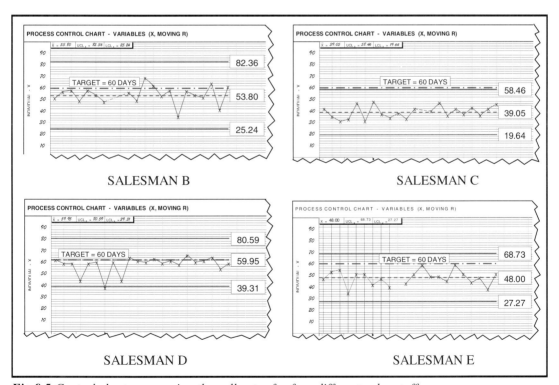

Fig 9.5 *Control charts comparing the call rates for four different sales staff.*

remain, then they would vary from one region to another, and be set at the level of the corresponding LCL.

An alternative to monitoring the number of calls, or the number of sales, is to monitor the time involved in the various processes involved in the sales function. This is brought out in the next case study which shows how one organisation has looked in detail at times involved with a documentation process.

Vehicle maintenance costs form the basis of Case Study 5.

9.6 CASE STUDY 5 SPILLERS MILLING

COMMERCIAL VEHICLE MAINTENANCE COSTS

9.6.1 Background to the company

Spillers Milling, part of Dalgety Food Ingredients (DFI), produces a range of flour for diverse UK food manufacturers involved in the production of bread, biscuits, cakes etc. In addition, it produces specialised flours for specific customers.

Over a two-year period in the late 1990's, the company provided a comprehensive SPC training programme for all management levels, to be followed at a later stage by training of the operational staff. This project is one of several that were undertaken in non-manufacturing areas.

9.6.2 The project

At the time, commercial vehicle maintenance costs were presented in a conventional numerical row and column format.

A typical layout of the data is shown in *Fig 9.6*.

There were difficulties in understanding this form of presentation. Identifying trends and patterns was anything but easy. A growing awareness of the benefits of SPC in this context meant that data currently shown in a form indicated above could provide a great deal more information when represented as a control chart. This required a simplification in all aspects of maintenance costs, with the result that trends would be more easily identifiable using SPC.

9.6.3 The control chart

Control charts were set up to monitor maintenance costs for both bulk product and product sold in bags.

This case study covered the costs associated with bulk maintenance.

Because monthly cost figures were available i.e. single readings, then (X, Moving R) charts were to be used.

The first control chart was set up to monitor the total costs involved with bulk transport maintenance for all six locations.

The chart is shown in *Fig 9.7 (overleaf)*.

The chart clearly shows an upward trend. The main reason for this was the increasing age of the vehicles in use, and the resulting costs associated with these vehicles.

Further control charts were then set up. These represented the bulk costs for each individual location. Costs associated with bag vehicles could then be used as a basis of another set of control charts.

9.6.4 Future action

The control charts identified patterns and trends in a much more effective way than the traditional tabular format. As a result, vehicle maintenance costs would increasingly be represented by control charts.

There was confidence that this better form of presentation could be used to forecast various features associated with all aspects of transport maintenance.

A final point relates to the trend shown in *Fig 9.7*. A further analysis was to follow in allowing for this trend and drawing in the control limits angled around the line of drift, as explained in Chapter 17.

This case study has looked at maintenance costs, a feature that affects the great majority of organisations in one way or another.

A further measure that affects all organisations is attendance levels. The next case study shows how a major engineering organisation is making use of an (X, Moving R) chart in handling absenteeism.

SITE	NO. OF VEHICLES	COST	BULK PERIOD			ACCUMULATIVE		
			MILEAGE	CPM	COST	MILEAGE	CPM	
TILBURY	8	6,764	19,788	31.18	22,425	74,873	29.95
BIRKENHEAD	14	7,709	35,950	21.44	41,493	143,025	29.01
GAINSBOROUGH	7	7,245	24,053	30.12	32,650	102,833	31.75
NEWCASTLE	8	10,743	28,914	37.16	32,922	145,392	22.64
AVONMOUTH	9	10,683	48,149	22.19	39,987	185,215	21.59
CAMBRIDGE	10	12,098	35,061	34.51	41,481	146,516	28.31
	56	55,242	191,915	28.78	210,958	797,854	26.44
PLATFORMS							
TILBURY	13	9,559	52,953	18.05	41,504	219,998	18.87
BIRKENHEAD	11	14,864	28,992	51.27	36,348	131,071	27.73
NEWCASTLE	7	2,406	24,898	9.66	16,854	107,118	15.73
AVONMOUTH	13	7,552	43,020	17.55	30,129	177,782	16.95
CAMBRIDGE	5	4,100	20,951	19.57	11,889	87,389	13.63
CARMARTHEN	1	290	1,843	15.74	1,641	8,370	19.61
	50	38,771	172,657	22.46	138,365	731,728	18.91

Fig 9.6 Typical tabular representation of vehicle maintenance costs.

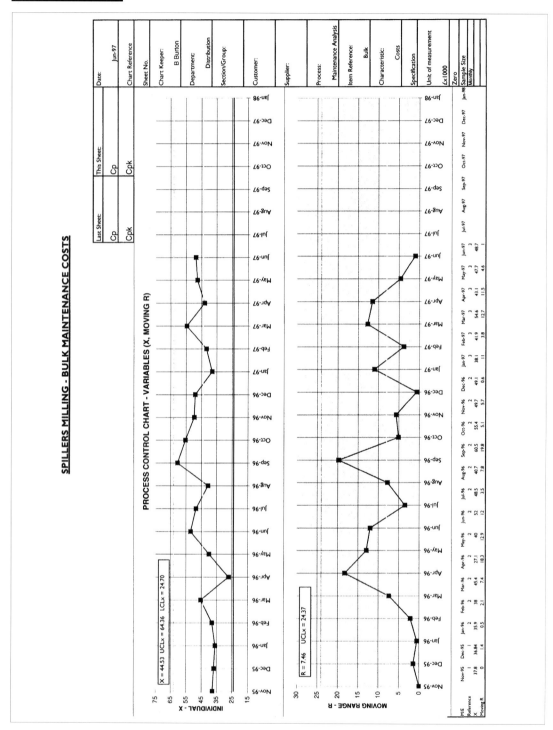

Fig 9.7 Control chart for total bulk-maintenance costs for all locations.

9.7 CASE STUDY 6 ORGANISATION A

ABSENTEEISM

9.7.1 Background to the company
The company is a medium-sized engineering organisation with a long-standing reputation for producing reliable products associated with the defence industry.

Control charts have been introduced spasmodically over a period of years, mainly in response to a company-wide improvement programme based uniquely on the Deming philosophy.

SPC was re-activated as a programme in its own right as a result of requirements from major customers. Various teams were set up in the plant, looking at different applications of SPC, and this particular project is based on an analysis of attendance levels.

9.7.2 Some background on the project
Absenteeism seemed an ideal topic to which to apply SPC techniques. Whilst the company had some feel for the level of absence, it really was not much more than that. The project should be useful in comparing its own level of absence with that of industry in general, and engineering in particular. The results should indicate whether there are any trends in absence patterns, and might point the way to what the company can do in improving performance in terms of attendance.

9.7.3 Data collection
Data was already held within a certain database. It represented only the performance of those employees who clock in. At this stage, this information was assumed to be typical of the workforce as a whole.

9.7.4 Data analysis
The I.T. department identified absence records from the indirect codes. The reports produced showed month-by-month absence. The figures were expressed as days lost as a percentage of days available to work. It was possible to obtain secondary reports that showed the secondary performance by department.

9.7.5 The control chart
Absenteeism figures for the company as a whole were used to create the control chart shown in *Fig 9.8 (overleaf)*.

The process was seen to be under control, and in that sense was satisfactory. However, the level of absenteeism was significantly higher than the national average for similar industries of 3.6%.

9.7.6 Further analysis
There was a need to look in more detail at the level of absenteeism within the different departments. Data was already available which showed the variation in performance between the different departments. For example, *Fig 9.9 (overleaf)* shows departmental absenteeism in bar chart form for 1997.

For confidentiality reasons the names of the departments have been left out.

Following the SPC course, there was an intention to replace this conventional bar chart format with control limits for absenteeism for each department.

9.7.7 Benefits of the project
In the first case, the charts were based on reliable data and gave a graphic interpretation of the variation over time, something not achieved under the current method of representing data.

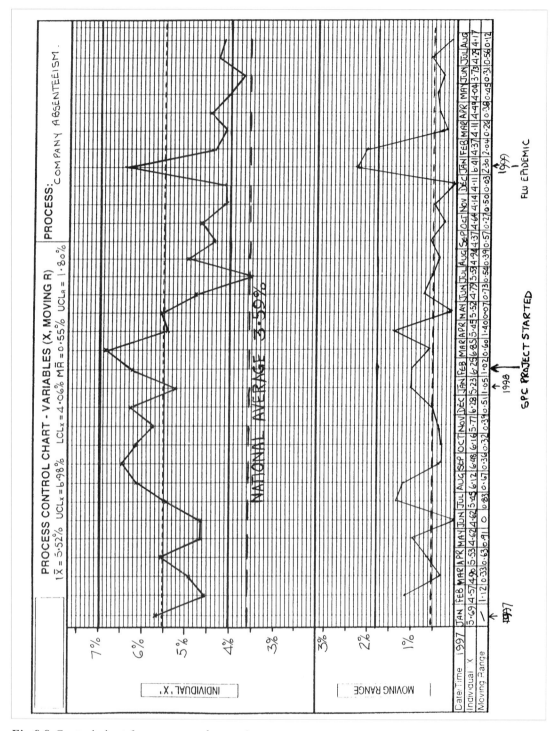

Fig 9.8 *Control chart for company absenteeism.*

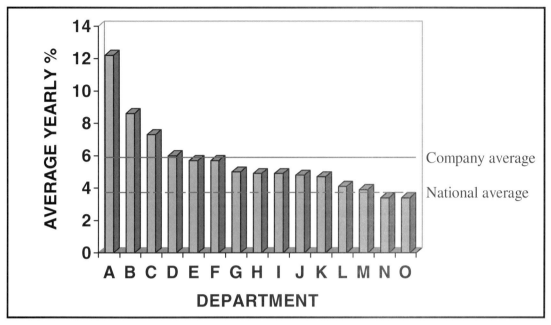

Fig 9.9 *Traditional method of representing departmental absenteeism figures.*

Secondly, there was an opportunity to compare the performance of one department against another. Finally, SPC would provide a useful benchmarking tool for the future.

9.7.8 Conclusions

The SPC initiative had prompted a keen interest in the use of control charts at senior management level.

In particular, the case study described here has resulted in consideration being given to ways of collecting data for employees who do not clock in.

The level of absenteeism as shown by the control charts was very surprising, and had not really been recognised previous to the use of a control chart. As a result, contact had already been made with unions to discuss the company's concern with high absence levels.

In future, there would be closer attention to the application of absence control procedures that were already in place. In addition, a monthly report to management would be introduced, using control charts as far as possible to indicate trends and patterns.

In providing SPC training and consultancy, we are often asked how we make use of the technique ourselves. Case Study 7 shows how a control chart provides a really useful monitor in providing repeated training courses.

9.8 CASE STUDY 7 TRAINING FOR EXCELLENCE

SCORES FOR TRAINING COURSES

9.8.1 Background to the company

Training for Excellence is an independent consultancy run by Mal Owen. For the last 10 years training and consultancy have been supplied to a variety of leading organisations in an increasing range of activity. Running a series of courses over many years provides a rich source of data that can be used to improve customer satisfaction.

9.8.2 Title and brief description

The project made use of 2 processes. The first one, based on response times for payment, provided interesting results. However, the process was not one that could be directly influenced. The second process, based on scores from repeated SPC courses, provided more useful information. The results were a direct reflection of the service provided by the trainer to course attendees – the customers involved.

9.8.3 Choice of topic

Providing training courses is a process, just as is managing a hotel, or drilling a hole in a component. It is repetitive, provides data, and can be improved indefinitely by feeding back information provided by customer assessment.

In considering the various options for setting up a suitable form of control chart, two alternatives were available.

1. Time for payment

The times taken for payment following the issue of an invoice were used as the basis of a control chart. A chart was set up using data relating to time for payment, as shown in *Fig 9.10*.

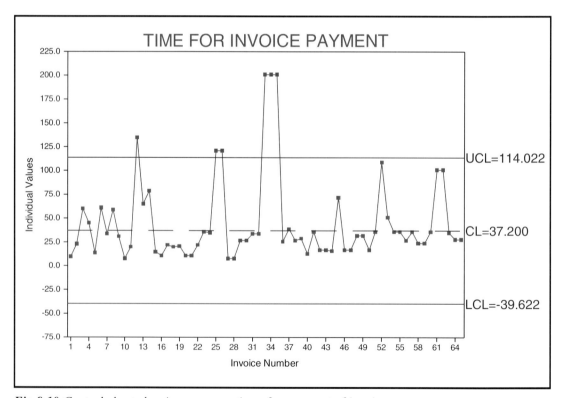

Fig 9.10 Control chart showing response times for payment of invoice.

Control limits were obtained based on the first 20 response times available, and these limits were then used to monitor ongoing times for payment. The analysis shows that on average there is a mean response time of thirty-seven days for payment, with an upper control limit indicating that sometimes I can expect to wait up to one hundred and fourteen days for payment. A typical payment date is within thirty days of receipt of invoice. However, customers often state other requirements, based on internal rules that take into account invoice runs, and so on. The software package used in this case shows a control chart with a theoretical negative LCL present. The natural value of the LCL in such cases is zero.

The process was clearly out of control and specific companies were associated with special causes.

In particular, sample nos. 12, 25, 26, 33, 34, 35, all corresponding to points outside the UCL, related to a common customer who regularly had to be prompted for payment. The organisation concerned operated a policy of delaying payment to any supplier until, as the saying goes, the supplier 'started to scream'. It seems that I was not the only one to suffer in this way. All suppliers to this company were in touch on a regular basis, asking why their invoices were not being paid. It is worth noting that when an SPC chart was set up for the score recorded for the training courses, as shown in the following section, the same company was associated with an out-of-control signal.

Also of interest, was sample no. 52 – just within the UCL but related to a case where the invoice had been mislaid, and a duplicate invoice had to be forwarded to the company before payment could be made.

Interesting as it may be, this first choice for setting up a control chart was not one that was likely to be too helpful. The control chart highlighted poor payers, but that was of little direct help to myself. I had no influence over these payments. The chart was monitoring a measure that was not really a reflection of the training course that had been provided.

A better measure was therefore required, one which adequately assessed the courses themselves. What was the best way to obtain feedback? How could the courses be measured in an effective way?

9.8.4 Assessing course questionnaires

It was decided to use data provided by course attendees on completion of an SPC course. The design of the course questionnaire was based on those typically used by various organisations. There was a need to keep the questionnaire as succinct as possible, and asking for a response to questions referring directly to the training course. A rating from 1 'poor' to 10 'good' was chosen for those questions that required a numerical response, and allowance was also made for more general comments relating to the training.

9.8.5 Collection of data

Data was collected from the individual responses following each course. The same questionnaire was to be used for both courses under review – the 2-day practitioner's course and the 1-day overview. The current analysis relates to the 2-day course, and the first 66 such courses for which data was available.

The data represented the instantaneous response from those attending the relevant SPC course. As far as possible, attendees were asked to complete the questionnaire before they left. There should be no difficulties. However, in some cases the questionnaires were completed but they were not handed in at the end of the training session. There must be some obscure reason for this, but it was difficult to determine. There was no request to identify the responses, and hence the returns were as far as possible anonymous.

9.8.6 Analysis of data

Fig 9.11(overleaf) represents a summary of the responses for a particular company.

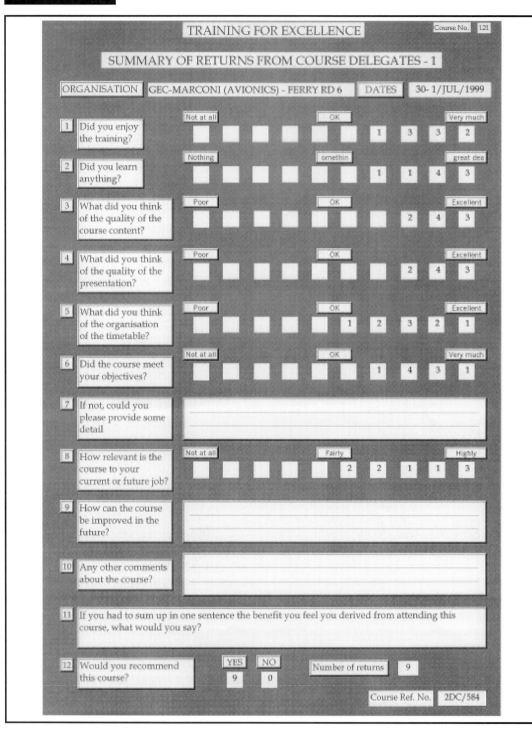

Fig 9.11 Summary of responses from attendees on a 2-day course.

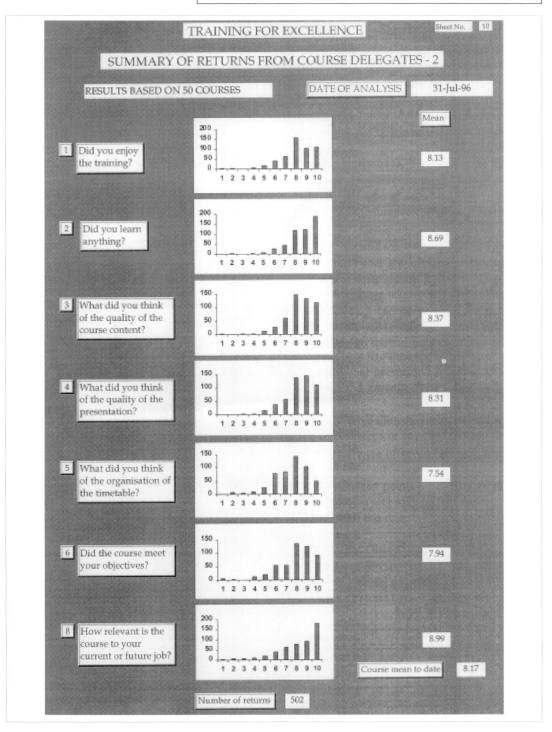

Fig 9.12 *Patterns of responses based on fifty courses.*

By using these results, histograms can be produced. The histograms reflect the different patterns relating to the particular question being asked. As more and more course results become available, then the histograms for each question begin to stabilise. *Fig 9.12* shows the results for the first fifty courses.

In general a histogram is of little use in controlling a process. However, in the current context, where the histogram is being used to reflect the different patterns that build up as more and more readings become available, its use in this way is quite acceptable. It is not being used to control the process as such. Its value is in showing different patterns.

Seven separate scores corresponding to each section of the questionnaire could be calculated, from which an overall score could be evaluated. There was therefore an opportunity for producing control charts for each of the sections, together with a chart for the overall score for each course. Because single readings were being used, the (X, Moving R) chart was chosen as the appropriate chart to use.

9.8.7 Chart results

Control charts were generated based on the results from the first 20 courses. *Fig 9.13* shows the control chart for the total score, using the first 20 samples to calculate the central line and the control limits.

A potential special cause was seen at sample no. 20. Was it a genuine unusual feature, or was the point there by chance as part of the system? In fact, there was a reason for the low reading, but at this stage it was considered part of the natural variation, and the calculations proceeded accordingly.

Fig 9.14 shows the control chart for total scores with the lines projected ahead and the results for sequential scores plotted on the chart. No further out-of-control signals were seen.

Further useful information was available from the various control charts relating to the separate tracking of scores corresponding to individual questions. In particular, Question 3, – "What did you think of the quality of the course content" – turned out to be especially helpful.

Fig 9.15 (overleaf) shows the control chart for scores relating to this question.

Again the reading corresponding to course number 20 was out of control. This reading corresponded to the same organisation that was late in paying invoices, and an interesting tale developed.

Initial pre-course discussions with the company had shown reluctance on behalf of the organisation concerned to spend any more money on SPC training above the minimum required. In particular, the company representative felt uneasy at the thought of paying a per-head delegate fee, a problem not experienced elsewhere, but obviously an issue to this organisation. The representative also indicated that calculators could be acquired through a local dealer at a cut-price rate. He also suggested that if I could forward the masters for the course-training manual, he would take on board the photocopying of these, to provide the basis of course manuals which he would then put together. In order to help the customer, I agreed. I had some reservations at the time, and later events confirmed that these were justified.

The final format of the training manual turned out to be not much short of a disaster. Pages were missing, or appeared upside down. The grid on the control charts, designed to provide a balance between showing lines sufficiently clear to be seen, yet at the same time not too dense as to cloud the movement of the plot itself, was not apparent. The company's photocopier was not sensitive enough. It also turned out that the SPC representative spent the best part of 2 days hogging the main photocopier in the administrative area in preparing the course manuals. As a result, other staff could not use the photocopier and were therefore frustrated because they could not get on with their normal activities.

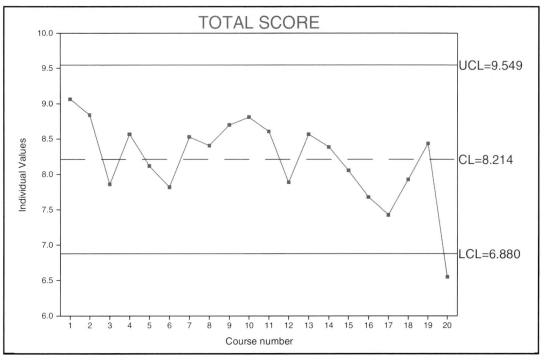

Fig. 9.13 *Control chart for overall course score based on the first twenty courses.*

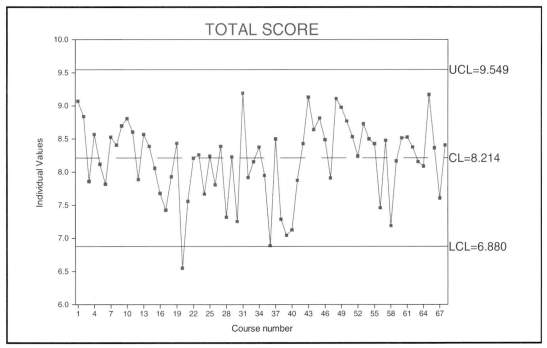

Fig. 9.14 *Control chart for overall course score.*

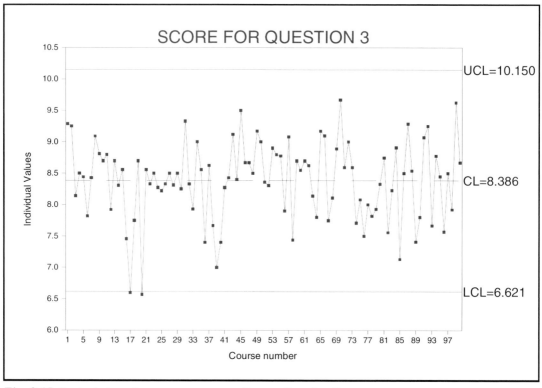

Fig. 9.15 *Control chart for scores corresponding to Question 3.*

On my own account, analysis of course questionnaires showed that I was often heavily criticised by course attendees from the same organisation because of the quality of the course materials. Subsequent discussion on project feedback days made the situation clear, and there was general recognition that the real cause was a misguided company policy on costs, and not any shortcomings on my own account regarding the quality of the manuals provided to course members.

Sample no 17, also given an out-of-control signal, related to another organisation. Investigation showed that it was one of a series for the same company. There was a very wide spread in the interests and abilities of those attending and likely to be the reason for the low score.

9.8.8 Any benefits obtained

More specific information was provided on how the courses can be improved.

In terms of providing SPC courses, it is not easy to directly identify material savings or cost improvements. Even so, two points are worth making.

One organisation trained over one hundred and twenty managers and key engineers over a period of nine months. In that time considerable savings, over the order of £0.25 million, were made by reducing the amount of materials used in the production processes. This could be attributed directly to the introduction of the SPC programme.

Secondly, there are the 'hidden costs' which Deming refers to. How can we measure the benefits that people gain by learning about the control chart, using it in their work, and take the technique with them to apply to their hobbies and leisure activities?

There is no doubt that a more scientific approach to the assessment of course scores can result in a host of benefits.

9.8.9 Conclusions

I had little doubt regarding the use of a control chart in handling training scores and the results confirmed my expectations. Using charts as part of the process of providing training courses gives an extra confidence in that you are applying the technique on your own data at the same time as expounding the general benefits to others.

This case study has possibly opened up new opportunities for applying SPC charts. In it there was a reference to using control charts outside the work area.

The last case study based on using the (X, Moving R) chart provides such an example. It deals with a very personal issue of trying to give up smoking.

9.9 CASE STUDY 8 Organisation B

GIVING UP SMOKING

9.9.1 Background to the company

This company is a medium-sized pharmaceutical business with headquarters in the south of the United Kingdom and with other locations across the country. Its medicines are widely known in the professional and consumer markets and the company also produces fine chemicals, healthcare and diagnostic products.

9.9.2 Organisation B and SPC

Over the years this company has made sporadic attempts to introduce SPC in one form or another. A couple of project-based training courses provided some very useful applications with scope for further development. However, at the time this training took place there was a considerable change in management structure and company direction taking place, and hence it was not surprising that it was not felt timely to further develop the SPC initiative.

A more recent training course has now sparked off renewed enthusiasm at a time when the company is seriously considering all the implications of teams and the newer techniques. There is therefore likely to be a strong drive on extending the SPC knowledge base over the months.

9.9.3 The project

Whilst the great majority of SPC projects relate directly to the use of the technique in the workplace, a few have to do with pastimes, hobbies, personal measures – out-of-work issues in general.

So it is with this case study which was presented at a feedback session. It dealt with an analysis of daily cigarette smoking.

9.9.4 Data collection

This was not a problem. For twenty successive days a record was kept of the number of cigarettes smoked each day. The data lent itself nicely to plotting on an (X, Moving R) chart.

9.9.5 The control chart

The control chart is shown in *Fig 9.16*. It showed some interesting features. First of all, the process is not under control. Two out-of-control points were noted.

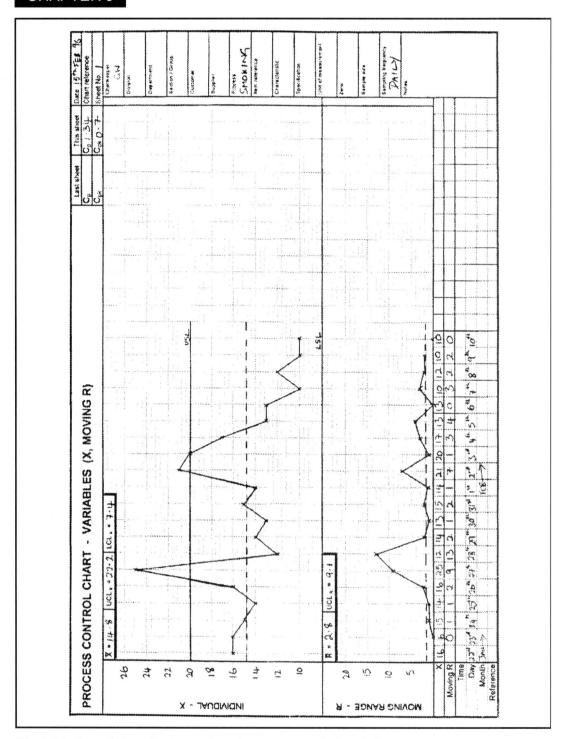

Fig. 9.16 *Control chart for the number of cigarettes smoked each day.*

The first one, on Jan. 27th, corresponded with a weekend. Aided by a few beers, cigarette consumption had increased and the chart reflected this.

On Feb 2nd, a second point fell above the UCL. As for the first point, the weekend had taken its toll and the number of cigarettes smoked had increased.

The ultimate aim of the project is to reduce to zero the number of cigarettes smoked.

To some extent the chart is showing that this aim is being gradually achieved in that there is a general drift downwards. However the problem lies with the weekend consumption.

Two options appeared to be open.

1. Reduce the number of cigarettes smoked over the weekend, which would greatly assist in achieving the aim.

2. Accept that cigarette smoking at the weekend is really a new process and start a new chart for this characteristic. At the same time keep the original chart going but only plot the figures corresponding to weekdays.

9.9.6 Conclusion

No detail is available of how the figures progressed, and, all being well, the numbers should trail away to zero and the problem is solved.

It is easy to dismiss this example as a little artificial, but don't underestimate how useful it is in suggesting new areas where SPC can be applied. One course delegate has used the technique to monitor daily readings taken on his child's asthma condition. Another used daily sugar level readings to produce a control chart. What was it that he had eaten yesterday which must have contained sugar that he was unaware of, but had been detected by an out-of-control signal on an SPC chart? Another colleague has being measuring attendance at a dog-training session he runs. Some one else has been using a control chart on golf scores. The list goes on.

These eight case studies have shown some varied applications for the (X, Moving R) chart. Useful as it is, there is another chart – the ($\overline{X}$, R) chart – which can also be applied with much success in an office area. The next chapter provides you with the detail you require to use this chart.

THE ($\overline{X}$,R) CHART

10.1 Introduction

Earlier, in Chapter 7, we looked at different formats which could be represented on a control chart. One of them made use of data which is measurable and which relates to single readings. The (X, Moving R) chart was seen to be the chart to use in this situation. If there is so much data that it is not possible to physically deal with each value, then we need to take samples from the process, and in this case we use the ($\overline{X}$, R) chart. It is this chart that has been used extensively in manufacturing industry when controlling dimensions on mass-produced components. The chart can apply equally as well in administrative areas. To some extent the applications are similar to those for which we used the (X, Moving R) chart, such as when dealing with response times of all types.

As in Chapter 8, this chapter covers the sequence of setting up the chart. Once again the calculations are not difficult. The approach is very similar to that followed previously. We again refer to tables of constants to help us with the calculations. There is slightly more arithmetic involved because of the fact that in using samples rather than individuals we naturally have more numbers to handle.

The ($\overline{X}$, R) chart is proving highly relevant in the office equivalent of mass production, e.g. where we have a large number of documents to deal with. Examples of the applications appear in Chapter 11 where four case studies are provided.

10.2 Some typical figures to work on

A set of data for which the ($\overline{X}$, R) chart could be used was shown in Section 7.3 in Chapter 7. The set is typical of that used in developing SPC projects, and a list of some general applications of the ($\overline{X}$, R) chart is shown in Fig 10.1.

In developing the sequence for setting up the ($\overline{X}$, R) chart, the first step is to make sure we understand the process we are going to measure.

Arrears in processing documents	*Supplier response times*
Monitoring of time standards	*Time taken to load deliveries*
Cost figures	*Payment of accounts*
New business processing	*Turnround time for enquiries*
Machine response times	*Travel and sickness claims*
Analysis of course admission figures	*Machine response times*
Downtime on computer facilities	

Fig 10.1 *Some applications of the ($\overline{X}$, R) chart in office areas.*

10.3 Defining the process

It is probably true to say that all organisations have some sort of administrative function which involves the handling of forms or documents. The documents could be of many types, relating to purchase orders, invoices, sales figures, delivery records, and so on.

Suppose we consider the process of ordering of items by a customer. The activity involves a specific document relating to the ordering process. There are a large number of orders placed each day and hence there are a large number of related documents to be handled.

Because of the limited resources, it is not practical to measure every document, and so we are forced to take samples.

The layout of the material in the next sections of this chapter follows the same sequence as in Chapter 8. We adopt the guidelines shown in the flowchart in *Fig 6.7*.

Collecting the data is the first step.

10.4 Collecting the data

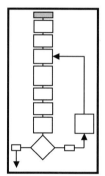

Collect data

Fig 10.2 shows data for the first two days in March. It is very likely that the raw data only recorded the date of ordering and the date of delivery. In collecting the data, therefore, the actual time to deliver would need to be calculated and recorded. There were approximately ten orders placed each day and *Fig 10.2* shows the first five items in each sample which were to be used in setting up the control chart. The sample size (n) is typically taken as five.

Previous knowledge of the ordering process, allied with a scan of some of the historical readings which were available, confirmed that it was acceptable to base the analysis on the first five items in that they were typically representative of all the items available on any day.

SUPPLIER DELIVERY PERFORMANCE				
SUPPLIER - Alan Twyford			Target - 10 days	
SAMPLE NO.	REF.NO	ORDER SENT	DELIVERY RECEIVED	TIME DAYS
1	AT/347	March 2nd	March 11th	7
	AT/348	March 2nd	March 11th	7
	AT/349	March 2nd	March 12th	8
	AT/350	March 2nd	March 10th	6
	AT/351	March 2nd	March 11th	7
	AT/352	March 2nd	March 13th	9
	AT/353	March 2nd	March 10th	6
2	AT/379	March 3rd	March 11th	6
	AT/380	March 3rd	March 12th	7
	AT/381	March 3rd	March 13th	8
	AT/382	March 3rd	March 5th	2
	AT/383	March 3rd	March 13th	8
	AT/384	March 3rd	March 13th	8
	AT/385	March 3rd	March 11th	6

Fig 10.2 *Section from data collection sheet recording delivery times for a certain supplier.*

This might not always be the case, and Case Study 21, covered in Chapter 17, brings out some of the difficulties of sampling in this way.

The supplier had a target delivery time of 10 days. This was critical, as any item which arrived later than this caused problems for the customer.

10.5 The control chart format to be used

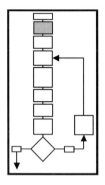

Decide on the chart to use

Use of the flow chart in *Fig 7.20* indicates that we use an ($\overline{X}$, R) chart.

The design of the ($\overline{X}$, R) control chart is of the same basic format as the (X, Moving R) chart, but there is a slight difference in the layout to allow for some additional calculations to do with the samples.

The version of the ($\overline{X}$, R) chart we shall be using is shown in *Fig 10.3*.

This chart allows for samples of up to size six, but we typically use only five of the boxes in a column.

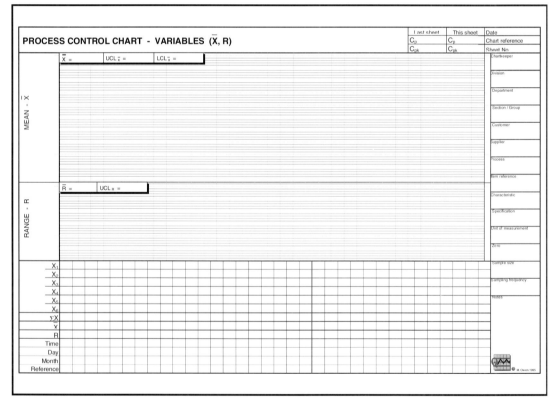

Fig 10.3 *Master version of ($\overline{X}$, R) chart.*

x_1	7	6	7	7	7	6	9	7	8	7	2	9	5	7	7	7	5	9	6	9
x_2	7	7	9	6	7	5	5	7	8	5	7	7	5	7	3	8	5	13	7	5
x_3	8	8	8	7	7	9	7	4	10	7	8	8	7	7	5	8	6	3	7	5
x_4	6	2	6	5	4	4	5	7	8	7	6	6	8	5	7	7	7	15	8	7
x_5	7	8	8	7	7	8	9	4	6	8	8	10	15	6	6	6	7	7	6	8

Fig 10.4 Data recording section of an ($\overline{X}$, R) chart with the boxes filled in.

10.6 Record data on chart

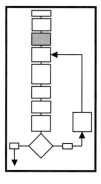

> **Record data
> on a blank
> control chart**

The data provided in the collection sheet shown in *Fig 10.2* can now be transferred into the appropriate boxes in the data recording section of the control chart. *Fig 10.4* shows part of the data recording section for the ($\overline{X}$, R) chart. The results for the first two samples shown in *Fig 10.2* have been recorded, as also have the readings for the next eighteen days.

The X_1, X_2, figures refer to the five individual values in each successive sample.

As usual, the descriptive information relating to the process needs to be recorded. *Fig 10.5* shows some of the completed boxes, which give information relating to the process of measuring response times.

At the same time, reference boxes at the bottom of the control chart, which refer to the date of the sample, are filled in. *Fig 10.6 (overleaf)* shows the completed boxes.

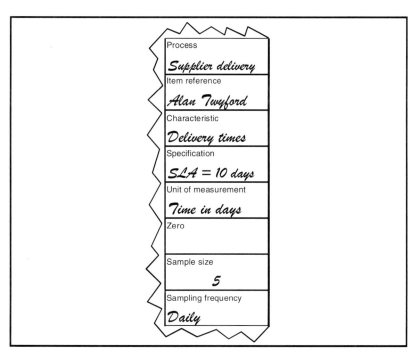

Process

Supplier delivery

Item reference

Alan Twyford

Characteristic

Delivery times

Specification

SLA = 10 days

Unit of measurement

Time in days

Zero

Sample size

5

Sampling frequency

Daily

Fig 10.5 Section from the control chart showing some of the completed process information boxes.

	2	3	4	5	6	9	10	11	12	13	16	17	18	19	20	23	24	25	26	27
March																				
1	2	3	4	5	6	7	8	9	10	11	12	13	14	15	16	17	18	19	20

Fig 10.6 *Section from the chart showing completed sampling times.*

10.7 Carrying out the required calculations

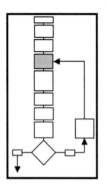

Calculate central lines and control limits

In order to calculate the central lines and the control limits, we need to calculate the mean and range for each of the samples.

10.7.1 Sample calculations

Calculations showing how to work out the mean and range were carried out in Section 5.7.2.

To remind you, we calculate the sample mean $\overline{X}$ from the formula $\overline{X} = \dfrac{\Sigma X}{5}$, where X is one of the readings in a sample of 5.

R is the Range.

For the first sample shown in *Fig 10.4*, $\Sigma X = 35$, $\overline{X} = 7.0$ and $R = 2$.

These values can now be recorded in the boxes corresponding to the first sample, as shown in *Fig.10.7*.

Values for the remaining nineteen samples can similarly be obtained, and the appropriate boxes filled in on the control chart. The result is shown in *Fig 10.8*.

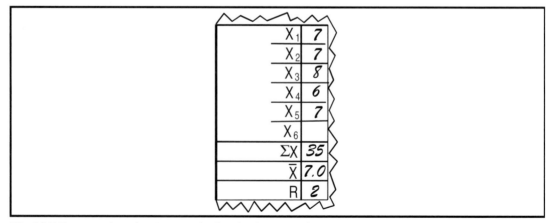

Fig 10.7 *Data section showing results for the first sample.*

X_1	7	6	7	7	7	6	9	7	8	7	2	9	5	7	7	7	5	9	6	9
X_2	7	7	9	6	7	5	5	7	8	5	7	7	5	7	3	8	5	13	7	5
X_3	8	8	8	7	7	9	7	4	10	7	8	8	7	7	5	8	6	3	7	5
X_4	6	2	6	5	4	4	5	7	8	7	6	6	8	5	7	7	7	15	8	7
X_5	7	8	8	7	7	8	9	4	6	8	8	10	15	6	6	6	7	7	6	8
X_6																				
ΣX	35	31	38	32	32	32	35	29	40	34	31	40	40	32	28	36	30	47	34	34
$\overline{X}$	7.0	6.2	7.6	6.4	6.4	6.4	7.0	5.8	8.0	6.8	6.2	8.0	8.0	6.4	5.6	7.2	6.0	9.4	6.8	6.8
R	2	6	3	2	3	5	4	3	4	3	6	4	10	2	4	2	2	12	2	4

Fig 10.8 Completed data boxes for the first twenty days' results.

With this data available, we can proceed with the next step, which is to calculate the central lines for both sections of the chart.

10.7.2 Calculation of central lines

For the $\overline{X}$ section of the chart: -

$$\overline{\overline{X}} = \frac{\Sigma \overline{X}}{20} = \frac{138}{20} = 6.90$$

For the R section of the chart: -

$$\overline{R} = \frac{\Sigma R}{20} = \frac{83}{20} = 4.15$$

10.7.3 Calculation of control limits

Control limits for the section of the chart

We use the notation UCL $_{\overline{x}}$ and LCL $_{\overline{x}}$ for the upper and lower control limits respectively.

Consider the $\overline{X}$ section of the chart first. We know that UCL $_{\overline{x}}$ and LCL $_{\overline{x}}$ are to be set at a distance of 3 standard deviations out from the central line $\overline{\overline{X}}$.

The method of getting the value of the standard deviation is different to that used when dealing with

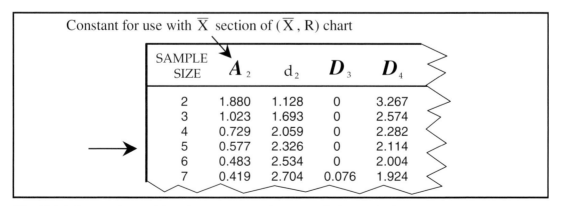

Constant for use with $\overline{X}$ section of ($\overline{X}$, R) chart

SAMPLE SIZE	A_2	d_2	D_3	D_4
2	1.880	1.128	0	3.267
3	1.023	1.693	0	2.574
4	0.729	2.059	0	2.282
5	0.577	2.326	0	2.114
6	0.483	2.534	0	2.004
7	0.419	2.704	0.076	1.924

Fig 10.9 Selection from tables of constants used in control chart calculations.

the (X, Moving R) chart. There is no need to get into the mathematics of why this is so. We just rely on the fact that there is an index A_2 available which is used in determining the standard deviation. By multiplying the A_2 value by the known value of $\overline{R}$, we finish up with 3 standard deviations directly. The standard deviation itself is hidden in the $A_2\overline{R}$ calculation, and we needn't worry about it.

A sub-section of the original tables appears in *Fig 10.9*.

This time we have highlighted the row corresponding to the sample size 5.

From the tables, A_2 for a sample size 5 is 0.577.

We know already that $\overline{R}$ is 4.15.

The control limits can then be calculated as follows: -

$$UCL_{\bar{x}} = \overline{\overline{X}} + A_2\overline{R}$$
$$= 6.90 + (0.577 \times 4.15)$$
$$= 6.90 + 2.39$$
$$= 9.29$$

Similarly,

$$LCL_{\bar{x}} = \overline{\overline{X}} - A_2\overline{R}$$
$$= 6.90 - 2.39$$
$$= 4.51$$

Control limits for the R section of the chart

As in the (X, Moving R) chart, we use UCL_R and LCL_R to denote the upper and lower control limits respectively for R.

Unlike the (X, Moving R) chart, however, R in this case represents the actual range in the sample and not a moving range.

We obtain the limits for R by using the same set of constants, but this time applying values of D_3 and D_4 corresponding to a sample size 5.

Fig 10.10 shows the same section of the table of constants, highlighting the D_3 and D_4 constants with n = 5.

To obtain UCL_R, multiply D_4 by $\overline{R}$ in the usual way. Similarly, to obtain LCL_R multiply D_3 by $\overline{R}$.

From the tables, with a sample size 5, D_4 is 2.114.

$$UCL_R = D_4\overline{R}$$
$$= 2.114 \times 4.15$$
$$= 8.77$$

With a sample size 5, D_3 is 0 and hence LCL_R is zero.

Constants for use with R section of ($\overline{X}$, R) chart

SAMPLE SIZE	A_2	d_2	D_3	D_4
2	1.880	1.128	0	3.267
3	1.023	1.693	0	2.574
4	0.729	2.059	0	2.282
5	0.577	2.326	0	2.114
6	0.483	2.534	0	2.004
7	0.419	2.704	0.076	1.924

Fig 10.10 Section from tables of constants used in control chart calculations.

10.8 Recording numerical values on chart

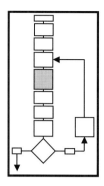

Record the values of the central lines and control limits

With the central lines and control limits calculated, the results can be recorded in the data boxes on the two sections of the chart.

The completed boxes are shown in *Fig 10.11*.

10.9 Choosing scales for the charts

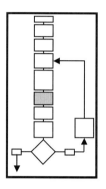

Choose scales for the charts

With the control limits known, they are used to determine suitable scales for the $\overline{X}$ and R sections of the control chart.

UCL_X is 9.29 and LCL_X is 4.51. The blank control chart has 10 major gridlines for the $\overline{X}$ section. By recording 5, 6, 7 etc at the tick marks corresponding to the major grid lines, a suitable scale is obtained. A section of the axis for plotting the $\overline{X}$ values is shown in *Fig 10.11*.

Similarly for the R section. UCL_R is 8.77 and LCL_R is 0. The blank chart has 5 major gridlines. A suitable scale is obtained by recording 2, 4, 6 etc at the tick marks corresponding to the major grid lines. A section of the axis for plotting the R values also appears in *Fig 10.12 (overleaf)*.

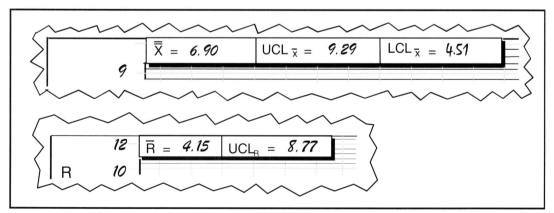

Fig 10.11 Data boxes showing values of central lines and control limits.

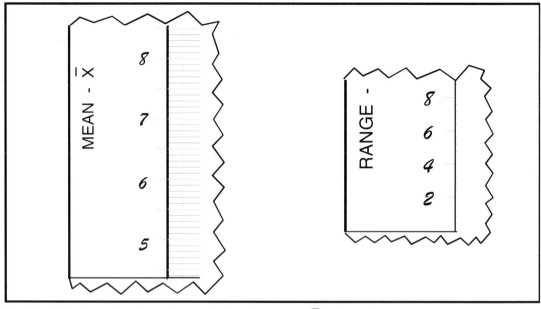

Fig 10.12 *Sections of scales to be used when plotting the $\overline{X}$ and R values.*

10.10 Plotting the sample results

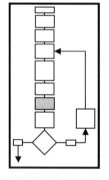

> **Plot the sample results**

With the scales completed, $\overline{X}$ and R values are plotted in the usual way, and the points then joined up. A section of the control chart showing the two plots is shown in *Fig 10.13*.

10.11 Drawing the central lines and control limits

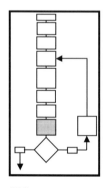

> **Draw the central lines and control limits**

The final step is to draw the central line and control limits for the two sections of the chart.

The control chart based on the first twenty readings is now shown in *Fig 10.14 (overleaf)*.

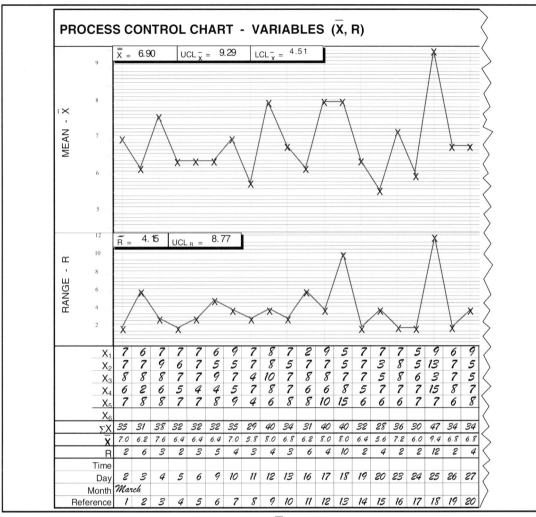

PROCESS CONTROL CHART - VARIABLES ($\overline{X}$, R)

$\overline{\overline{X}}$ = 6.90   UCL$_{\overline{X}}$ = 9.29   LCL$_{\overline{X}}$ = 4.51

$\overline{R}$ = 4.15   UCL$_R$ = 8.77

MEAN - $\overline{X}$

RANGE - R

X_1	7	6	7	7	7	6	9	7	8	7	2	9	5	7	7	7	5	9	6	9
X_2	7	7	9	6	7	5	5	7	8	5	7	7	5	7	3	8	5	13	7	5
X_3	8	8	8	7	7	9	7	4	10	7	8	8	7	7	5	8	6	3	7	5
X_4	6	2	6	5	4	4	5	7	8	7	6	6	8	5	7	7	7	15	8	7
X_5	7	8	8	7	7	8	9	4	6	8	8	10	15	6	6	6	7	7	6	8
X_6																				
ΣX	35	31	38	32	32	32	35	29	40	34	31	40	40	32	28	36	30	47	34	34
$\overline{X}$	7.0	6.2	7.6	6.4	6.4	6.4	7.0	5.8	8.0	6.8	6.2	8.0	8.0	6.4	5.6	7.2	6.0	9.4	6.8	6.8
R	2	6	3	2	3	5	4	3	4	3	6	4	10	2	4	2	2	12	2	4
Time																				
Day	2	3	4	5	6	9	10	11	12	13	16	17	18	19	20	23	24	25	26	27
Month	March																			
Reference	1	2	3	4	5	6	7	8	9	10	11	12	13	14	15	16	17	18	19	20

Fig 10.13 Section of control chart showing plot of $\overline{X}$ and R values.

10.12 Interpret the chart

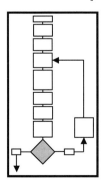

Are special causes present?

The chart is now interpreted to see if there are any special causes present. We use the four rules introduced earlier in the book and shown again overleaf.

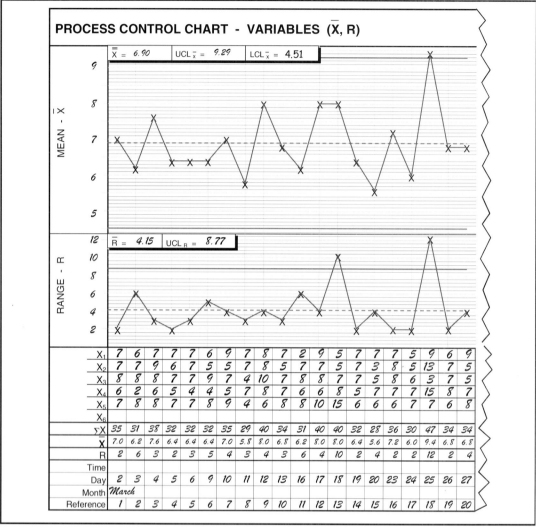

PROCESS CONTROL CHART - VARIABLES ($\bar{X}$, R)

	1	2	3	4	5	6	7	8	9	10	11	12	13	14	15	16	17	18	19	20
X_1	7	6	7	7	7	6	9	7	8	7	2	9	5	7	7	7	5	9	6	9
X_2	7	7	9	6	7	5	5	7	8	5	7	7	5	7	3	8	5	13	7	5
X_3	8	8	8	7	7	9	7	4	10	7	8	8	7	7	5	8	6	3	7	5
X_4	6	2	6	5	4	4	5	7	8	7	6	6	8	5	7	7	7	15	8	7
X_5	7	8	8	7	7	8	9	4	6	8	8	10	15	6	6	6	7	7	6	8
X_6																				
ΣX	35	31	38	32	32	32	35	29	40	34	31	40	40	32	28	36	30	47	34	34
$\bar{X}$	7.0	6.2	7.6	6.4	6.4	6.4	7.0	5.8	8.0	6.8	6.2	8.0	8.0	6.4	5.6	7.2	6.0	9.4	6.8	6.8
R	2	6	3	2	3	5	4	3	4	3	6	4	10	2	4	2	2	12	2	4
Time																				
Day	2	3	4	5	6	9	10	11	12	13	16	17	18	19	20	23	24	25	26	27
Month	March																			
Reference	1	2	3	4	5	6	7	8	9	10	11	12	13	14	15	16	17	18	19	20

Chart annotations: $\bar{\bar{X}} = 6.90$ $UCL_{\bar{X}} = 9.29$ $LCL_{\bar{X}} = 4.51$
$\bar{R} = 4.15$ $UCL_R = 8.77$

MEAN - $\bar{X}$

RANGE - R

Fig 10.14 *Section showing completed ($\bar{X}$, R) control chart for the first 20 points.*

RULE 1   Any point outside one of the control limits.
RULE 2   A run of seven points, all above or all below the centre line, or all increasing or all decreasing.
RULE 3   Any unusual patterns or trends within the control limits.
RULE 4   The number of points within the middle third of the region between the control limits differing markedly from two-thirds of the total number of points.

Two samples need to be looked at. Sample no.13 on March 18th gave an out-of-control signal on the range chart. This was due to a high value of 15 days corresponding to one document. Sample no. 18 on March 25th also had an out-of-control signal on the range chart, due to the reading of 15 days. This reading, when combined with the other high value of 13 days in the same sample, resulted in a further out-of-control signal on the $\bar{X}$ section of the chart.

A further investigation of the two samples was required. The order taking 15 days in sample no. 13 was due to a specific problem which was the supplier's responsibility. The value of 15 days in sample no. 18 was due to a unique combination of reasons, one of which was the responsibility of the customer.

10.13 Removing values resulting in special causes

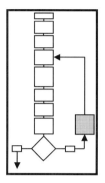

Remove values from the first set of 20 readings

Because the reasons are known the values corresponding to the two out-of-control signals are removed and the control limits recalculated using the remaining eighteen samples.

10.14 Carrying out the required calculations

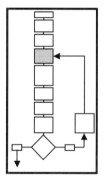

Calculate central lines and control limits

New central lines and control limits are determined.
The calculations are as follows: -

$$\overline{\overline{X}} = \frac{\Sigma \overline{X}}{18} = \frac{120.6}{18} = 6.70$$

$$\overline{R} = \frac{\Sigma R}{18} = \frac{61}{18} = 3.39$$

$$\begin{aligned}
UCL_{\overline{X}} &= \overline{\overline{X}} + A_2\overline{R} \\
&= 6.70 + (0.577 \times 3.39) \\
&= 6.70 + 1.96 \\
&= 8.66
\end{aligned}$$

Similarly,
$$\begin{aligned}
LCL_{\overline{X}} &= \overline{\overline{X}} - A_2\overline{R} \\
&= 6.70 - 1.96 \\
&= 4.74
\end{aligned}$$

$$\begin{aligned}
UCL_R &= D_4\overline{R} \\
&= 2.326 \times 3.39 \\
&= 7.89
\end{aligned}$$

$$LCL_R = 0$$

The scales remain unchanged and the values have already been plotted. The next requirement, based on our flowchart, is to draw lines based on our new results for the central lines and the control limits.

10.15 Drawing the new central lines and control limits

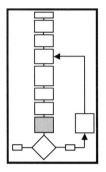

Draw the central lines and control limits

With new central lines and control limits available, these are now drawn on the chart, giving the result shown in *Fig 10.15*.

10.16 Interpreting the chart

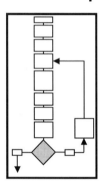

Are special causes present?

The process is again checked for the presence of any special causes. In practice, it is highly unlikely that there will be any special causes remaining at this point. However, it is possible that one of the other rules for the presence of something unusual may apply, and therefore it is worth following the sequence in the flowchart.

In our case no special causes were found and therefore we move to the next stage of the analysis.

10.17 Projecting lines ahead

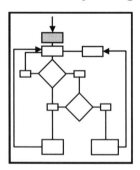

Draw lines onwards

The central lines and control limits are now extended to the end of the first control chart sheet. The results are shown in *Fig 10.16 (overleaf)*.

10.18 Continue monitoring the process

Using the control chart with the lines projected to the end of the sheet, further readings are taken and the results plotted in sequence on the chart. Each value of $\overline{X}$ and R is assessed using the rules for out-of-control signals, and appropriate action taken.

Fig 10.17 (Page 145) shows the final control chart with the results for the next eight samples plotted. The process continues to remain under control. Further points are plotted until the sheet is completed.

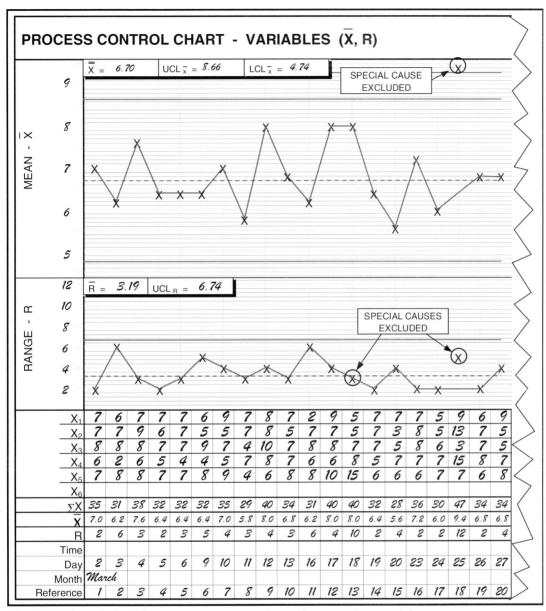

PROCESS CONTROL CHART - VARIABLES ($\overline{\text{X}}$, R)

X_1	7	6	7	7	7	6	9	7	8	7	2	9	5	7	7	7	5	9	6	9
X_2	7	7	9	6	7	5	5	7	8	5	7	7	5	7	3	8	5	13	7	5
X_3	8	8	8	7	7	9	7	4	10	7	8	8	7	7	5	8	6	3	7	5
X_4	6	2	6	5	4	4	5	7	8	7	6	6	8	5	7	7	7	15	8	7
X_5	7	8	8	7	7	8	9	4	6	8	8	10	15	6	6	6	7	7	6	8
X_6																				
ΣX	35	31	38	32	32	32	35	29	40	34	31	40	40	32	28	36	30	47	34	34
$\overline{X}$	7.0	6.2	7.6	6.4	6.4	6.4	7.0	5.8	8.0	6.8	6.2	8.0	8.0	6.4	5.6	7.2	6.0	9.4	6.8	6.8
R	2	6	3	2	3	5	4	3	4	3	6	4	10	2	4	2	2	12	2	4
Time																				
Day	2	3	4	5	6	9	10	11	12	13	16	17	18	19	20	23	24	25	26	27
Month	*March*																			
Reference	1	2	3	4	5	6	7	8	9	10	11	12	13	14	15	16	17	18	19	20

In the chart: $\overline{\overline{\text{X}}} = 6.70$, $\text{UCL}_{\overline{\text{x}}} = 8.66$, $\text{LCL}_{\overline{\text{x}}} = 4.74$, SPECIAL CAUSE EXCLUDED; $\overline{\text{R}} = 3.19$, $\text{UCL}_{\text{R}} = 6.74$, SPECIAL CAUSES EXCLUDED

Fig 10.15 *Control chart for customer response times after removing special causes.*

A new sheet is then used with the central lines and control limits from the previous sheet drawn on.

10.19 Other issues relating to the ($\overline{\text{X}}$, R) chart

10.19.1 Choice of sample size

A sample size of five has been used in the working example in this chapter. In office areas it is doubtful if a different sample size will be used, and so you are advised to stick with n = 5.

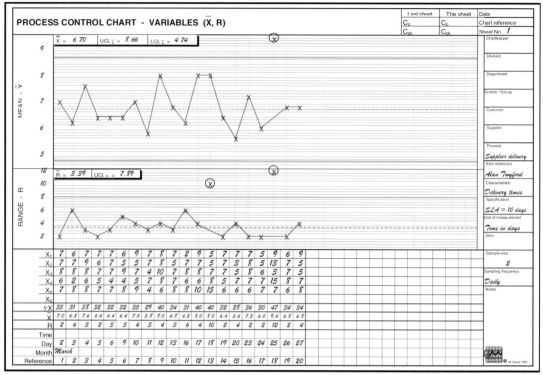

Fig 10.16 *Control chart with lines drawn ahead.*

This will make things easier in that you need not bother with constants corresponding to other sample sizes when using this particular type of control chart. If it so happens that you need to use a value of n other than five, then simply carry out the calculations exactly as we have done, using the values of the constants corresponding to the sample size in question.

10.19.2 Improving the process

The response times indicated in *Fig. 10.17* reflect a process which is under control and predictable. However, it may not be satisfying the customer requirements which have been specified for the process. At the same time, it is not improving, either in terms of reducing the mean response time, or narrowing the variation in the readings about the mean response times.

These are important issues. Satisfying the customer requirements is a capability issue, and Chapter 14 provides a lot of detail on this. Using the control chart to detect signals which reflect improvement in the process is covered in Chapter 17.

10.19.3 The R chart

When discussing the (X, Moving R) chart, the point was made that for various reasons the Moving R section of the chart was not seen to be of much relevance.

We must not take the same view with the R section of the ($\overline{X}$, R) chart. The R chart in this case is extremely important. It provides a direct measure of the variation in the process. In the working example, for instance, we saw how the R chart highlighted an excessively high reading in a sample. Further, it provides the basis for process improvement – to be discussed in Chapter 17.

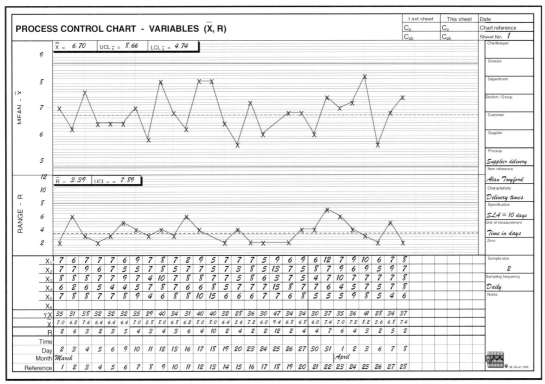

Fig 10.17 *Control chart for response times with further results plotted.*

10.20 Summary of symbols and formulae

Symbols

n	Sample size
$\overline{X}$	Mean of X values
$\overline{\overline{X}}$	Mean of sample means, sometimes known as the grand mean
R	Range of a sample
$\overline{R}$	Mean of sample ranges
UCL $_{\overline{X}}$	Upper control limit for $\overline{X}$
LCL $_{\overline{X}}$	Lower control limit for $\overline{X}$
UCL$_R$	Upper control limit for R
LCL$_R$	Lower control limit for R
A_2	Constant used in determining UCL $_{\overline{X}}$ and LCL $_{\overline{X}}$
D_4	Constant used in determining UCL$_R$
D_3	Constant used in determining LCL$_R$

Formulae

$$\overline{X} = \frac{\Sigma X}{n} \ . \ \text{n is generally 5.}$$

$$\overline{\overline{X}} = \frac{\Sigma \overline{X}}{20}$$

$$\overline{R} = \frac{\Sigma R}{20}$$

$$\text{UCL}_{\overline{X}} = \overline{\overline{X}} + A_2 \overline{R}$$
$$\text{LCL}_{\overline{X}} = \overline{\overline{X}} - A_2 \overline{R}$$
$$\text{UCL}_R = D_4 \overline{R}$$
$$\text{LCL}_R = D_3 \overline{R}$$

10.21 Key points and summary

- Make sure the process is well defined.
- Choose a suitable measure for plotting on the chart.
- For the ($\overline{X}$, R) chart the measure is likely to be time.
- Use a flow chart to decide that the ($\overline{X}$, R) chart is the appropriate one.
- Keep the sample size options to a minimum by choosing n = 5.
- Make sure that you use $A_2 \overline{R}$ when calculating 3 standard deviations.
- Don't be tempted to use standard deviation keys when calculating the standard deviation.
- Always choose suitable scales for the axes.
- The R section of the ($\overline{X}$, R) chart is much more important than the corresponding Moving R section of the (X, Moving R) chart.
- A stable process does not necessarily mean that the process is satisfactory.
- Values corresponding to special causes in the first twenty readings should be removed and new central lines and control limits calculated using the remaining readings.

In this chapter you have been shown the relevant steps in developing an ($\overline{X}$, R) chart.

Whilst not as generally applicable as an (X, Moving R) chart, the ($\overline{X}$, R) chart can have many uses in office areas. The four case studies which follow in the next chapter show how useful the chart we have looked at in this chapter has been in helping various organisations improve their competitive position.

THE ($\overline{X}$, R) CHART – CASE STUDIES

11.1 Introduction

Chapter 10 took you through the sequence for setting up an ($\overline{X}$, R) chart. The various steps involved in collecting the data, setting up the chart and interpreting it were explained in some detail. Some key points associated with the chart were also introduced, and at the end of the chapter you should have felt reasonably comfortable with the idea of taking samples, and plotting results based on those samples.

This chapter provides you with some examples of how the ($\overline{X}$, R) chart has been applied effectively in a variety of situations. From a bank to a finance company, an insurance organisation to a flour milling company, – the possibilities are the same. It is probably true to say that in office areas there are relatively fewer examples of the ($\overline{X}$, R) chart than the (X, Moving R) chart. That does not at all mean that the chart is less important. It just so happens that there is a lot more data in office areas for which the (X, Moving R) chart is the more appropriate chart.

Having said that, there is little doubt that the traditional ($\overline{X}$, R) chart has proven potential in administrative functions and the case studies to follow should show this.

11.2 CASE STUDY 9 Organisation C

STANDARD ORDER PROCESSING TIMES

11.2.1 Background to the company

The organisation concerned is a major industrial company based in the South of England. For more than forty years the company has been setting standards in the production of industrial consumables. Today, the company continues to build on a reputation for innovation, technical excellence, total quality and, above all, a dedication to customer satisfaction.

Some 100 orders are received by the company each month, the majority of which are for standard products. These orders are received in the sales office in a number of ways – post, fax, telephone, telex and e-mail. Prior to attending an in-house SPC course, the personnel involved carried out no formal measurement. The topic of order processing was seen to be ideal as the basis of an SPC project.

11.2.2 Targets

In the absence of a target set by customers (other than lead times), the group had been aiming for a target of 24 hours to process 'problem-free standard product orders'. The word 'processing' is used to describe interpreting the order, and entering it into the computer. This target was set a number of years ago, and was based on what was reasonable without any real reference to the process itself. Because orders were only date stamped and not time stamped, the target was difficult to achieve without adding another administrative task into the process. For the purpose of the project, therefore, it was decided that any order entered on the day of receipt (regardless of the actual time received) would be counted as

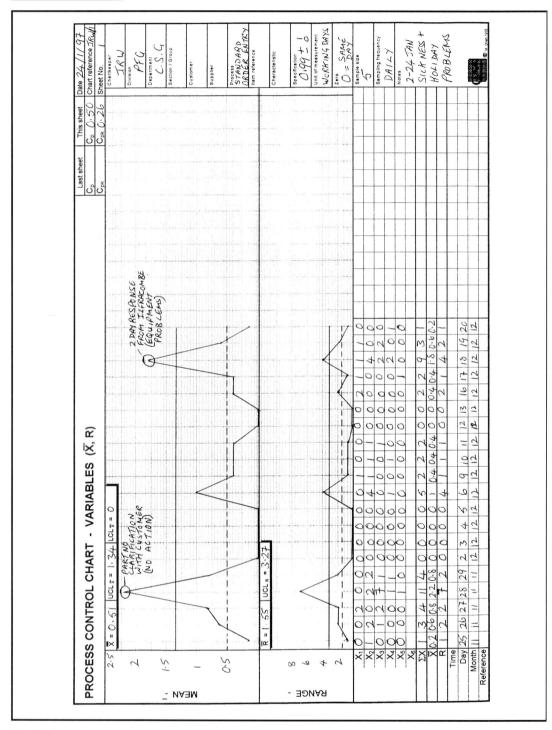

Fig 11.1 *Control chart for time to enter customer order onto the system.*

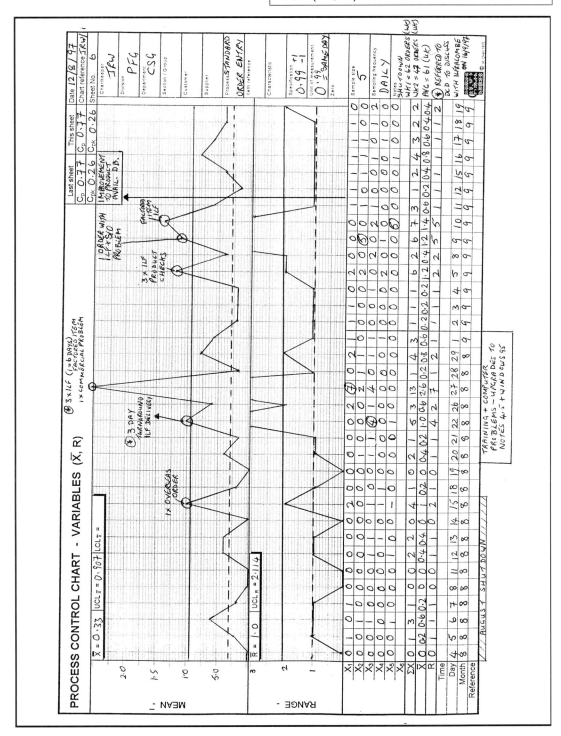

Fig 11.2 *Control chart for processing times used in a monitoring sense.*

'0' days to process. If the order was entered on the next day, it would be counted as '1' day to process, and so on. The process specification becomes 0.99 + 1, (same day + 1).

11.2.3 Initial measurement

The information was gathered from a query report, which listed all orders entered on a given day. Five standard product orders were taken each day and the receipt date obtained from the sales order file.

The results for the first twenty days were used to set up the control chart, shown in *Fig 11.1*. The chart highlighted two special causes.

One was the result of difficulty by the sales staff to resolve a part number problem due to the absence of the customer's key personnel. The second was due to the introduction of a new database by the sales office to agree delivery dates with the manufacturing plant. The system developed technical problems, which affected the response time. The PC Support Department relating to the Customer Services Notes Servers was already instigating corrective action.

Because the reasons for these two special causes were known, the points were eliminated. The control limits were recalculated using the remaining eighteen points and then projected ahead to continue monitoring the process. Further readings were then plotted and analysed, and the control chart as it appeared at a later date is shown in *Fig 11.2*.

11.2.4 Process improvements

The Customer Services Group, which was responsible for order entry, met to discuss the project and talked generally about prioritising workloads to improve the process. It was decided to discuss with the manufacturing plants how the timing of an order entry affected the lead times of the orders. This meeting brought to the group a greater awareness of the process and the realisation that achieving improvements was the result of working smarter, not harder. For example, it was believed (incorrectly as it turned out) that an order received and entered at 17.15 on one day had no real advantage over one entered at 9.00 the next day.

The group decided to focus initial efforts on entering all orders on the same day where possible, but without compromising on quality. Along with a new awareness of manufacturing's routine, this has helped to improve the process.

11.2.5 Process mapping

Now that the group had a greater awareness of the process and the improvements that were trying to be achieved, it was agreed to look at one of the inputs into the process i.e. receipt of orders into the Sales Office and the speed and accuracy of the activity. A process mapping of the receipt of the post to the various sales offices was carried out, and for four weeks the time taken to receive postal orders was measured. At the same time the number of items incorrectly routed was noted. *Fig 11.3* and *Fig 11.4* show the flow mapping for the distribution of orders for two of the three floors occupied by the organisation.

The flow charts highlighted how the lack of training in carrying out a straightforward task of directing orders resulted in quite distinct processes. Many areas for improvement were found, and these were then worked on. For example, it was recognised that: -

1. Post/order distribution is a shared job, and each person does the task in a different way.
2. There were unnecessary people in the distribution chain.
3. Distribution needed to be more accurate and much faster.
4. Orders and general post needed to be given different priorities.
5. With a few exceptions, the second delivery of post was held until the next morning for distribution.

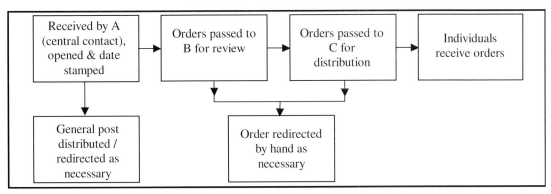

Fig 11.3 *Flow map of distribution of orders for Floor 1 post/orders.*

6. The numerical results attained during the four weeks emphasised these issues. For example, 119 orders were presented as 'process' orders, but 32, i.e. 26%, were redirected to other sales offices.

11.2.6 Further activities

Further areas for identification and possible improvements in the future were identified. These included:

1. A process map of orders received by fax.
2. The identification of common handling problems – price, discounts, part numbers, lead times.
3. The measurement of the response time of delivery database once PC support's corrective actions are in place.
4. The identification of regular misrouted orders and talking to customers regarding amending their records to correct/enhance the addressing.

This case study provides an excellent example of making use of another technique in addition to the control chart in improving the service provided to the customer. It is easy enough to forget that effective use of control charts needs the support of other quite simple, yet equally useful, process improvement tools.

Problem solving is also referred to in Case Study 10, which also includes some explanation of how cost savings can be associated with an SPC project.

11.3 CASE STUDY 10 Rover Finance

DO WE PAY OUR SUPPLIERS TOO EARLY?

11.3.1 Background to the company

Rover Finance is a joint venture company between Lombard North Central plc and Rover Group Limited. The company provides credit finance via instalment credit and leasing, both direct and through the Rover dealer network. The main offices are in Shirley, Birmingham, employing approx. one hundred and fifty office-based staff and a peripatetic sales force of fifty who service the dealer network.

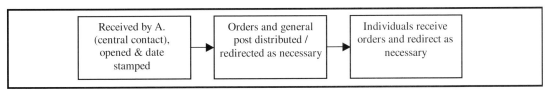

Fig 11.4 *Flow map of distribution of orders for Floor 2 post/orders.*

As part of a restructure in 1994, the purchase ledger function was moved out of the Lombard head office and up to Rover Finance's offices in Shirley. The payment practices adopted by the parent company were reviewed to ensure cash flow was being maximised.

The case study looked at current payment practices relating to purchase invoices within the retail/group staff sections. If it were found that there was sufficient variation between the invoice date and the existing payment date, then it would suggest that the adoption of a 'just-in-time' payment process would reduce the company's funding requirements.

The project looked at administration expenses only. No attempt at this stage was made to look at payment to vehicle suppliers.

11.3.2 Current practice

The department currently received invoices, set them on the purchase ledger system and then dispatched them for authorisation. Once the authorised invoice was returned, it was scheduled for payment.

At the time the project was instigated, no attempt was made to match payments against the invoice due date. All authorised invoices were paid on the first cheque run following authorisation. The only exception to this was where early payment would lead to a discount. In these cases there was a reliance on staff recognising the relevant invoices.

11.3.3 Relevance of SPC project to the department

The current purchase ledger system offers the facility to enter payment terms information for each supplier. The idea of adopting a 'just-in-time' payment process had been toyed with for some time. However, there was first a need to ascertain whether the additional work involved in loading and maintaining settlement terms was going to be worth the effort.

The project would enable the company to quantify how far payments were made from the due date. In time, this would then enable a reasoned decision to be made on whether to implement the new payment processes.

Any measures adopted would enable money to be retained for a longer period, and would be to the company's benefit if the costs of compliance did not exceed the saving. At the same time, there was a clear requirement to make sure that any new approach did not antagonise the suppliers.

RANDOM SAMPLE OF INVOICES FROM WEEKLY PAYMENT RUNS											
Payment date	No.	Invoice No	Supplier	Amount (£)	Invoice date	Terms (days)	Postal/BACS delay (days)	Theoretical due date	Paid in advance arrears (days)	Mean (days)	Range (days)
28-Jun-94	1	1453	A	41418.75	08-Jun-94	30	3	11-Jul-94	13		
28-Jun-94	2	1327	B	35.25	09-Jun-94	30	3	12-Jul-94	14		
28-Jun-94	3	1432	C	80.00	10-May-94	30	3	12-Jun-94	-16	9.4	47
28-Jun-94	4	1363	D	4073.61	15-Jun-94	14	3	03-Jul-94	5		
28-Jun-94	5	1373	E	39.30	26-Jun-94	30	3	29-Jul-94	31		
05-Jul-94	1	1518	F	18.40	30-Jun-94	7	3	10-Jul-94	5		
05-Jul-94	2	1537	G	1833.00	27-Jun-94	30	3	30-Jul-94	25		
05-Jul-94	3	1484	H	2350.00	31-May-94	30	3	03-Jul-94	-2	7.2	30
05-Jul-94	4	1469	I	450.00	15-Jun-94	30	3	18-Jul-94	13		
05-Jul-94	5	1345	J	11.75	13-Jun-94	14	3	30-Jun-94	-5		
12-Jul-94	1	1688	K	28.50	06-Jul-94	7	3	16-Jul-94	4		
12-Jul-94	2	1814	L	77.00	21-Jun-94	10	3	04-Jul-94	-8		
12-Jul-94	3	1808	M	421.25	09-Jun-94	30	3	12-Jul-94	0	-1	13
12-Jul-94	4	1514	N	1057.50	29-Jun-94	15	3	17-Jul-94	5		
12-Jul-94	5	1681	O	15.22	23-Jun-94	10	3	06-Jul-94			

Fig 11.5 Section from data collection sheet for monitoring weekly invoice payment runs.

11.3.4 Data collection

The initial source of all data used was the weekly payments proposals. There were two runs each week, one for cheques and one for BACS transfers. Both payment proposals were produced on the same day, normally a Tuesday.

A sample of 5 invoices was taken at random from the large number of invoices available from the weekly payment runs. Staff expense payments were excluded from the samples.

The details on payment run date, supplier and invoice no. were noted on a spreadsheet, a section of which is shown in *Fig 11.5*. The individual invoices were then traced and the invoice date and any specific payment terms noted. Where no payment terms were given, 30 days were assumed.

11.3.5 Calculation of theoretical payment date

In order to find out the deviation of the actual payment date from one using the payment terms, a theoretical payment date had to be collected.

By adding the credit period to the invoice date, the due date for the invoice could be determined. It was then just a case of working back to the first available payment run. In doing so, the project manager ensured that there was at least three days between the invoice payment run and the due date to allow for receipt of the cheque/processing of the BACS payment.

11.3.6 The measure of payment performance

By subtracting the actual payment date from the theoretical payment date, the measure to use was obtained. This represented the number of days early or late that the invoice was paid, and was an appropriate measure of the efficiency.

11.3.7 The control chart

An ($\overline{X}$, R) chart was used, and *Fig 11.6 (overleaf)* shows the completed control chart.

The section of the chart was seen to be under control. It appears that suppliers were being paid 10 days early. The suppliers were being kept happy although at a cost to Rover Finance.

The R section of the chart was out of control. This was due to a special cause on 6th September 1994, the result of one invoice which had an abnormally long payment term.

The overall goal of the process was to reduce the R-values and to drag the values down towards zero. Care has to be taken to ensure that as few invoices as possible fell below 0, as this would cause friction with the suppliers.

The above results were to be viewed with an element of caution. The investigation was confined to the invoice due dates, and had ignored value. Problems could still be caused if payment was a day late on a £3m invoice.

11.3.8 Savings

The result of paying the suppliers 10 days early is an interest cost, and some rough calculations were made. An average payment run in the region of £108,500 was assumed as was an interest rate of approximately 6%. If the payment period could be brought down to 0 days, an annual saving of approx. £9000 is possible.

11.3.9 The future

The next step is to introduce the supplier payment terms. Following the successful implementation of these, the results will be monitored and process improvements tracked. Once the process has settled down following the change, process improvements will be looked for involving the whole department.

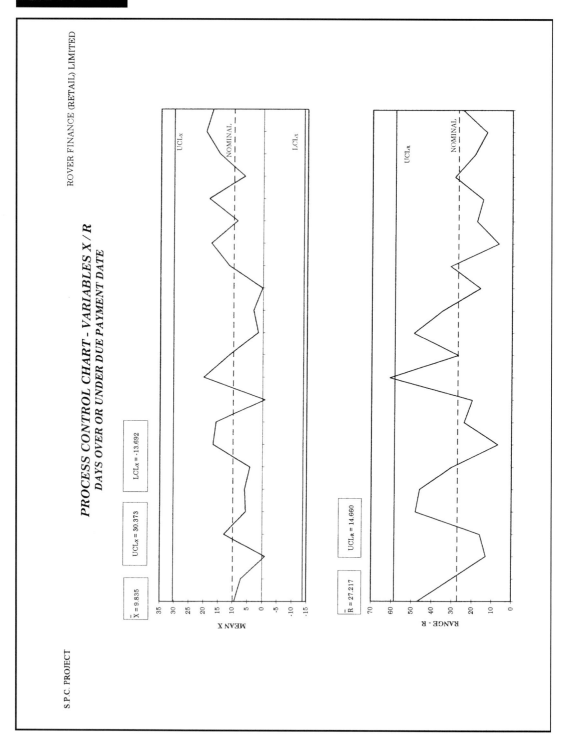

Fig 11.6 *Control chart for days over or under due payment date.*

It is envisaged that brainstorming will be used extensively as part of the next stage of this process improvement programme.

This case study provides a good example of how the use of a control chart gives a good measure for the process of monitoring payments. In addition, it highlights how the level of the process can be equated to costs, and how possible cost savings can be directly measured in control chart terms.

Response times provide a common theme for SPC projects. They feature again in Case Study 11 that looks at times to carry out customer transactions in a bank.

11.4 CASE STUDY 11 NatWest – UK Retail Banking Services

RESPONSE TIME TO CUSTOMER TRANSACTIONS AT THE COUNTER

11.4.1 Background to the company

NatWest UK is the main domestic financial services arm of the NatWest group. It is organised into five units: -

- Retail Banking Services covers the personal and small business markets and is responsible for the branch network.
- Mortgage Services offers mortgages for residential properties to personal customers, and further loans for major purchases.
- Insurance Services undertakes insurance broking activities and offers independent financial advice on life and pensions products.
- Card Services issues credit, charge and debit cards and manages currency acquisition and card processing for retail businesses.
- Corporate Banking Services deals with mid-sized and large corporate customers including international trade finance services.

The Retail Banking Network has 6.6 million personal customers, and offers its services through 1,750 branches, 24-hour telephone banking and a wide network of cash machines.

11.4.2 Introduction

SPC techniques were introduced into NatWest UK's Retail Banking Services arm in the early 1990's. Comprehensive training in the use of control charts was provided to key staff involved with processing activities. At this point, staff exposed to the training were employed as productivity managers, or similar functions, both centrally placed and in the regions.

A requirement of attendance at the SPC training course that had been provided was that personnel should work on applying the technique in their own area of activity. This particular project investigated how SPC could be used in analysing customer response times.

11.4.3 Some background

Responding to customers is a crucial issue to those employed by NatWest. Various approaches had been adopted over the years in measuring, in one way or another, how this could be achieved. Balanced Business Score cards, customer service indices and similar programmes all offered different, yet in many ways similar guides on how to assess the performance of the bank.

SPC offered yet another way. Those who fully understood variation and how to measure it suggested that it was the only way of really measuring how the bank is performing in providing a particular service.

At the stage when this project was being set up, SPC training had only been provided to managerial/ supervisory staff. Training for those involved at the sharp end in the branches was rightly seen as a later step in the programme. However, in developing projects on the potential for using the technique in the branch network, staff had access to a mass of actual or potential data, which related directly to bank activity.

The project to be discussed is one of a series which made use of such data.

11.4.4 The project

The project in question was based on the time taken to handle customer transactions at a specific branch at a specific time of day.

NatWest was already aware that the pattern of customer attendance varied across the day. The number of people attending a branch, and the nature of their business at the branch, was different for the first hour of the day, from what it was over the lunch hour, from what it was for the last hour. Similarly, the pattern for Monday was different from Tuesday, and so on.

For the purpose of the project, it was decided to monitor response times over a lunch period – between 12.30 and 13.30 each day.

11.4.5 Collecting the data

The times taken to serve the first five customers arriving after 12.30 each day were noted, and the procedure repeated for twenty successive days. To avoid introducing possible further variation, the same clerical assistant was used. Using different bank staff for the exercise would not in fact turn out to be an issue because there was no variation in the long term between the way the staff dealt with customers as they were all experienced.

The data was collected by the member of staff concerned. A simple data collection sheet was set up, and a stopwatch used to time how long it took to serve a customer.

11.4.6 The control chart

The readings were converted to the control chart, calculations carried out and the final control chart appears in *Fig 11.7*.

The chart showed some interesting results.

At first glance, the times seem very short. It would appear that the customers are being served much more quickly than would be expected. On reflection, however, these small times are to be expected. Many transactions involve routine paying of gas or other service bills, cashing a cheque or paying cheques into an account, etc. Hence an average service time of just less than two minutes is quite natural.

The lower limit on the section of the chart is actually negative, but this does not make sense in practice and hence we have a lower control limit of 0.

11.4.7 Analysing the results

The chart shows $\overline{X}$ to be under control but R out of control.

The R section of the chart shows two special causes corresponding to samples numbered 10 and 12. These are due to the high readings of 611 seconds and 667 seconds respectively. The readings related to the same customer who was paying in a large amount of money in small coinage – the takings from a local 'penny bazaar', as described by the project manager.

11.4.8 Future action

The chart was useful in highlighting a customer whose business was unusual in comparison with the normal counter activities. This means that with a known pattern over the weeks, it might be possible to set up a special counter to deal with any activities which are unusual and hence take a longer time to handle.

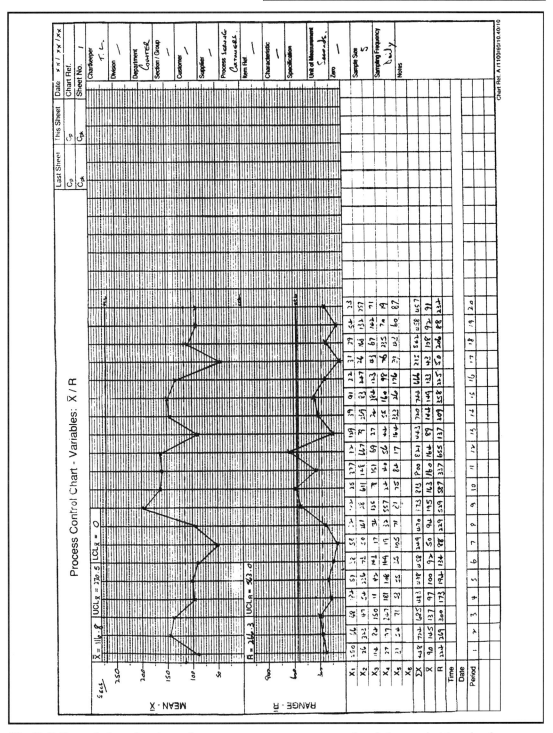

Fig 11.7 Control chart for time taken to serve customers over a lunchtime period in a bank.

The mean time of 116.8 seconds to serve a customer can also be useful. In another sense, this means that on average 30.8 customers could be served in that hourly period. This figure can be used to look at staffing resources. For example if there was a notional target of 35 customers to be dealt with in an hour, then the process is not capable of meeting that requirement.

The project has concentrated on customer response times for the lunch hour period only. Further control charts could be set up for measuring the response times for other hours during the day. In addition, it would be possible to develop other charts for the other days of the week to see what variation there is across the week.

The case study opens up the considerable potential for applying SPC in measuring customer response times in any environment. It is difficult to see how we can really measure any process without physically using a stopwatch, or a similar piece of equipment. Conferences, seminars and workshops are generally available on a range of issues centred on measuring customer satisfaction. It is rare for any to include material based on the approach adopted in this case study.

Times are not the only feature for which the ($\overline{X}$, R) chart can be used, as the next Case Study shows. It illustrates how costs can be monitored and compared when looking at the various options in acquiring company cars.

11.5 CASE STUDY 12 Spillers Milling

COMPANY CARS

11.5.1 Background to the company

Spillers Milling is an operating company within Dalgety Food Ingredients (DFI). Within DFI there is a large company car fleet that is managed by the operations department of Spillers Milling for the whole DFI group. Spillers Milling manufactures and distributes flour whilst other parts of DFI manufacture other food products.

11.5.2 Introduction

Historically, cars were purchased without the support of quantitative research. Procurement and policy were determined on the basis of opinions and historical experience that was never effectively challenged. Rather than continuing to purchase cars, DFI decided to contract hire in order to improve cash flow. This generated a requirement to review the cost effectiveness of the car scheme. There were also criticisms from car drivers about the limited choice of cars. The objective was therefore to revise the car scheme with enhanced choice at neutral or reduced cost.

11.5.3 Management actions

A simple statistical procurement process was adopted whereby cars of a similar specification from a variety of manufacturers were compared in terms of monthly cost reflecting all cost elements within a contract hire cost (e.g. purchase cost, finance charges, depreciation, maintenance etc). A new limit on the amount a car could cost for a given specification (e.g. 4 door saloon) was derived from the simple formula of the mid-point plus mean deviation of all values from the mid-point. Cars or manufacturers that cost more than this upper limit were either delisted or manufacturers could provide extra discount to reduce the operating cost. As a result, new manufacturers were introduced which provided greater choice but also stimulated competition that reduced cost.

The next step was to measure the effectiveness of this method and develop a means of control which would graphically show suppliers (car manufacturers) how they are measured by Spillers Milling.

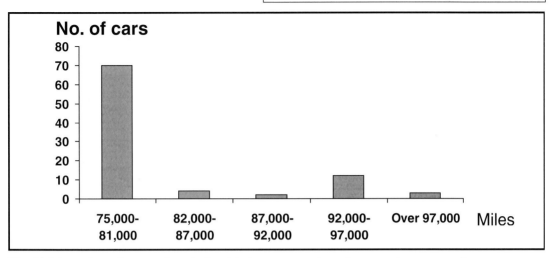

Fig 11.8 Bar chart showing the relationship between number of cars and contract mileage.

11.5.4 Data collection

Data was available relating to characteristics such as contract length and contract mileage dating from when contract hire replaced purchasing. For example, *Fig 11.8* shows a frequency analysis of contract mileage.

This representation provided some basic information to work on, but it did not provide any time-based data.

In control chart terms, there was sufficient data about to allow the use of the ($\overline{\text{X}}$, R) chart.

There were various options available to initiate the control chart. As a start, it was decided to concentrate on costs associated with expensive executive specification cars with high mileage and costly depreciation over a very short period of time.

Data was available for quotations for these types of cars prior to the policy changes and then gathered subsequently. These were in periodic batches in approximately fortnightly intervals representing five different suppliers. A total of twenty readings were used to set up the control chart.

11.5.5 The control chart

The control chart appears in *Fig 11.9 (overleaf)*.

It highlights very effectively the policy change and the overall savings that can be measured by the reduced level of expenditure over the latter portion of the chart. In addition, the chart emphasises the difference in cost variability between the two policies. The control chart demonstrated the need to use statistical methods to manage underlying cost performance rather than rely on subjective opinions.

11.5.6 Future action

The initial use of a control chart had proved its effectiveness, and the technique will be applied to other car specifications and also to other similar procurement activities.

This case study provides an excellent example of using a control chart with effect in an area little seen as having any relevance to SPC. The project was one of many similar ones undertaken by Spillers Milling in office and support areas.

We have covered two charts so far, but neither is of help when dealing with situations where we have categories of faults, types of errors etc. The third type of chart we will look at – the multiple characteristics chart – gives us a means of handling data such as customer complaints, document errors, etc.

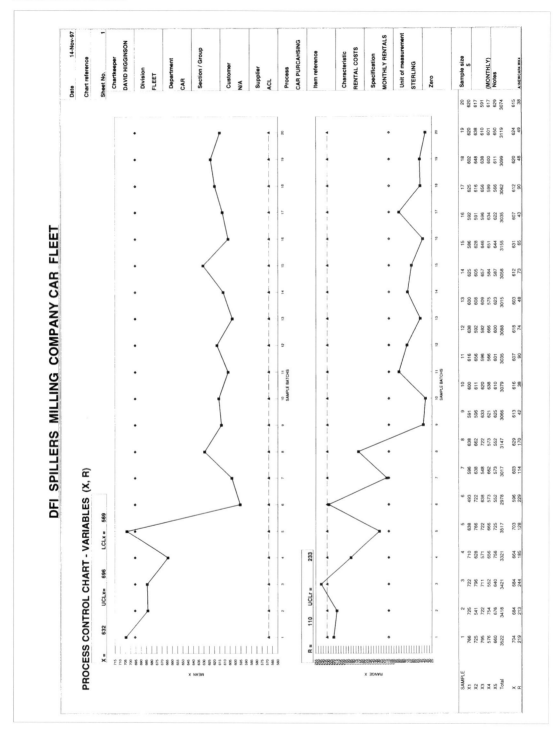

Fig 11.9 *Control chart showing car rental costs.*

CHAPTER 12

THE MULTIPLE CHARACTERISTICS CHART

12.1 Introduction

The different data sets displayed in Chapter 7 have resulted in two specific control charts so far.

In Chapter 8 we showed how an (X, Moving R) chart is used when dealing with single readings. Chapter 10 covered the ($\overline{X}$, R) chart for use with samples. The remaining data type is covered in this chapter.

We use the Multiple Characteristics chart for features such as errors, faults, omissions, etc. Customer complaints, errors in documents, reasons for failure, etc can be recorded and plotted in a very effective way by using the Multiple Characteristics chart. It is quite simple in its layout. Its potential in the office environment is considerable, and yet it is surprising that it is not a commonly known method for at least collecting data, if not moving on to the control chart stage.

As in Chapters 8 and 10, so in this chapter. The bulk of the material, up to Section 14, covers the sequence of setting up the chart. A core of the calculations are identical to those in Chapter 8 because we again make use of the (X, Moving R) routine. However because of the nature of the data being used, there is an additional bonus in that we can apply the Pareto principle in conjunction with the chart. Detail on this appears in Section 15.

12.2 Some typical figures to work on

In Chapter 7, typical sets of data for which the Multiple Characteristics chart could be used were shown in *Fig 7.15*, *Fig 7.16* and *Fig 7.17*. Some general applications of the Multiple Characteristics chart appear in *Fig 12.1*.

As with the previous two charts we have looked at, i.e. the (X, Moving R) chart and the ($\overline{X}$, R) chart, the first requirement is to understand the process that is being monitored.

12.3 Defining the process

Whatever the size of the organisation, and irrespective of its nature of business, administrative activities of one sort or another must be in place. These activities will almost certainly involve the use of documents, whether paper based or in electronic format, and hence there is potential for errors to occur.

Allocation of departmental errors	*Types of customer enquiries*
Reasons why invoices are not being paid	*Nature of inadequate information*
Causes of photocopier m/c failure	*Types of errors in orders*
Classification of complaint	*Categories of injuries*

Fig 12.1 *Some applications of the Multiple Characteristics chart in office areas.*

ANALYSIS OF SALES RETURN FORM				
WEEK COMMENCING	ERROR TYPE	FREQUENCY	TOTAL NO. OF ERRORS	TOTAL NO. OF FORMS
March 3rd	Post code	/	1	
	Customer reference	//	2	
	Unauthorised discount	////	4	
	Bank details	ЖГ ////	9	
	Other	//	2	
TOTAL			18	20
March 10th	Post code	///	3	
	Payment type	/	1	
	M/c data	//	2	
	List price	////	4	
	Unauthorised discount	//	2	
	Bank details	ЖГ ///	8	
	Other	///	3	
TOTAL			23	23
March 17th	Post code	//	2	
	Area code	///	3	
	Payment type	///	3	
	Customer reference	//	2	
	Unauthorised discount	/	1	
	Bank details	ЖГ ЖГ /	11	
	No trade code	////	4	

Fig 12.2 *Section of a data collection sheet for errors in a sales order form.*

In the case of the previous two charts, analysing the data meant some form of measuring. In this chapter, we are looking at error rates, i.e. assessing attribute data relating to faults, errors, rejections, whatever is the appropriate measure of the process being considered.

The data to be used as the basis of the working example relates to the number of errors which result from the completion of a sales order form. These forms are completed by field staff, and are then sent to head office for analysis.

The figures are essentially those as used by the organisation concerned. As a result, a specific issue arises which brings out a good learning point. This will be discussed in Section 12.15.3

Fig 6.7 provided a flowchart for developing an appropriate control chart. The same sequence will be adopted in this chapter.

As in the previous cases, collecting the data is the first step.

12.4 Collecting the data

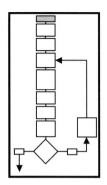

Collect data

Fig 12.2 shows a typical data collection sheet for recording errors of different types relating to the sales order form in question.

The data sheet enables a record of the number of errors associated with a specific type to be recorded. Corresponding totals can be obtained, as can the number of errors as a proportion of the number of forms available.

12.5 The control chart format to be used

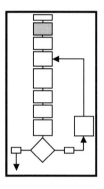

Decide on the chart to use

Use of the flow chart in *Fig 7.20* suggests that the correct chart to use is a Multiple Characteristics chart.

The design of this particular control chart is somewhat different from the two other charts we have looked at so far. It is different in that the chart allocates a section to record the type of error being considered and the number of times this type of error occurs.

The Multiple Characteristics chart we shall be using is shown in *Fig 12.3 (overleaf)*.

12.6 Recording data on chart

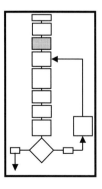

Record data on a blank control chart

The data available in the data collection sheet shown in *Fig 12.2* can now be transferred to the relevant data recording section of the control chart.

The first step is to record the error type in the 'Class/Characteristic' section of the Multiple Characteristics chart.

Fig 12.4 (overleaf) shows how the different error types have been recorded. In doing so it is important to make sure that sufficient weekly results, along the lines shown in *Fig 12.2,* have been utilised in order to detect all the likely error types. Even then, it is very likely that a category defined 'Other' will be necessary in the early stages.

The chart has been designed to allow for up to fourteen categories. If you find that you have more

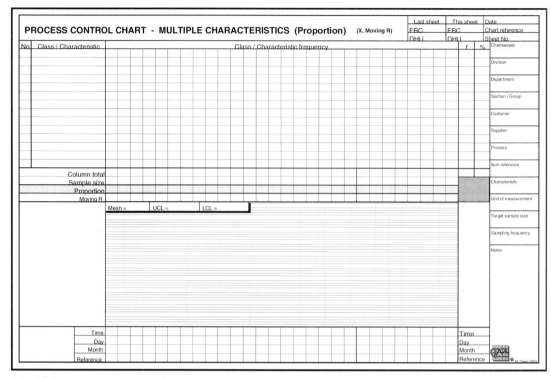

Fig 12.3 *Master version of the Multiple Characteristics chart.*

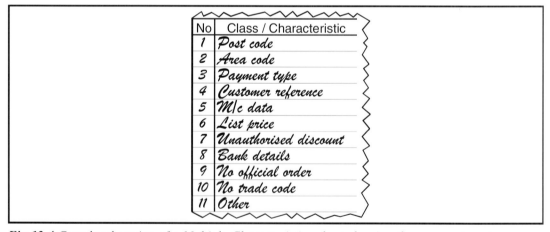

No	Class / Characteristic
1	Post code
2	Area code
3	Payment type
4	Customer reference
5	M/c data
6	List price
7	Unauthorised discount
8	Bank details
9	No official order
10	No trade code
11	Other

Fig 12.4 *Completed section of a Multiple Characteristics chart showing the error categories.*

than fourteen, and hence forced to use another sheet, then you have probably not classified the data adequately. A case study in Chapter 13, based on customer complaints recorded by a Trading Standards Department, provides further detail.

With the categories known, the corresponding frequencies, as indicated in *Fig 12.2*, can now be recorded in the appropriate cells in the 'Class/Characteristic frequency' section of the chart.

No	Class / Characteristic	Class / Characteristic frequency																			
1	Post code	1	3	2		1		1	2	1			3	1		1		1			3
2	Area code			3	2		1	1	3	1	2			1	2		2		2	2	1
3	Payment type		1	3	2				2			1		1		1		2		2	
4	Customer reference	2		2	2	2	1	2	4	2	4	1	3	2	4		1	3	2	2	3
5	M/c data		2					1				1									
6	List price		4		2		5			3		1			2		1		2		
7	Unauthorised discount	4	2	1	3		2	2	7		3	3		3	1	2	8	1	1	3	3
8	Bank details	9	8	11	4	10	14	8	7	7	15	11	14	13	3	14	11	6	12	4	14
9	No official order				3	3		2			2	4		4		1		2	2		3	1
10	No trade code				4	3	2	3	3	2	3	3	3	1	2	1		1	2	3	3	3
11	Other	2	3	2	5	3	1	1	1	2	8	1	12		1	1			3	3	5	3

Fig 12.5 *Multiple characteristics chart showing error categories and corresponding frequencies.*

The results are shown in *Fig 12.5*.

At the same time as recording the data relating to the error types, we need to record the descriptive data relating to the process which is being monitored.

Fig. 12.6 shows the completed boxes which give information relating to the process of analysing errors in sales order forms.

It is also timely to now complete the data boxes at the bottom of the chart which refer to the week no. etc, as shown in *Fig. 12.7*.

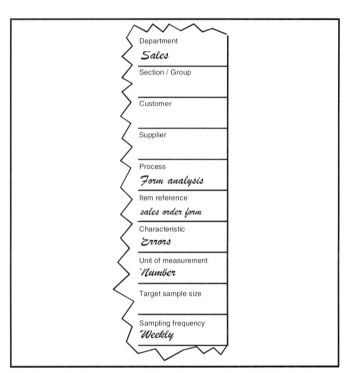

Department
Sales
Section / Group
Customer
Supplier
Process
Form analysis
Item reference
sales order form
Characteristic
Errors
Unit of measurement
Number
Target sample size
Sampling frequency
Weekly

Fig 12.6 *Section from the control chart showing completed process information boxes.*

Day	3	10	17	24	31	7	14	21	28	5	12	19	26	3	10	17	24	1	8	15
Month	*March*					*April*				*May*				*June*				*July*		
Reference	48	49	50	51	52	1	2	3	4	5	6	7	8	9	10	11	12	13	14	15

Fig 12.7 *Section showing completed boxes referring to sampling times.*

12.7 Carrying out the required calculations

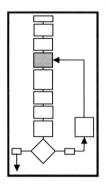

Calculate central lines and control limits

Before we can calculate the central lines and the control limits, some intermediate calculations are required using data available for the first twenty weeks, some of which was shown in *Fig 12.2*.

12.7.1 Sample calculations

The number of forms looked at each week varies. To allow for this the characteristic to be plotted is the number of errors expressed as a proportion of the number of forms.

The first calculation is to determine the total number of errors.

Referring to *Fig 12.5* and *Fig 12.7*, the first data set we use corresponds to week no. forty-eight, commencing on March 3rd.

The total number of errors for that week is: -

$$1 + 2 + 4 + 9 + 2 = 18.$$

Fig 12.2 tells us that twenty forms were scanned during the week, and hence the required proportion is 18/20 = 0.9

Proportions for the next nineteen weeks were similarly calculated and data boxes completed on the control chart as shown in *Fig 12.8*.

In terms of setting up a control chart, these twenty proportions are now considered as single readings, i.e. traditional 'X' values. They will be used to set up an (X, Moving R) chart, as shown earlier in the book, and more specifically in Chapter 8.

Nineteen moving ranges are calculated in the usual way, and the results recorded on the control chart as shown in *Fig 12.9*.

With the sample calculations completed, we can now determine the central lines and the control limits.

18	23	28	26	21	27	21	28	21	39	21	35	25	14	22	27	21	24	26	28
20	23	21	19	19	19	19	18	20	22	21	22	22	19	20	19	19	19	19	21
0.90	1.00	1.33	1.37	1.11	1.42	1.11	1.56	1.05	1.77	1.00	1.59	1.14	0.74	1.10	1.42	1.11	1.26	1.37	1.33

Fig 12.8 *Completed data boxes relating to sample values.*

	Column total	18	23	28	26	21	27	21	28	21	39	21	35	25	14	22	27	21	24	26	28
	Sample size	20	23	21	19	19	19	19	18	20	22	21	22	22	19	20	19	19	19	19	21
	Proportion	0.90	1.00	1.33	1.37	1.11	1.42	1.11	1.56	1.05	1.77	1.00	1.59	1.14	0.74	1.10	1.42	1.11	1.26	1.37	1.33
	Moving R		0.10	0.33	0.04	0.26	0.31	0.31	0.45	0.51	0.72	0.77	0.59	0.45	0.40	0.36	0.32	0.31	0.15	0.11	0.04

Fig 12.9 *Section from the control chart showing completed data boxes for moving ranges.*

12.7.2 Calculation of central lines

For the X section of the chart: -

$$\overline{X} = \frac{\Sigma X}{20} = \frac{24.68}{20} = 1.234$$

For the Moving R section of the chart: -

$$\overline{R} = \frac{\Sigma R}{19} = \frac{6.53}{19} = 0.344$$

12.7.3 Calculation of control limits

The layout of the Multiple Characteristics chart only requires the X section of an (X, Moving R) chart to be plotted. Hence we only need to determine UCL_X and LCL_X.

$\overline{R}$ is needed, however, in order to calculate the control limits for X.

In Chapter 8, we showed that providing we always use a sample size two when calculating the moving ranges, then UCL_X and LCL_X can be obtained directly from: -

$UCL_X = \overline{X} + (2.66 \times \overline{R})$

$LCL_X = \overline{X} - (2.66 \times \overline{R})$

$\therefore UCL_X = \overline{X} + (2.66 \times \overline{R})$

$\qquad = 1.234 + (2.66 \times 0.344)$

$\qquad = 1.234 + 0.915$

$\qquad = 2.149$

Similarly,

$LCL_X = \overline{X} - (2.66 \times \overline{R})$

$\qquad = 1.234 - 0.915$

$\qquad = 0.319$

12.8 Recording numerical values on chart

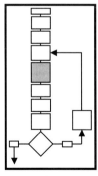

Record the values of the central lines and control limits

With the central line and control limits calculated, the results are now recorded in the data boxes on the control chart.

The completed data boxes are shown in *Fig 12.10*.

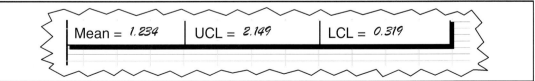

Mean = *1.234* | UCL = *2.149* | LCL = *0.319*

Fig 12.10 Data boxes showing values of the central line and control limits.

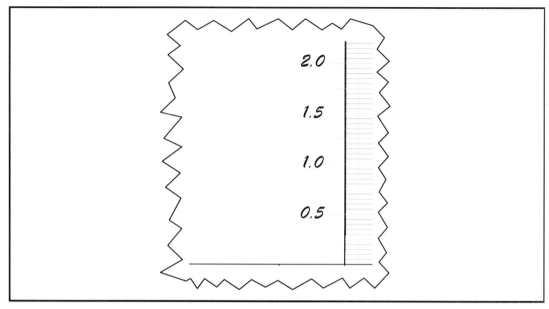

Fig 12.11 Section of the scale to be used when plotting the proportions.

12.9 Choosing a scale for the chart

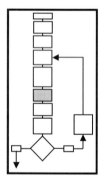

Choose scales for the charts

The values of the control limits are now used use to determine a suitable scale for the control chart.

We know that UCL_x is 2.149 and LCL_x is 0.319. The blank control chart has 10 major gridlines shown. By recording 0.5, 1.0, 1.5, 2.0 at the tick marks corresponding to these major grid lines, we end up with a suitable scale to use. A section of the axis for plotting the proportions appears in *Fig 12.11*.

12.10 Plotting the sample results

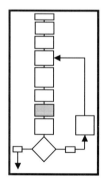

Plot the sample results

With the scale determined, the values of the proportions are plotted in the usual way, and the points then joined up. A section of the control chart showing the run chart now appears in *Fig 12.12*.

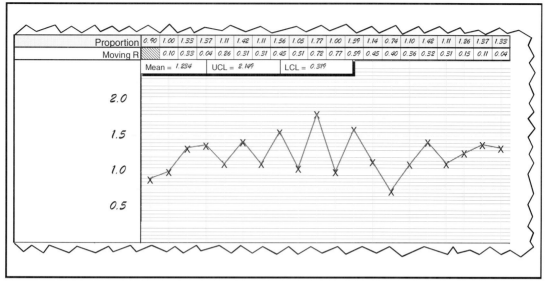

| Proportion | 0.90 | 1.00 | 1.33 | 1.37 | 1.11 | 1.42 | 1.11 | 1.56 | 1.05 | 1.77 | 1.00 | 1.59 | 1.14 | 0.74 | 1.10 | 1.42 | 1.11 | 1.26 | 1.37 | 1.33 |
| Moving R | | 0.10 | 0.33 | 0.04 | 0.26 | 0.31 | 0.31 | 0.45 | 0.51 | 0.72 | 0.77 | 0.59 | 0.45 | 0.40 | 0.36 | 0.32 | 0.31 | 0.15 | 0.11 | 0.04 |

Mean = 1.234   UCL = 2.149   LCL = 0.319

Fig 12.12 Section of control chart showing plot of proportion values.

12.11 Draw the central line and control limits

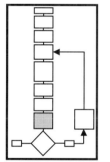

Draw the central lines and control limits

The final step is to draw the central line and control limits for the first twenty points of the chart.

The control chart is now shown in *Fig 12.13 (overleaf)*.

12.12 Interpreting the chart

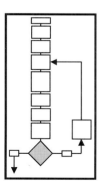

Are special causes present?

We use the four rules we should now be familiar with to see if the process is under control.

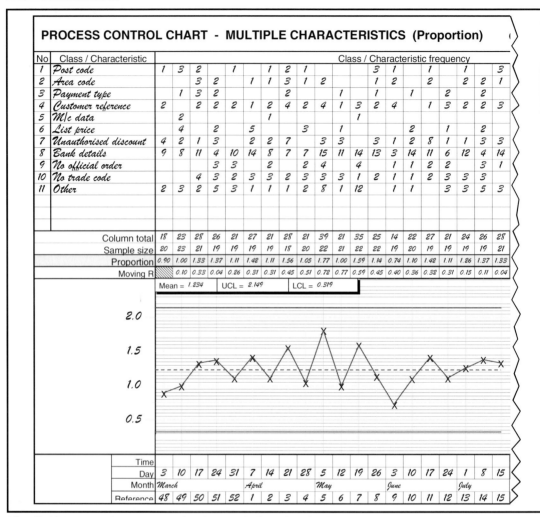

PROCESS CONTROL CHART - MULTIPLE CHARACTERISTICS (Proportion)

No	Class / Characteristic	Class / Characteristic frequency																			
1	Post code	1	3	2		1		1	2	1			3	1		1		1		1	3
2	Area code		3	2		1	1	3	1	2		1	2		2			2	2	1	
3	Payment type		1	3	2			2			1	1		1		2		2			
4	Customer reference	2		2	2	2	1	2	4	2	4	1	3	2	4		1	3	2	2	3
5	M/c data		2					1				1									
6	List price		4		2		5			3		1			2		1		2		
7	Unauthorised discount	4	2	1	3		2	2	7		3	3		3	1	2	8	1	1	3	3
8	Bank details	9	8	11	4	10	14	8	7	7	15	11	14	13	3	14	11	6	12	4	14
9	No official order				3	3		2		2	4		4		1	1	2	2		3	1
10	No trade code			4	3	2	3	3	2	3	3	3	1	2	1	1	2	3	3	3	
11	Other	2	3	2	5	3	1	1	1	2	8	1	12		1	1		3	3	5	3
	Column total	18	23	28	26	21	27	21	28	21	39	21	35	25	14	22	27	21	24	26	28
	Sample size	20	23	21	19	19	19	19	18	20	22	21	22	22	19	20	19	19	19	19	21
	Proportion	0.90	1.00	1.33	1.37	1.11	1.42	1.11	1.56	1.05	1.77	1.00	1.59	1.14	0.74	1.10	1.42	1.11	1.26	1.37	1.33
	Moving R		0.10	0.33	0.04	0.26	0.31	0.31	0.45	0.51	0.72	0.77	0.59	0.45	0.40	0.36	0.32	0.31	0.15	0.11	0.04

Mean = 1.234   UCL = 2.149   LCL = 0.319

	Time																				
	Day	3	10	17	24	31	7	14	21	28	5	12	19	26	3	10	17	24	1	8	15
	Month	March					April				May				June				July		
	Reference	48	49	50	51	52	1	2	3	4	5	6	7	8	9	10	11	12	13	14	15

Fig 12.13 *Section showing completed control chart for the first twenty points.*

Here are the four rules again.

RULE 1	Any point outside one of the control limits.
RULE 2	A run of seven points, all above or all below the central line, or all increasing or all decreasing.
RULE 3	Any unusual patterns or trends within the control limits.
RULE 4	The number of points within the middle third of the region between the control limits differing markedly from two-thirds of the total number of points.

None of the rules apply. The process is stable and predictable.

This does not mean that we are satisfied with the error rate. Reducing this requires appropriate action, and one way is shown in Section 12.15

Now that the process is predictable, the next step is to use the control chart to continue to monitor it.

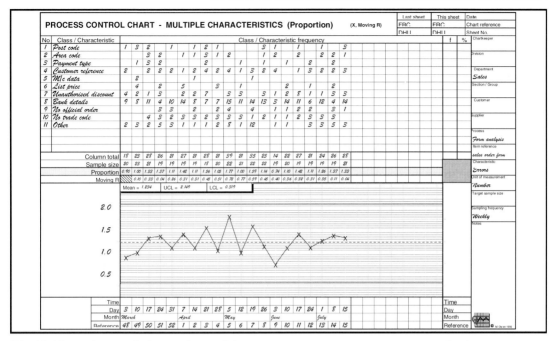

Fig 12.14 *Final control chart to be used for monitoring ongoing error rates in sales form.*

12.13 Projecting lines ahead

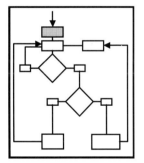

Draw lines onwards

The central line and control limits are now extended to the end of the first control chart sheet. The results are shown in *Fig 12.14*.

12.14 Continue monitoring the process

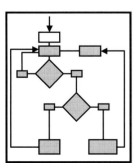

Error values are now recorded corresponding to the next set of results, commencing on July 22nd. The situation is assessed using the flow diagram shown symbolically here, with various actions following depending on the nature of the result.

Using this approach, further readings were recorded and results plotted until the control chart sheet was completed, as shown in *Fig 12.15 (overleaf)*.

The process is under control. Further analysis is now possible.

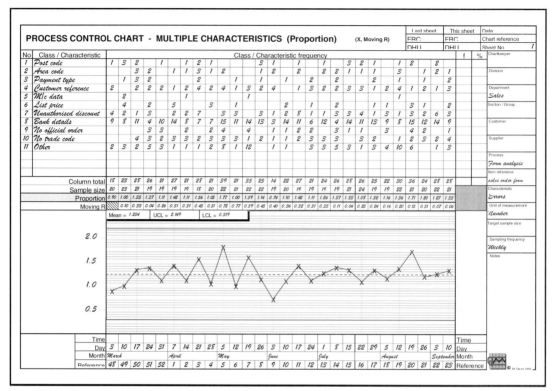

Fig 12.15 *Completed control chart sheet for monitoring total errors in a sales form.*

12.15 Further analysis

12.15.1 Highlighting the major problem

The generic flow chart we have been using does not cover the specific case when using the Multiple Characteristic chart in deciding how to proceed in making best use of the data we have available.

The control chart shown in *Fig 12.15* gives an indication as to whether the level of errors in the sales form is remaining at a predictable level. This is the first requirement in handling any data. However, the Multiple Characteristics chart has an additional attraction in that we can make a record of the total number of errors of a particular type, and then use that data to decide on where to concentrate our efforts in improving the process, i.e. reducing the overall error rate.

We progress by adding up the total number of occurrences of a particular error. This is the frequency, and the result is recorded in the column headed 'f'. A secondary step is to convert these frequency figures to percentages.

Fig 12.16 shows the section of the control chart with the corresponding columns completed.

Now note how very effective a Multiple Characteristics chart is in highlighting those characteristics or features that need addressing first. The control chart brings out the application of the Pareto Principle. By analysing the contribution identified under the % column, we can concentrate, in order of priority, on those items which make the major contribution to the overall problem.

Fig 12.17 shows that the major problem area (40.1%), and by a clear margin, is due to the category of 'Bank details'.

No	Class / Characteristic	Class / Characteristic frequency																											f	%
1	Post code	1	3	2		1		1	2	1				3	1		1			1		3	2	1		1	2		2	28	3.9
2	Area code			3	2		1	1	3	1	2			1	2		2	2	1	1	1		3		1	2	1			32	4.5
3	Payment type		1	3	2			2			1		1	1		2		2			2		1		1			2		21	2.9
4	Customer reference	2		2	2	2	1	2	4	2	4	1	3	2	4		1	3	2	2	3	3	1	2	4	1	2	1	3	59	8.3
5	M/c data		2								1							1			1									5	0.7
6	List price		4		2		5			3		1			2		1		2			1	1		3	1			2	28	3.9
7	Unauthorised discount	4	2	1	3		2	2	7		3	3		3	1	2	8	1	1	3	3	4	1	3	1	3	2	6	3	72	10.1
8	Bank details	9	8	11	4	10	14	8	7	7	15	11	14	13	3	14	11	6	12	4	14	11	13	9	8	15	12	14	9	286	40.1
9	No official order			3	3		2		2	4		4			1	1	2	2		3	1	1		3		4	2		1	39	5.5
10	No trade code				4	3	2	3	3	2	3	3	1	2	1	1	2	3	3		3	2		1	2	3	2	4		59	8.3
11	Other	2	3	2	5	3	1	1	1	2	8	1	12			1	1		3	3	5	3	1	3	4	10	6		1	3	85	11.9
	Column total	18	23	28	26	21	27	21	28	21	39	21	35	25	14	22	27	21	24	26	28	26	25	22	30	36	24	28	28	714	

Fig 12.16 Section of chart showing weekly readings and totals for first twenty eight weeks.

12.15.2 Setting up a new control chart

It is a logical step to now set up a control chart for monitoring those figures that relate to 'Bank details'. The result may show up a special cause on this particular category only. Either way, we need to recognise the need to refer to other tools and techniques in improving the process. You will find an appropriate tool kit in Chapter 16.

The characteristic to be plotted in this case is the number of errors corresponding to the category 'Bank details' expressed as a proportion of the number of forms.

The column totals are now the values for the number of errors corresponding to category 8. We have more than twenty readings available, but we adopt the usual convention and use the first twenty readings only in setting up the chart. New proportions are calculated, from which nineteen new moving ranges can be determined.

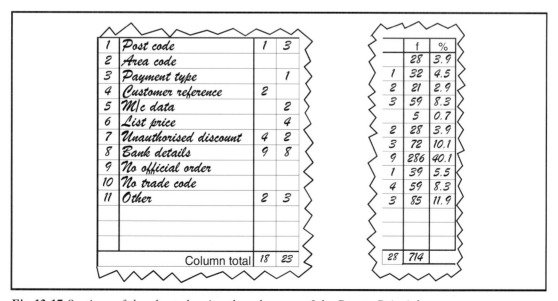

Fig 12.17 Sections of the chart showing the relevance of the Pareto Principle.

Column total	9	8	11	4	10	14	8	7	7	15	11	14	13	3	14	11	6	12	4	14	11	13	9	8	15	12	14	9
Sample size	20	23	21	19	19	19	19	18	20	22	21	22	22	19	20	19	19	19	19	21	24	19	19	22	21	20	22	21
Proportion	0.45	0.35	0.52	0.21	0.53	0.74	0.42	0.39	0.35	0.68	0.52	0.64	0.59	0.16	0.70	0.58	0.32	0.63	0.21	0.67	0.46	0.68	0.47	0.36	0.71	0.60	0.64	0.43
Moving R		0.10	0.17	0.31	0.32	0.21	0.32	0.03	0.04	0.33	0.16	0.12	0.05	0.43	0.54	0.12	0.26	0.31	0.42	0.46	0.21	0.22	0.21	0.11	0.35	0.11	0.04	0.21

Fig 12.18 *Completed data boxes relating to sample values for category 'Bank details'.*

The results are as shown in *Fig 12.18*.

With the sample calculations completed, the central line and the control limits can be calculated.

$$\overline{X} = \frac{\Sigma X}{20} = \frac{9.66}{20} = 0.483$$

$$\overline{R} = \frac{\Sigma R}{19} = \frac{4.70}{19} = 0.247$$

$$\begin{aligned}
UCL_X &= \overline{X} + (2.66 \times \overline{R}) \\
&= 0.483 + (2.66 \times 0.247) \\
&= 0.483 + 0.657 \\
&= 1.140
\end{aligned}$$

Similarly,

$$\begin{aligned}
LCL_X &= \overline{X} - (2.66 \times \overline{R}) \\
&= 0.483 - 0.657, \text{ which we take as zero.}
\end{aligned}$$

With the control limits known, a scale can be chosen, the results plotted, the central line and the UCL recorded and lines drawn as appropriate.

The usual rules for detecting special causes are applied and the process is found to be under control. The lines are projected onwards to the end of the page and the remaining eight readings plotted. No out-of-control signals are indicated.

The final control chart appears in *Fig 12.19*.

12.15.3 Repeating the procedure

Reference to *Fig 12.16* shows that the next problem area is 'Other'. Since this classification is a combination of several smaller contributions, then little is gained by developing a control chart for this overall category. However, the high % corresponding to this group does suggest a redefinition of the categories. This issue will be discussed in the next section.

The next ranked problem after 'Other' is 'Unauthorised discount' at 10.1%. The corresponding weekly readings are used to calculate new proportions, and a further control chart is developed and analysed in the usual way.

This procedure is repeated, dealing with the categories in order of priority, and using as many as are felt to be useful.

12.16 Other issues relating to the Multiple Characteristics chart

12.16.1 Use of (X, Moving R) chart

In the working example, we have allowed for varying sample sizes by plotting proportions, each proportion being considered as an X value and then used to generate an (X, Moving R) chart.

If the sample size is constant, or not known (as, for example when monitoring customer complaints, or office m/c breakdowns), then we plot the total number of errors, faults etc, directly. Because there is

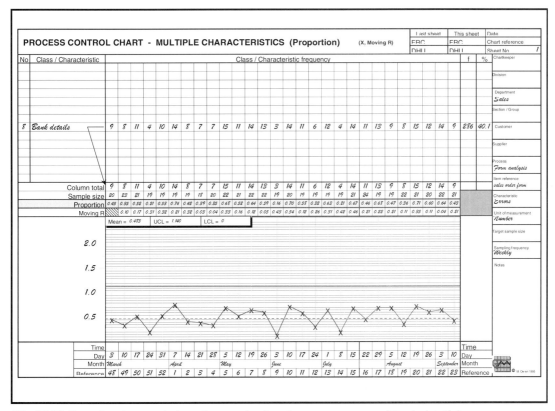

Fig 12.19 *Completed control chart for monitoring the error category 'Bank details'.*

no need for rows recording sample size and proportion, then the design of the master chart is changed to allow for this. *Fig 12.20* shows a section from a Multiple Characteristics chart for recording types of customer complaints, where the total number of complaints leads directly to corresponding moving ranges.

Technically, there are specific attribute charts available which cover a range of options. More detail on these can be obtained by reference to other books on SPC, as suggested in the Appendix. It is an advantage if someone in the organisation is familiar with these attribute charts. Having said that, there is no real problem, initially, in considering all attributes as single readings and using the (X, Moving R) chart as we have done. The point has already been made that a major objective of this book is to keep the approach as simple and practical as possible. Introducing a lot of additional options when dealing with attributes is not likely to be of benefit to those who want a basic, yet adequate introduction to the use of control charts in office areas.

Column total (X)	7	9	4	10	4	6	8	3	8	2
Moving Range (R)		2	5	6	6	2	2	5	5	6

Fig 12.20 *Section from a Multiple Characteristics chart based on numbers, not proportions.*

12.16.2 Classifying the data

It is worth spending time early on at the data collection stage to make sure that sufficient and relevant classifications have been decided upon.

The Multiple Characteristics chart allows for fourteen classes/characteristics to be defined. If we finish up with three or four classes, for example, then we may not have not gone into enough detail. If an initial breakdown provides more classes than the chart will allow for, then the initial analysis has probably resulted in too much detail.

An initial category defined, as 'Other', is necessary. It is quite likely that in the early stages of collecting the data then not all the possible classes will be known. At a later stage there may be a need for redefining some of the classes. This is indicated by the fact that the 'Other' category forms a major classification in itself. This feature was seen in the working example. The nature of the figures suggested that more should have been done to provide a clearer definition of categories.

If the 'Other' category is significant, then it is advisable to form separate classifications for some of the items grouped collectively under 'Other'. At the same time some existing categories with few readings, such as 'M/c data' and 'Payment type', could be transferred to the 'Other' category.

12.16.3 Number or value?

The Pareto principle was used in the working example to decide on the importance of the problems, on the basis of the number of errors occurring in a certain category.

If it is possible to allocate a cost figure to each type of error, then a preferable use of the Pareto principle is to rank the features in financial terms, i.e. from those with the highest cost implications to those with the least. For example, a multiple characteristic chart for accident figures will show that there are typically more 'cuts' than 'fractures'. However in cost terms, 'fractures' is ahead of 'cuts'. It may not be so easy to do this analysis using office-based figures, but the point needs to be borne in mind. If you have the information, then another option would be to prioritise according to the likely impact on customer satisfaction.

12.17 Summary of symbols and formulae

f   Frequency

12.18 Key points and summary

- Make sure the process is well defined.
- Choose a suitable measure for the process.
- Ensure that you have defined the classes/categories adequately.
- You should have no more than fourteen categories, i.e. use only one sheet to record the data.
- You will need to include a category 'Other' when first collecting the data.
- Whether we are handling numbers or proportions, then use these as X values and calculate moving ranges as before.
- We only plot the X section of the conventional (X, Moving R) chart.
- We still need $\overline{R}$ to enable us to calculate UCL_x and LCL_x.
- Use the 'f' and '%' columns to allow the use of the Pareto Principle.
- Draw up further charts in order of priority.
- A Pareto analysis based on cost totals would give better information than a Pareto analysis based on numbers.
- Other more detailed attribute charts are available, but keep things simple at first by using an (X, Moving R) approach with multiple characteristic data.

This chapter has shown you how to deal with data that is common to all office areas. Errors in forms, mistakes in computer input, nature of enquiries, customer complaints – these and many others can be handled in a very neat way using the layout of the Multiple Characteristics chart. In addition, we have had no need to introduce any new methods for calculating control limits. We continue with the (X, Moving R) approach and this makes things a lot easier.

We have done some further calculations, but these have been necessary so that we can use the chart in a very effective way in conjunction with the Pareto principle.

With the detail of the Multiple Characteristics chart covered, some case studies should now help you in seeing the usefulness of this chart. In Chapter 13, case studies are presented based on the experiences of five different organisations.

THE MULTIPLE CHARACTERISTICS CONTROL CHART – CASE STUDIES

13.1 Introduction

Chapter 12 explained the procedure in creating a Multiple Characteristics control chart. As with the other two charts we have looked at, you were taken through the various steps of collecting the data, setting up the chart and interpreting it. Key points associated with this chart should have helped in reminding you that this type of chart has a lot of scope in dealing with error rates, complaints, reasons for unacceptability, and so on. At the end of the chapter you should have had confidence in using the Multiple Characteristics chart, initially as a very useful data collection sheet, and subsequently as the source of a series of control charts which use the Pareto principle to track the progress of a series of characteristics.

In this chapter you have five examples of varying uses of the Multiple Characteristics chart. They come from different organisations in different areas of commercial activity. These examples should assist in showing you how useful this chart is. The organisations represented might not be in exactly the same activity as your own, but that shouldn't be a barrier. You must have data of this type available somewhere, stored in files or capable of being generated afresh.

The first example makes use of data which has to be common to any organisation – that which relates to errors in letter writing.

13.2 CASE STUDY 13 NPI

ERRORS IN LETTER WRITING

13.2.1 Background to the company

NPI, a subsidiary of AMP, was founded in 1835 as the National Provident Institution. One of its earliest policyholders was Charles Dickens. Today the company has over 500,000 policyholders and manages funds of around £10 billion. NPI specialises in pension products and aims to be regarded as the pension specialist within the financial services industry.

13.2.2 Introduction

SPC was introduced into the various business operations over a period of months with two-day training courses. These focused on the use of (X, Moving R) and ($\overline{X}$, R) charts and the application of the Journey to Improvement problem solving process. A number of projects have been successfully undertaken, resulting in reduced cycle times and costs, and increased customer satisfaction as we have gained greater understanding of our processes.

13.2.3 The case study

The case study looks at quite a different aspect of our SPC applications, however. Letter writing.

Pensions and investments can be quite technical subjects, particularly with all the taxation and legal jargon involved. The pension specialist may understand it, but the majority of policyholders are unlikely to have such expert knowledge.

NPI has produced its policy documents in Plain English for some time, but the quality of customer correspondence did not match these standards. General mistakes in addressing and grammar were compounded by the use of technical phrases and jargon that simply confused the policyholders.

Measuring the 'errors' using a Multiple Characteristics chart seemed an ideal way to pull together the data needed for an improvement project. SPC would help in identifying problem areas so that appropriate training could be provided to staff within the team environment. Various reasons were put forward for using SPC in this way. For example, SPC should show how it would help in:-

- Providing an original way to collect data.
- Identifying 'out-of-control' situations.
- Prompting process reviews.
- Showing the effects of training operational staff.
- Showing the effects of introducing change.
- Showing an improved process.

13.2.4 Background

It was felt that the measurement process should not only measure the errors, but also encourage the relevant team to do something about them.

EPS - F LETTER AND MEMO WRITING CHECK LIST

CHECKER THIS WEEK : | WEEK BEG.

CATEGORY / Clerk's initials:	Enter the number of errors per category below										TOTAL
Addressed correctly											
Salutation/Sign - off correct											
Heading - correct case and bold											
Heading - meaningful											
Grammar correct											
Punctuation correct											
Spelling correct											
Plain English											
Appropriate tone											
Accurate information given											
OTHER BAD IMPRESSION POINTS											
1											
2											
3											
COMPLIANCE ISSUES											
No opinions expressed											
Writing to authorised person											
Suggesting they contact an IFA											
TOTAL ERRORS FOR CLERK											

Instructions:

1. 10 letters must be audited every week by that week's auditor.
2. Put a zero in any boxes if everything is fine.
3. Enter the number of errors for that category and clerk in the box.
4. Any Compliance issues must be shown to the Ops Controller
5. If in doubt, ask your Ops Controller or another member of staff.
6. Feedback the weekly results to the team in the weekly feedback slot
7. Send the original of this form to Chris Wood (CA05A). Put a copy on our file.

Fig 13.1 *Data collection sheet used for analysing errors in letter writing.*

Letter checking courses were set up, and staff encouraged to attend. A vital element of the course was the provision of training to identify common error types found in non-standard letters. Training in Plain English and a series of supporting competitions, guidelines and hints helped maintain momentum.

13.2.5 Collection of data

Data was gathered by referring to the team's letter-audit file. This contained details of letters audited on a daily basis. The number and type of error is recorded in each case against the clerk responsible for the letter.

A typical data collection sheet is shown in *Fig 13.1.*

13.2.6 Difficulties experienced in collecting the data

Several problems were experienced when gathering the data:-
- Getting staff to accept that common cause and special cause errors had been identified on their letters.
- A lack of willingness from staff to submit their letters on a daily basis.
- Some staff were too set in their ways and didn't want to accept change.
- Constructive criticism, meant in a helpful way, was not taken to heart.
- Staff were not using 'spellchecker' programs.

A combination of communication, coaching, tact and diplomacy eventually overcame these difficulties and people began to recognise that what was being looked at was 'the process' and not their personal performance. After all, letter writing is a pretty personal and potentially subjective issue.

13.2.7 Importance of the data

The data collected is very important because it clearly identifies specific areas where training is needed. Clear, precise and accurate letters will project a professional image to NPI clients.

13.2.8 Analysis of data

In progressing this project, three non-standard letters a day were examined over a twenty-day period. This information provided the basis for SPC analysis.

A Multiple Characteristics chart was used to assess the number of errors, and how they were split according to the type of error.

13.2.9 Control chart

The control chart used is shown in *Fig 13.2.*

The process was under control with no special causes. However, the point close to the control limit was identified as corresponding to a new member of the team who had just started to reply to complaints.

Referring to *Fig 13.2,* a breakdown of the totals corresponding to error types showed that 'Plain English' was the major problem (37%), closely followed by 'punctuation' (30%).

The analysis revealed that staff still have a lot to learn when it comes to letter writing. Eighty-four percent of all errors accounted for the basics, most of which are still taught at school i.e. spelling, Plain English, grammar and punctuation. The analysis also provided conclusive evidence that some staff were not using the spellchecker facility. It also suggested that many do not read their letters before posting them.

Results based on control charts for the performance of teams in other departments showed similar problems.

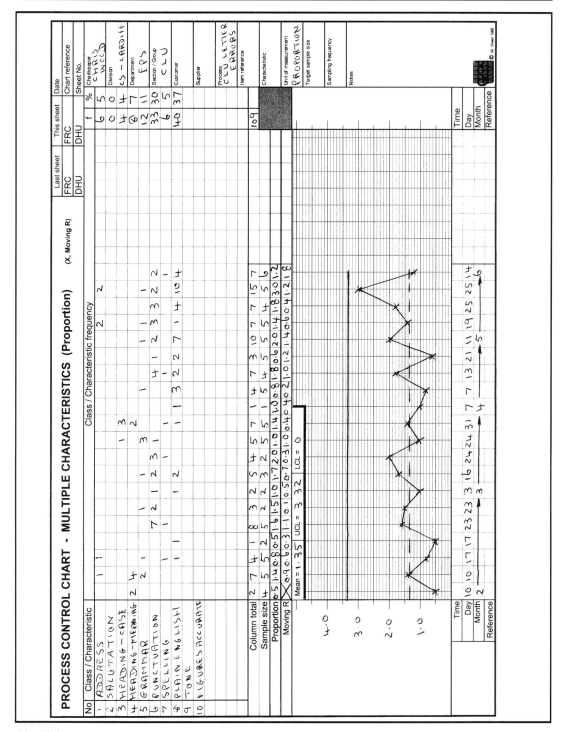

Fig 13.2 *Multiple characteristics chart for errors in letter writing.*

13.2.10 Further action

The measurement at both team and company level is being continued, though on a less frequent basis as the effects of the improvement activity, and particularly the training, takes hold. Within three months, errors reduced by 50% and the control limits were adjusted to reflect this improvement. For the moment, though, the control chart has been discontinued following the less frequent measurement, but on-going monitoring using the 'multiple-characteristic' section of the chart shows the error rate is still falling.

13.2.11 Deming's fourteen points

Several of Deming's points were found to be relevant to this project. For example, all processes must be continuously monitored if the company was to maintain consistently high standards.

Neatly presented and well-written letters will earn respect and, in some cases, admiration from customers. In the insurance industry it is no longer the cost of the product which is important. It is the quality of service and improved service standards, which matter.

Comprehensive training in letter writing has been provided for all staff. These training sessions will eventually remove the barriers that rob people of pride of workmanship.

By striving for continuous improvement, the company was taking positive action to accomplish the transformation that will distinguish NPI from being just another pensions office to being the pensions specialist.

Analysing errors in this way provides a common approach. The next case study, no. 14, shows how the Multiple Characteristics chart has been utilised in handling details on shortages.

13.3 CASE STUDY 14 Aerospace Composite Technologies

THE ANALYSIS OF WEEKLY RECORDED SHORTAGES

13.3.1 Background to the company

The origins of Aerospace Composite Technologies (ACT) lie in the establishment of a flight accreditation test centre which D. Napier & Sons set up in 1940. The company changed hands twice in the 1960's and 1970's, during which the product range extended to include aircraft transparencies and electroluminescent lighting panels.

In 1993 Lucas Industries announced the sale of the company, then known as Lucas Engineering & Heating Systems Division as part of its 'non-core' diversification programme. The management team at that time sought to gain the necessary investment for a management buy out. This was successfully completed in August 1993 when Aerospace Composite Technologies was born.

In July 1997, GKN plc, the international automotive, industrial services and aerospace and defence group, announced that GKN Westland Aerospace (GKN WAe) had acquired Aerospace Composite Technologies Ltd. GKN is principally engaged in the design and manufacture of aircraft structures for civil and defence aircraft and transmission systems for aircraft engines.

Throughout the past 55 years one specific company objective has remained fundamental – to deliver, through Total Quality Management, the optimum product to meet customer and market requirements. ACT is a market leader in its chosen fields and supplies components as original equipment to some of the most advanced aircraft world-wide as well as providing full in-service support and repairs, spare and exchange stock.

13.3.2 The company and SPC

ACT is a key supplier to British Aerospace (Warton). A programme of SPC was initiated in 1997 resulting in various training courses, some of them project based. These prompted increasing interest

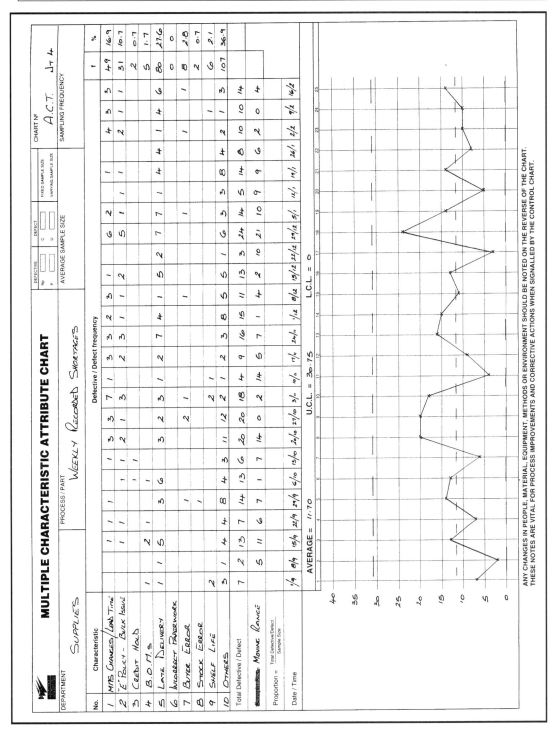

Fig 13.3 *Control chart for recording shortages in the Supplies Dept.*

in the use and scope of control charts. Understandably, initial interest concentrated on the operations management section. As with other companies, there was a general acceptance that in the first stages of SPC implementation, there would be more clearly identified measurable benefits resulting from applying SPC in production areas.

Even so, it was recognised that in order to obtain any award under the BAe supplier assessment programme, ACT needed to extend the use of SPC into non-production areas. Whilst this was seen as a secondary step, an enthusiasm for SPC in the Purchasing Department resulted in the following case study.

13.3.3 The project

A first attempt at using a control chart was based on the recording of the amount of items booked into Goods Receiving in a day as recorded on the computer system. Some information came out of the project, but not enough to warrant continuing.

It was felt that more benefit could be obtained by making use of attribute data relating to errors and reasons. In particular, errors in late deliveries resulting in shortages seemed to provide an ideal application for SPC, and as a result fresh data was collected.

A Multiple Characteristics chart was used to record the various reasons for shortages in the Supplies section. The completed chart is shown in *Fig 13.3*.

As is the custom, the first twenty results were used to calculate the central line and the control limits.

13.3.4 The control chart

On the basis of the first twenty points, the process was found to be under control. As a result, the central line and control limit were projected ahead and further readings recorded and plotted. No special causes were found.

Because the process was under control, totals were obtained for the frequency and % columns. The major problem area was seen to be 'Other'.

The case study brought out the same point as in the working example that formed the basis of Chapter 12. If the biggest problem area is seen to be 'Other', then it suggests that a re-classification of the error categories is required.

13.3.5 Future action

The process of monitoring shortages was under control, and therefore predictable. What does that tell us?

Well, at least ACT now knew what the error rate was, and what needed to be done to reduce it. A reclassification of the categories would then give a better guide as to the major reasons to work on, and this was set in hand.

There was an intention to target key suppliers regarding their performance, using SPC charts as indicators and as a means of comparing one organisation with another. Monitoring response times by using (X, Moving R) charts for various suppliers has opened up a huge area for further analysis using control charts. Early results have been most positive, and it seems clear that ACT have opened up a real opportunity for improving their processes by using SPC charts as a means of involving, and upgrading the performance of the various suppliers.

Handling a feature such as shortages in this way is typical of the use of a Multiple Characteristics chart.

In a purely service area, such as a bank, the chart can show equally impressive results. NatWest has used the Multiple Characteristics chart to great effect in handling downtime on a service till, as Case Study 15 demonstrates.

13.4 CASE STUDY 15 NatWest – UK Retail Banking Services

THE ANALYSIS OF DOWNTIME AT AN AUTOMATIC TELLER MACHINE – (ATM)

13.4.1 Background to the company

Detail on NatWest Bank was provided with the NatWest project on the ($\overline{X}$, R) chart which appeared in Section 11.4.

13.4.2 Introduction

The SPC training provided for the Retail Banking Services arm of NatWest Bank was project based. As a result, some seventy-five case studies were developed, providing a rich source of examples of real-life application of control charts in banking operations.

This particular example provides a very visual example of the power of the Multiple Characteristics chart.

13.4.3 The case study

The example relates to downtime on an ATM. A senior executive who had recently moved across into the Retail Banking Services from another Division initiated this particular project. One of his first exposures to data representation involved ATM downtime. Traditionally, the data was presented in the form of a rainbow chart, as described in Section 4.4.4 in Chapter 4. Line graphs plotted over time, referring to each reason for downtime, were plotted and the area between each line coloured in. The charts looked very attractive, but no more than that. Fired with his enthusiasm for SPC, and supported by the many successful applications he had seen whilst involved with the other division of NatWest, the executive suggested to a colleague that SPC techniques would provide a much better picture.

Fig 13.4 (overleaf) shows the control chart that was developed.

13.4.4 The control chart

A Multiple Characteristic chart was used to record the downtimes and the corresponding reasons. Strictly speaking, a Multiple Characteristic chart has conventionally been used to record reasons, or types. For example, if a form is rejected, then it can be rejected for more than one reason, and the corresponding frequencies recorded in the boxes in the usual way.

The manner in which NatWest was now using the chart represented a break with tradition.

13.4.5 Interpreting the chart

The control chart for total downtime shows a sequence of high points towards the end of the run.

A scan of the other charts quickly shows that the four points in question correspond to four high points on the control chart for downtime due to the magnetic card-reader.

Further investigation proved necessary. As a result, it was found that the magnetic card-reader was down for an unusually long time because of dirt and material falling behind the card-reader. Customers tend to fiddle with their bankcards. As a result, the magnetic strip starts to chaff and disintegrate, and consequently when cards in this state are used in the reader, there is an increase in the amount of debris which drops behind the card reader.

A modification to the card reader to deal with this problem was required. Plastic guards were installed behind the card readers to prevent unwanted material from dropping into the mechanism. As a result, downtime due to magnetic card-readers dropped significantly, as shown in the specific control chart. This led directly to a reduction in the total downtime.

The combination of the power of software technology and the simplicity of the control chart resulted

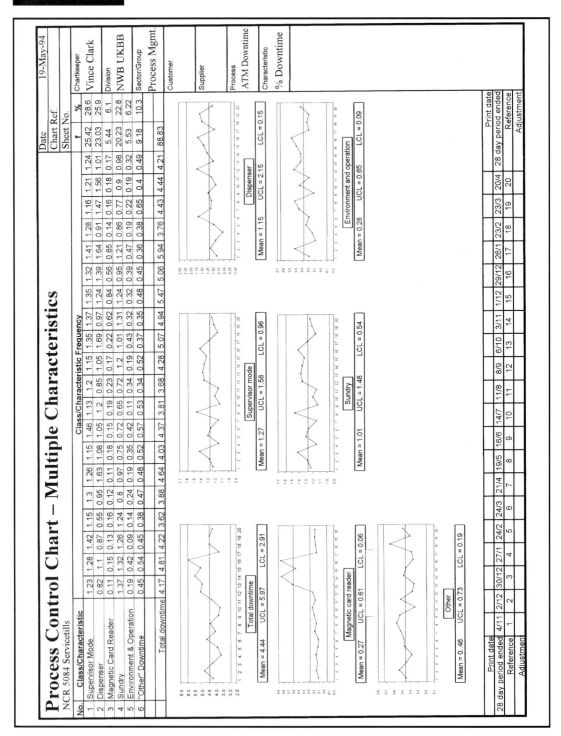

Fig 13.4 *Control chart for assessing reasons for downtime on a service till.*

in a very impressive combination. Further work was in hand to reduce the total level of downtime by working on the various reasons in turn.

This case study has shown how the control chart, combined with appropriate software, can revolutionise decision-making. It has provided an excellent example of the use of a Multiple Characteristics control chart, combining the simplicity of the chart with the power of a computer. It reflects well on a banking organisation that it has used this technique in a very effective way

Errors in orders and invoices provide a common base from which to develop an SPC project. Errors in invoicing are frequent, and the next example, Case Study 16, illustrates how a major organisation involved with the defence industry has made use of a control chart in checking on error rates in handling invoice errors.

13.5 CASE STUDY 16 GEC-MARCONI Avionics

SERVICE ORDER INVOICE ERRORS

13.5.1 Background to the company

The Radar Systems Division of GEC-Marconi Avionics was formed from the merger of Ferranti Defence Systems and the Radar Group of GEC-Marconi. Since this project was set up, it has become part of BAE SYSTEMS. It has over forty years of experience at the forefront of airborne radar technology. This dates back to the early 1950's with the design, development and production of the A1 23 air-intercept radar for the Lightning Aircraft – the world's first high-performance monopulse radar to enter squadron service.

GEC-Marconi Avionics is Europe's largest avionics supplier. The company was formed in January 1993 with the merger of four GEC-Marconi companies – GEC Ferranti, GEC Avionics, GEC Sensors and GEC Aerospace. GEC-Marconi Avionics continues at the leading edge of airborne radar techniques, with current projects including the Foxhunter radar for the Tornado F3, the Blue Vixen radar for the Sea Harrier FRS2, the Blue Kestral radar for EH101 Merlin and the ECR90 Radar for the Eurofighter 2000.

13.5.2 Introduction

The company has gradually started a long-term programme of introducing SPC, initiated primarily as a result of the requirements of major customers such as British Aerospace, now BAE SYSTEMS. Initial exposure to the technique has resulted in several projects that offer real scope for process improvement. This has confirmed a view previously expressed in the company that SPC provides measurable benefits and should be utilised independently of the requirements of customers.

This particular case study refers to invoicing errors – a feature that is common to any organisation.

13.5.3 Data collection

Each month, service order invoices were analysed and the number of errors of different types recorded on a Multiple Characteristics chart.

After 12 weeks no invoices were transferred prior to the end of the financial year. Over the same time period the transfer of an Excel spreadsheet was being developed in the accounts department. As a result, there was a gap of five weeks before further readings were taken.

13.5.4 The control chart

The Multiple Characteristics chart is shown in *Fig 13.5 (overleaf)*.

Control limits were calculated using the first twelve points. It was recognised that more readings would have been preferable, but twelve was still felt to be a sufficient number to enable some assess-

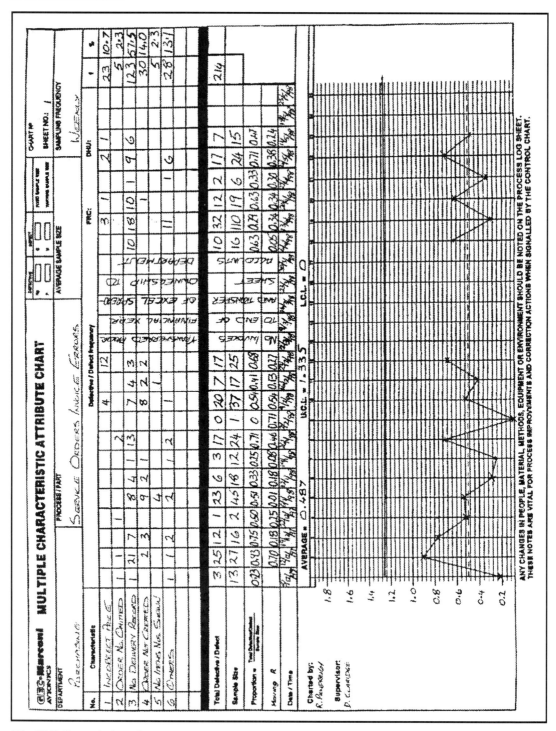

Fig 13.5 Control chart for monitoring errors in service order invoices.

ment of the process to take place. The changes taking place in the period March 2nd to April 6th did not seem to reflect a different pattern on the chart.

The Pareto analysis indicated that 58% of the problems are due to 'No delivery record'.

A further chart was to be plotted for this category only, and then other charts plotted for the remaining categories of errors.

13.5.5 Future action

Initial discussions were to take place with key suppliers regarding the use of SPC in the supply base. GEC Marconi intended to make the use of SPC a requirement for suppliers, and documentation was in the course of being developed which would spell this out.

13.6 CASE STUDY 17 BROMLEY COUNCIL

COMPLAINTS ANALYSIS

13.6.1 Background to the organisation

Bromley Council is the largest in area of the thirty-two London boroughs. Extending from Penge in South London to the ridge of the North Downs, Bromley provides not only urban facilities but also the amenities of the countryside. The Environmental Services Department provides a wide range of services aimed at protecting and improving the natural, built and working environments.

Located within this department is the Environmental Health & Trading Standards service. With ISO 9002 certification, two Citizen's Chartermark Awards (1993 and 1996) and winners of the 1997 Unisys/ Management Today Award for Service Excellence in Public Services, this group has a reputation for finding ways to improve quality and value for money.

13.6.2 Bromley Council and SPC

Up until recently, however, SPC had not figured in the quality 'toolkit' of the Environmental Health & Trading Standards Department. Not that there was any strong opposition to looking into its potential. As is often so, it was more a case of misunderstanding it, mistakenly believing it was a production engineering technique which had little relevance to running a local authority.

Following a half-day presentation to various senior members of the Authority, pilot SPC programmes were looked into. Control charts were set up to consider response times of different types. This particular case study, however, looked at the nature and number of customer complaints which, over the months, had been logged by the Environmental Health & Trading Standards Department.

13.6.3 The project

Traditionally, complaints have been recorded on a data sheet, and then transferred to a database. A sample copy of one of the monthly records is shown in *Fig 13.6 (overleaf)*.

A wealth of information was hidden in these sheets.

As a start, it was decided to look at the data relating to the types of complaints.

13.6.4 Handling the data

The data relating to complaints was categorised by a code and a description. The total number of complaints of a particular type was recorded, and it was this figure that was to be used in the analysis.

In order to make the data more manageable, the first step was to reduce the overall number of categories. For example, all the complaints relating to 'Food' were to be grouped under a single

EHCS COMPLAINTS – RESPONSE PERFORMANCE ANALYSIS
Statistics are based on working days taken from initial receipt
to first response for complaints received in selected period.

28/01/98

		Selected dates	01/12/1997 - 31/12/1997
		Complaint Group	ALL
		Department	ALL
		Officer Code	ALL
		Ref. Restriction	0070800 – 0079999

COMPLAINT TYPE

		%	Total	Aim Dys	Ave Dys	Numbers			%		
						−	=	+	−	=	+
AA	FOOD HYGEINE	0.5	5	3	0.8	5	0	0	100	0	0
AT	FOOD TRADE ADVICE	0.1	1	3	0.0	1	0	0	100	0	0
BA	NOISE ALARMS	2.8	30	1	0.3	23	6	1	77	20	3
BB	NOISE ANIMALS	0.8	9	3	1.2	8	1	0	89	11	0
BC	NOISE DOMESTIC	13.2	144	3	0.9	140	3	1	97	2	1
BD	NOISE COMMERCIAL	0.3	3	3	1.0	3	0	0	100	0	0
BI	NOISE INDUSTRIAL	3.9	42	3	0.5	42	0	0	100	0	0
BJ	NOISE IN STREETS	0.2	2	3	0.0	2	0	0	100	0	0
BK	AIRCRAFT NOISE	0.2	2	3	9.0	0	1	1	0	50	50
BL	NOISE CONSTRUCTION	0.3	3	3	0.3	3	0	0	100	0	0
BX	SOUND INSULATION	0.1	1	3	1.0	1	0	0	100	0	0
CA	ADVICE ONLY (TS)	15.2	166	2	0.0	166	0	0	100	0	0
CF	CIVIL COMPLAINT (TS)	5.0	54	3	0.4	50	4	0	93	7	0
DC	PUBLIC SEWER BLOCKED	9.7	106	3	0.3	106	0	0	100	0	0
DD	DRAINAGE	1.9	21	3	0.1	21	0	0	100	0	0
DO	DOMESTIC DRAINAGE	5.6	61	3	0.1	61	0	0	100	0	0
DW	DOG WARDEN	1.7	18	3	0.2	18	0	0	100	0	0
EP	EMPTY PROPERTY	0.1	1	3	0.0	1	0	0	100	0	0
FA	FOOD COMPLAINTS	1.7	188	3	0.4	17	0	1	94	0	6
FC	FOOD STANDARDS COMP.	0.2	2	3	1.0	2	0	0	100	0	0
FG	FOOD ADVICE - HA/OA	0.1	1	3	0.0	1	0	0	100	0	0
FS	SUSPECTED FOOD POIS	0.7	8	3	0.5	8	0	0	100	0	0
HA	HOUSING - CARAVANS	0.1	1	3	1.0	1	0	0	100	0	0
HB	BROOMLEIGH PROPERTY	0.6	7	3	1.1	5	2	0	71	29	0
HC	HOUSING CONDS PRIV	2.4	26	3	0.9	24	1	1	92	4	4
HM	HMO - COMPLAINT	0.3	3	3	0.3	3	0	0	100	0	0
LS	CONTAMINATED LAND	0.5	5	3	0.0	5	0	0	100	0	0
NA	ANIMALS FOULING	0.1	1	3	0.0	1	0	0	100	0	0
NB	ANIMAL KEEPING	0.1	1	3	1.0	1	0	0	100	0	0
NC	BONFIRES COMMERCIAL	0.3	3	3	1.0	3	0	0	100	0	0
ND	BONFIRES DOMESTIC	o.8	9	3	0.0	8	0	1	89	0	11
NF	DIRTY PREMISES	0.2	2	3	1.0	2	0	0	100	0	0
NI	RUBBISH COMMERCIAL	0.7	8	3	0.1	8	0	0	100	0	0
NJ	RUBBISH DOMESTIC	1.4	15	3	0.7	15	0	0	100	0	0
NL	SMELL	1.2	13	3	0.5	13	0	0	100	0	0
NM	SMOKE INDUSTRIAL	0.1	1	3	2.0	1	0	0	100	0	0
NN	NUISANCE OTHER	1.9	21	3	0.4	21	0	0	100	0	0
PA	ASBESTOS	0.1	1	3	0.0	1	0	0	100	0	0
RF	FLEAS	0.7	8	3	2.3	2	6	0	25	75	0
RH	INSECTS	0.5	5	3	0.2	5	0	0	100	0	0
RI	MICE	2.4	26	3	1.8	16	10	0	62	38	0
RX	RATS	4.7	51	3	1.2	39	11	1	76	22	2
RL	WASPS	0.9	10	3	0.6	8	2	0	80	20	0
RS	SQUIRRELS	0.4	4	3	0.0	4	0	0	100	0	0
SD	HEALTH AND SAFETY	1.1	12	3	0.3	12	0	0	100	0	0
SO	EMPLOYEE 3 DAY ACCID	1.3	14	3	0.6	13	1	0	93	7	0
SQ	EMPLOYEE MAJOR ACCID	0.2	2	3	0.0	2	0	0	100	0	0

Fig 13.6 *Typical print out of data relating to customer complaints in the Environmental Health &Trading Standards Dept.*

category called 'Food', and so on for 'Noise', etc.

In undertaking this project, the results for sixteen months only were available. Data from these sixteen sheets was then broken down into its appropriate categories, fourteen in all including 'Other'. An initial scan of the sheets gave a good indication of the smaller categories that were to be grouped together in 'Other'.

The computer database did not allow for these separate groups to be obtained automatically, and so the routine had to be carried out manually. This was a long and tedious job, but there was no alternative if any sense was to be made from the numbers.

13.6.5 The control charts
The data was ideal for use on a Multiple Characteristics chart.

The first control chart, shown in *Fig 13.7*, indicates the pattern of customer complaints for the sixteen months that were available.

The control chart shows a special cause in July of Year 2. Was that due to a factor that influenced one specific category of complaint, or was it due to a general effect, i.e. something which influenced all the categories in the summer?

Further analysis was required.

13.6.6 Studying the detail
The total number of complaints of a particular type was obtained and the results recorded. The totals are already shown in *Fig 13.7*.

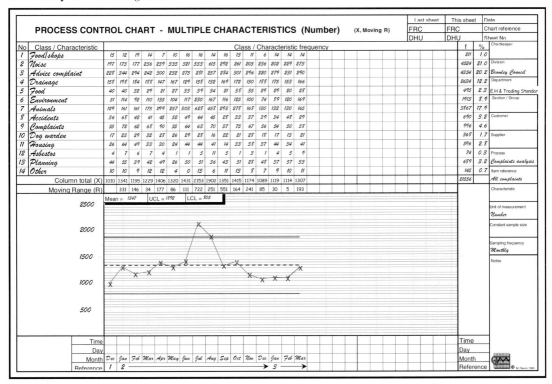

Fig 13.7 Multiple characteristics chart for customer complaints.

Some care needed to be taken because the process is out of control and so, technically, not too much credence can be put on the use of the Pareto principle. Bearing this in mind, the figures nevertheless indicated 'Advice complaint' as the major reason, followed closely by 'Noise'. The 'Advice complaint' figures showed no obvious unusual features, but the 'Noise' ones did. It was therefore decided to look at the 'Noise' figures in more detail.

A further analysis of the 'Noise' figures was now required. The original figures corresponding to type and nature of noise were used.

A new Multiple Characteristics chart was set up as shown in *Fig 13.8*.

The process was out of control for both July and August of year 2.

By referring to the totals on the right hand side of *Fig 13.8* it was seen that well over half the complaints were due to the category 'Domestic noise'. A further control chart was then set up to track this category, as shown in *Fig 13.9*.

Out of control signals occurred in July and August for Year 2. It now seemed clear that the main reason for the out of control points in the control chart for 'Noise' – *Fig, 13.8* – was the fact that 'Domestic noise' was also out of control.

The second highest total on the right hand side of *Fig 13.8* was 19 % due to 'Industrial noise'.

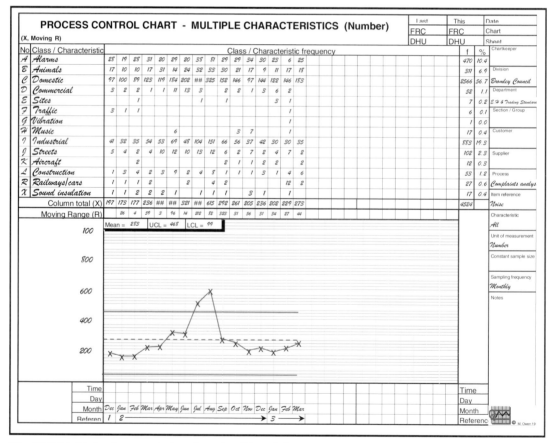

Fig 13.8 *Multiple characteristics chart for 'Noise' figures.*

A control chart for this category would be needed to see if the high figure of 104 was also out of control.

It was to be expected that both 'Domestic noise' and 'Industrial Noise' would be an issue in the summer months, and would need to be looked at.

13.6.7 Tackling the problem

The huge rise in 'Noise' complaints over the summer led to a series of actions. Brainstorming, fishbone diagrams and force-field analysis were used to identify issues and implement a number of solutions.

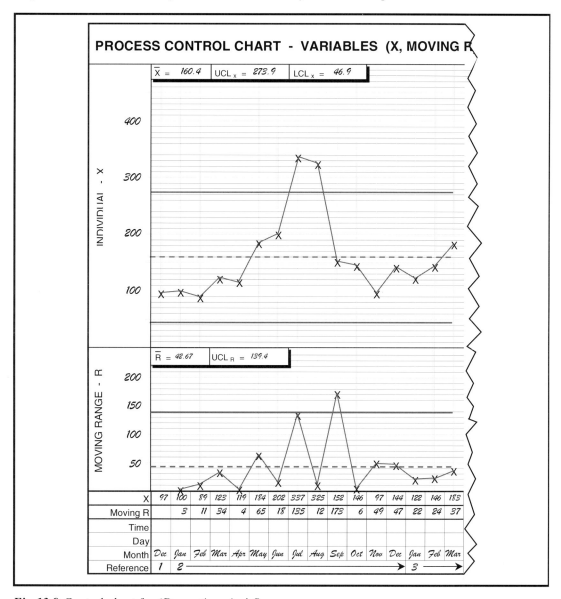

Fig 13.9 *Control chart for 'Domestic noise' figures.*

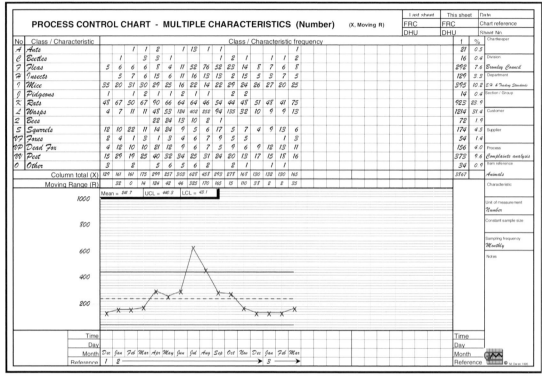

Fig 13.10 *Multiple characteristics chart for 'Animals' figures.*

These included:

- Extended operating hours in the summer
- Production of flow-charted procedures so that staff from other sections can be quickly trained and moved into the noise complaint team during peak periods.
- Development of an 'out-of-hours' complaint kit, a case containing everything an inspector needs – street maps, torch, procedures, blank forms and statutory notices, mobile telephone, etc.
- A neighbour mediation service whereby neighbour disputes can be resolved without the need for legal action.

13.6.8 Further charts

Referring back to the control chart for all categories of complaint – *Fig 13.7* – the next highest total after 'Noise' is 'Animals' at 17.9 %.

A further control chart was now produced for the breakdown of 'Animals' categories, with the result shown in *Fig 13.10*.

Not unexpectedly, summer months produce high figures and an out of control situation.

A further breakdown showed some interesting results, as shown in *Fig 13.11*.

It is pretty obvious that there will be a lot of complaints about wasps in the summer, as shown in the left-hand side of the figure. But why should there be a special cause in the 'Rats' chart for April?

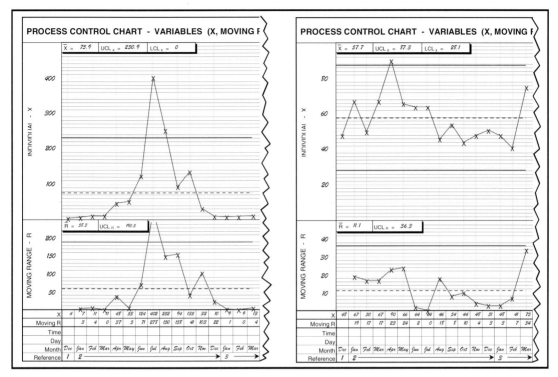

Fig 13.11 *Control charts for complaints regarding (a) wasps and (b) rats.*

13.6.9 Future action

The use of the Multiple Characteristics chart on customer complaints proved to be very useful. In the first place it confirmed events which had been known before but had not been portrayed so vividly. Secondly, it raised questions that had never been considered by simply looking at rows and columns of numbers. Thirdly, it led to charts being developed on other data, in particular that which relates to response times of different types of complaints (service requests). These response times have to be measured and reported to the Audit Commission on an annual basis as they form part of the key performance indicators for local authority services. SPC is again helping to improve performance in this area.

This particular case study provides an excellent example on how the Multiple Characteristics chart can be used with a common problem – the handling of customer complaints.

Several organisations now offer software packages that, it is claimed, provide effective ways of handling customer complaints. It comes as no surprise that Multiple Characteristics charts are conspicuously missing.

Having now covered three charts in detail, and provided many Case Studies that demonstrate the use of these, we need to return to the issue of satisfying customer requirements. This is capability, and the next chapter goes into the practical detail of developing numerical indices that can quickly indicate how a process is performing against customer requirements.

CAPABILITY – CAN THE PROCESS DELIVER?

14.1 Introduction

Customer requirements are irrelevant when going through the initial stage of setting up a control chart for a process. However, these requirements cannot be ignored and therefore it is necessary to define and interpret numerical indices which can quickly give us an indication of how our process is performing against customer requirements. Balancing customer needs and process performance is a real issue and the crux of this chapter gives adequate detail on how to use these numerical indices.

The first section reminds us of the 'voice of the process' and the 'voice of the customer'. Section 14.3 uses the histogram as an introduction to the first capability index, the C_p index, which is dealt with in Section 14.4. One index is not sufficient to completely define a process, and so we need a second one, the C_{pk} index, described in Section 14.5. The bulk of the chapter is taken up with the detail involved in calculating and interpreting C_p and C_{pk}. We must not forget that we also need capability indices for attributes, and this comes in the next section. A useful flow chart giving guidance on the choice of capability index appears in Section 14.7, to be followed by a final reminder of the relationship between control and capability in assessing the state of a process.

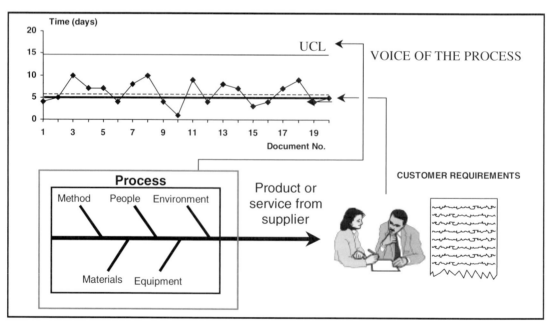

Fig 14.1 *Comparing the 'voice of the customer' with the control chart for the process.*

14.2 Two voices

Up to this point, the book has concentrated on the performance of a process as represented by a control chart. The chart is the best indicator available of the 'voice of the process'.

The 'voice of the process', however, has to match the 'voice of the customer'. *Fig 1.3* showed how the two voices could be compared, and that there was a gap between the two. The customer was requiring documents to be delivered in no more than five days, whilst the process was delivering on average in six days.

Fig 14.1 shows *Fig 1.3* with the 'voice of the process' represented, preferably, by a control chart. It is now possible to see that the situation is considerably worse than was shown in the original diagram. The SLA of five days is generally interpreted as being an upper limit, and when this value is compared with the UCL of 14.6 days there is a considerable difference. If the process is to match the customer requirements, then the UCL must be reduced so that it is the same as the SLA, or better.

Comparing these two voices is essentially assessing the capability of the process. Capability compares the inherent variation in a process with a tolerance band specified by the customer, and at the same time, checks on the level at which the process is running against the target level that has been set or agreed.

In explaining exactly what we mean by capability it makes things easier visually if the natural variation of the process is represented by a histogram rather than a control chart. In practice, of course, it is a control chart that is used to monitor the process. And remember that a process must be under control before any detailed assessment can be made regarding capability. A process that is out of control is inherently unstable, and it is therefore not possible to say that in the future any customer requirements can be met.

14.3 How are the processes doing?

Fig 14.2 shows the performance of five different suppliers in shipping items to a common customer.

The customer has an upper specification limit, which is one of the elements of the SLA. No items are to be shipped which are delivered beyond this value.

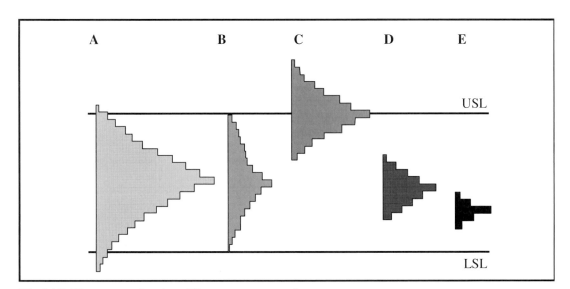

Fig 14.2 Histograms showing different process performances.

Equally, items delivered too early are a problem in terms of storage, inconvenience, etc. Hence part of the SLA also stipulates a lower specification limit (LSL).

What is *Fig 14.2* telling us about the processes?

Process A is incapable of meeting the customer requirements. The natural variation in the process, represented by the base width of the histogram, is wider than the difference between USL and LSL. Management action is required to reduce the variation in the process.

Process B is just capable. A minimum number of items lie outside the tolerance band. A generally accepted statistical definition of what we mean by 'a minimum number' is discussed in Section 14.5.3. There is no room for error, however. If it is vital that no items are greater than the USL or less than the LSL, then the process is somewhat on a knife-edge. The setting of the process now becomes crucial, and any move that results in the setting not being on the nominal will mean some items falling either below LSL or above USL.

Process C is inherently capable but the process is running at a level which is resulting in some 50% of the readings falling above USL. If it is the USL value that is critical in this process, then the process is in trouble.

Process D is capable. There is no problem in satisfying the requirements that the base width of the histogram is less than USL – LSL. However, a further decision on the performance depends on whether USL or LSL is the critical specification in terms of the setting of process D.

Process E is highly capable. There is still some work do be done in getting the setting to the right level if, for example, there is a requirement that the setting should be as low as possible, yet, at the same time, a negligable number of readings are below LSL. Rather than talk in general terms as we have done, it is better if we can obtain a numerical value to represent the relationship between the process performance and the customer requirements. This is called a capability index.

In fact there are two capability indices that we make use of – the C_p index and the C_{pk} index.

14.4 The C_p index

14.4.1 Defining and interpreting the C_p index

Fig 14.3 shows two of the processes shown previously in *Fig 14.2*, process A and process E.

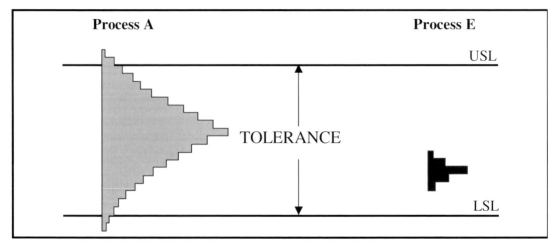

Fig 14.3 *An incapable and a capable process.*

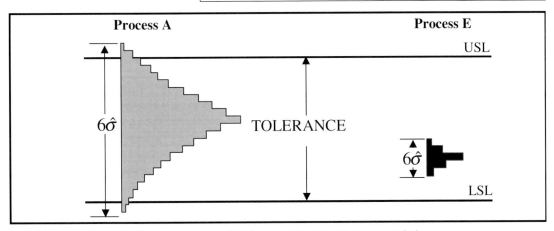

Fig 14.4 *Comparison of two processes with the specification limits provided.*

For process A the variation in delivery times is greater than the tolerance for the process. The histogram corresponding to the response times indicates that we can expect some results to fall outside the tolerance band.

Process E, on the other hand, seems acceptable. The histogram lies entirely within the tolerance band and hence all the delivery times are below the USL or above the LSL.

The process appears to be capable, but we need to be cautious because things are not always as they seem. Using a purely visual approach to assess capability in this way can lead to misleading conclusions. For that reason it is preferable to measure capability by first calculating the standard deviation $\hat{\sigma}$. $6\hat{\sigma}$, the base width of the histogram, is then compared with the tolerance to provide a measure of the capability of the process.

Fig 14.4 shows how the tolerance can be compared with the $6\hat{\sigma}$ values for process A and process E.

Process A is inherently incapable because the base width of the histogram, i.e. $6\hat{\sigma}$ is greater than the tolerance. From now on the tolerance will be denoted by TOL.

In other words, $\text{TOL} < 6\hat{\sigma}$

or $\dfrac{\text{TOL}}{6\hat{\sigma}} < 1.$

For process E, the base width of the histogram i.e. $6\hat{\sigma}$, is less than the tolerance.

i.e. $6\hat{\sigma} < \text{TOL}$

or $\dfrac{\text{TOL}}{6\hat{\sigma}} > 1$

$\dfrac{\text{TOL}}{6\hat{\sigma}}$ is a bit of a mouthful and so we make things easier for ourselves by calling this the capability index C_p.

Improving a process so that it changes from an incapable process to one that is capable is equivalent to changing the C_p value from one that is < 1 to one that is > 1 and then working on increasing it further.

Now that we have an understanding of C_p we can use it to interpret the five processes shown in *Fig 14.2*. *Fig 14.5* (overleaf) shows the same processes but this time with the corresponding values attached.

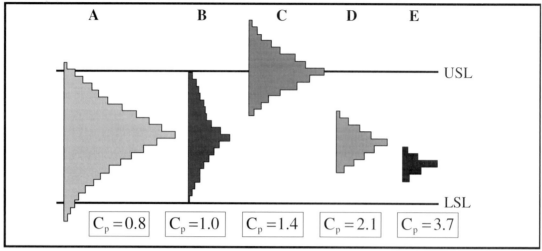

Fig 14.5 *Using values to indicate process improvement.*

14.4.2 Calculating and recording the C_p index

We have a process for which there is an SLA for deliveries specifying a target delivery for a particular service, i.e. a nominal, of 14 days. There is a window of 2 days on either side of the target, i.e. the USL is 16 days and the LSL is 12 days.

An (X, Moving R) chart for delivery times gives a value for $\overline{R}$ of 0.95 days.

In order to calculate C_p we need $\hat{\sigma}$, and we calculate this in the usual way using $\hat{\sigma} = \dfrac{\overline{R}}{d_2}$.

$$\therefore \hat{\sigma} = \frac{0.95}{1.128} = 0.84$$

Hence $C_p = \dfrac{\text{TOL}}{6\hat{\sigma}} = \dfrac{4}{6 \times 0.84} = 0.79$

This value is <1, indicating that the process is incapable and the SLA cannot be met.

On the (X, Moving R) chart, and also on the ($\overline{X}$, R) chart, allowance has been made for recording the C_p index.

The value is recorded in the box corresponding to 'This sheet', as shown in *Fig 14.6*.

Note that the calculation of the C_p index is the same whether we are using an (X, Moving R) chart or an ($\overline{X}$, R) chart.

14.4.3 Limitations of the C_p index

The C_p index is purely a measure of the potential ability of the process to satisfy both a USL and an LSL. It is no guide as to whether a process is set correctly, i.e. is the process on target, however that is defined.

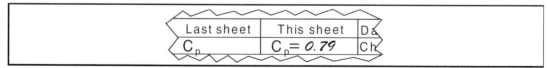

Fig 14.6 *Completed box for recording the value.*

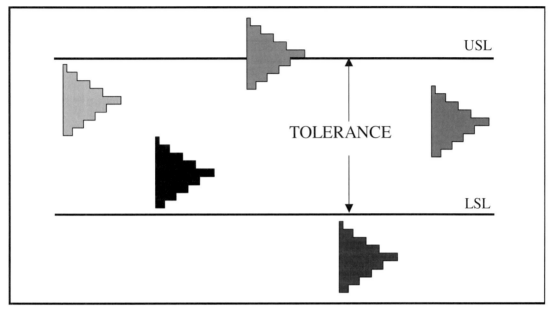

Fig 14.7 *Five identical processes but at different locations.*

This limitation is brought out in *Fig 14.7*.

Here we have five different processes as before, but this time the inherent variation is the same for each process. This will not always be so but it will be easier to explain the limitation of the C_p index if the assumption is made at this stage.

For each of the processes the calculated C_p value is the same because $6\hat{\sigma}$ is the same, i.e.

$$C_p = \frac{TOL}{6\hat{\sigma}} = \text{constant.}$$

The histogram used in *Fig 14.7* is actually process D in *Fig 14.5*, for which the C_p value is 2.1. Hence all five processes have $C_p = 2.1$, but that does not help us to discriminate between the different processes. In other words, knowing that $C_p = 2.1$ does not tell us which of the five situations shown, or indeed any other situation, relates to our C_p value. *Fig 14.8 (overleaf)* summarises the problem.

So how can we proceed?

It is clear that we need another index that tells us the level at which the process is running. This is the second capability index .

14.5 The C_{pk} index

The formulae for C_{pk} depend on whether we are referring to an (X, Moving R) chart or an ($\overline{X}$, R) chart.

We start with the (X, Moving R) chart, using it to explain the rationale behind the calculations. The approach for the ($\overline{X}$, R) chart then follows in a similar vein.

The interpretation we adopt for the C_{pk} value depends on three situations.

14.5.1 Nominal is critical

Cases such as this occur when, for example, we have a nominal time for delivery, and we want the process, as represented by an (X, Moving R) chart, to have a central line $\overline{X}$ which is to be as close as

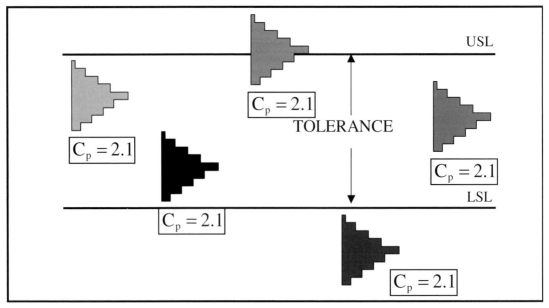

Fig 14.8 *Limitation of the C$_p$ value.*

possible to the nominal. In other words, a decreased mean delivery time is as equally unwanted as is an increased delivery time.

We have two specification limits as usual – USL and LSL.

The formulae for calculating C$_{pk}$ are as follows: -

$$C_{pk} \text{ is either } \frac{USL - \overline{X}}{3\hat{\sigma}} \text{ or } \frac{\overline{X} - LSL}{3\hat{\sigma}}.$$

Why two alternatives, and how do we decide which formula to use?

We refer to *Fig 14.9* to help us.

Here we have a SLA defined by USL and LSL.

Two processes are represented, each having a different mean value, .

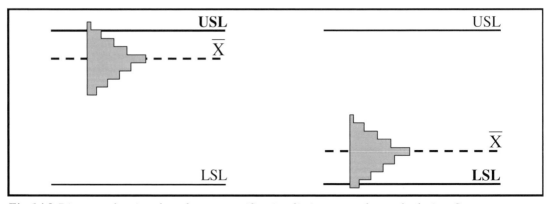

Fig 14.9 *Diagram showing the relevant specification limit to use when calculating C$_{pk}$.*

In calculating a C_{pk} value, two alternatives are offered to allow for the position of the mean.

If $\overline{X}$ is closer to USL than it is to LSL, as it is on the left hand side of *Fig 14.9*, then we use the formula for C_{pk} which makes use of USL.

i.e. $C_{pk} = \dfrac{USL - \overline{X}}{3\hat{\sigma}}$

Similarly if $\overline{X}$ is closer to LSL than it is to USL, as shown on the right hand side of *Fig 14.9*, then we use the formula for C_{pk} which makes use of LSL.

i.e. $C_{pk} = \dfrac{\overline{X} - LSL}{3\hat{\sigma}}$

Having calculated C_{pk} using one or other of these two formulae, and we show a typical calculation in the next section, then we need to interpret the value. What does it actually mean?

So as not to introduce an extra unnecessary element at this stage, we consider a process where the variation does not change over time, and it is the position of the process with respect to the SLA's that is important.

Fig 14.10 shows a series of processes with the same variation. All the processes are inherently highly capable, the C_p value being 2.2. The setting, $\overline{X}$, changes over time, and the seven cases to be discussed correspond to the different positions of $\overline{X}$.

Case 1. Here we make use of the C_{pk} formula which involves USL, i.e. $C_{pk} = \dfrac{USL - \overline{X}}{3\hat{\sigma}}$, because

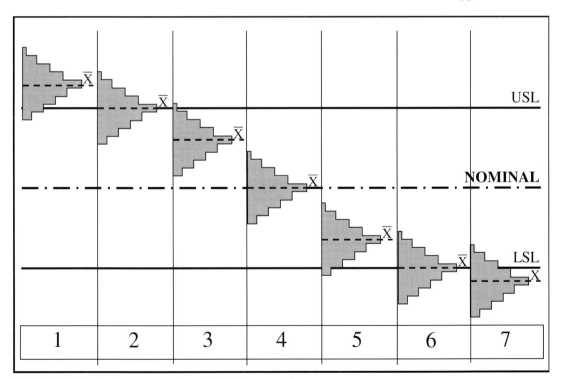

Fig 14.10 Identical processes but with different settings.

$\overline{X}$ is closer to the USL than it is to LSL. Because $\overline{X}$ is greater than USL, USL - $\overline{X}$ is negative and therefore C_{pk} is negative.

In **Case 2** we again make use of USL. The process mean $\overline{X}$ is exactly on the USL. USL - $\overline{X}$ is zero and therefore C_{pk} is zero.

Case 3 represents the situation where $\overline{X}$ drops below USL and moves towards the nominal. For any position of $\overline{X}$ in the zone between USL and the nominal, we use the C_{pk} formulae based on USL. USL - $\overline{X}$ is always positive, and gradually increasing, and hence C_{pk} is always a positive and gradually increasing value.

In **Case 4**, the mean $\overline{X}$ is exactly on the nominal. A little bit of algebraic juggling, which we needn't go into, shows that in this case the C_{pk} value is equal to the C_p value. This result is independent of the C_{pk} formula used.

As $\overline{X}$ moves below the nominal, then we go through a sequence that is the reverse of **Cases 1, 2** and **3**

Because $\overline{X}$ is now closer to the LSL than it is to the USL then we use the formula $C_{pk} = \dfrac{\overline{X} - LSL}{3\hat{\sigma}}$.

In **Case 5**, $\overline{X}$ - LSL is always positive, and gradually decreasing. C_{pk} is positive anywhere in the zone between the nominal and the LSL, and also decreasing as we move towards the LSL.

Case 6 is where $\overline{X}$ is exactly on the LSL. In this case $\overline{X}$ - LSL is zero and therefore C_{pk} is again zero.

Finally, in **Case 7**, $\overline{X}$ moves below the LSL. Because $\overline{X}$ is less than LSL, then $\overline{X}$ - LSL is negative and therefore C_{pk} is negative.

Fig 14.11 indicates how the various C_{pk} values relate to the cases we have discussed.

Four key messages come out of this.

1. The C_{pk} value can never be greater than the C_p value.
2. When the process is running on the nominal value, then the C_{pk} value and the C_p value are identical.
3. Process improvement requires increasing the C_p value whilst at the same time making sure that the C_{pk} value remains as far as possible equal to C_p.
4. In order to completely assess a process, then we need both the C_{pk} and the C_p values. Knowing only the C_{pk} value isn't enough, in the same way, as we saw in Section 14.4.3, that knowing only C_p is insufficient.

Now that we have gone through the interpretation of the C_{pk} value, it is important to actually carry out the calculation of C_{pk}.

14.5.2 Calculating and recording the C_{pk} index

We will use the same data as in Section 14.4.2 when calculating C_p.

The (X, Moving R) chart for delivery times gave a value for $\overline{X}$ of 13.2 days.

Is this value nearer to the USL of 16 days or the LSL of 12 days? 12 days is the answer, which guides us to using the C_{pk} formulae involving the LSL, i.e. $C_{pk} = \dfrac{\overline{X} - LSL}{3\hat{\sigma}}$.

$\hat{\sigma}$ has already been calculated as 0.84.

CASE	1	2	3	4	5	6	7
C_{pk}	−	0	+	C_p	+	0	−

Fig 14.11 Table relating C_{pk} values to the position of the process.

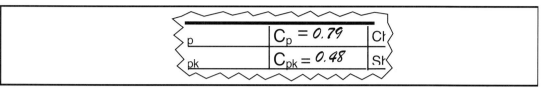

Fig 14.12 Section from the control chart showing the value recorded.

$$\therefore \; C_{pk} = \frac{\overline{X} - LSL}{3\hat{\sigma}} = \frac{13.2 - 12}{3 \times 0.84} = 0.48$$

The fact that C_{pk} is not the same as C_p is confirming that $\overline{X}$ is some distance from the nominal.
This C_{pk} value is recorded in the appropriate data box as indicated in *Fig 14.12*.
So this is how we interpret C_{pk}. If it is the same as C_p, then the process is running on the nominal.
What happens if we are not interested in a nominal? How do we interpret C_{pk} when it is one of the specification limits, either USL or LSL, that is more important?

14.5.3 USL or LSL is critical
In the previous section we considered cases where the requirement was that the process mean consistently runs on the nominal as far as possible.

This is not going to be the situation in all administrative cases. Often the need is to make sure that we do not have any items exceeding the USL or alternatively, being less than a LSL. For example, we could have a case where there is an upper limit for response times that must not be exceeded. We want to make sure that there is an acceptable number of items not exceeding this value.

Remember that whilst we may not like items falling outside our SLA's, it is a statistical fact of life that these values will occur at some time. That is not the same as the case where it is physically impossible to have a value outside an SLA. More detail on this is in the next section.

So what do we mean by the statement "an acceptable number of items occurring outside either the USL or the LSL"?

Fig 14.13 might help.

We have to recognise that it is impossible to locate $\overline{X}$ so that no items fall above the USL. It doesn't matter how far down on a vertical scale we locate the process mean, it is inevitable that we have some items falling above the USL value. We therefore have to define a position for $\overline{X}$ so that there is an acceptably very small risk of an item occurring above the USL value.

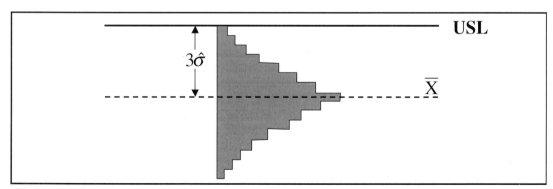

Fig 14.13 Optimum position for the location of a process where USL is critical.

Where do we set this level?

Well, we come back to our three standard deviations. It makes sense to set our mean at three standard deviations below the USL. In other words, and for the (X, Moving R) chart only, the UCL is to be on the USL.

This is therefore our agreed definition of acceptability. We do know that every now and again we will have a reading above the USL, in the same sort of way as on rare occasions we can have a special cause occurring outside the UCL.

Let's try to attach a capability index to reflect this new situation.

If there is a lower limit present, then we can calculate a C_p index. It does have some value, even though it is the USL that is determining our actions. However, it is the C_{pk} value that is going to be more important here.

Since we are using a USL then the appropriate formula for C_{pk} is: -

$$C_{pk} = \frac{USL - \overline{X}}{3\hat{\sigma}}$$

We have set the mean value $\overline{X}$ so that it is at a distance $3\hat{\sigma}$ below USL. This means that USL - $\overline{X}$ is $3\hat{\sigma}$.

and therefore C_{pk} is $\dfrac{3\sigma}{3\sigma}$ i.e.1.

This may suggest how we interpret C_{pk} in this case. The process level $\overline{X}$ should always be set so that the C_{pk} value is never less than 1.

Fig 14.14 shows how we use this rule in improving the process, recognising that we do not wish to have any items occurring above the USL value.

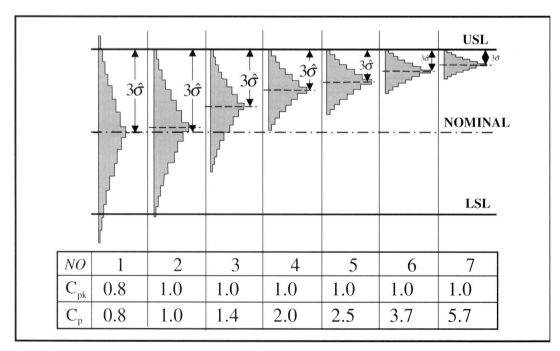

NO	1	2	3	4	5	6	7
C_{pk}	0.8	1.0	1.0	1.0	1.0	1.0	1.0
C_p	0.8	1.0	1.4	2.0	2.5	3.7	5.7

Fig 14.14 *Process improvement and C_{pk} and C_p values where the USL is critical.*

In **Case 1** we have an incapable process, set on the nominal because C_p and C_{pk} are the same.

As the process improves, represented by the readings becoming more consistent through **Cases 2** to **6,** then the C_p values increase. At the same time, the setting changes, reflecting the reduced variation. At each stage of the improvement process the mean is set at three standard deviations below the USL so that C_{pk} is always equal to 1.

In this analysis we have assumed that USL is critical. It may be that the LSL is critical, and if so then the analysis is very similar except that the process moves downwards in steps. So this is how to interpret C_{pk} where one of the SLA's is important. Aim for an increasing C_p value, whilst at the same time ensuring that C_{pk} does not become less than 1. Yet another interpretation of C_{pk} occurs when we have genuine one-sided situations, as discussed in the following section.

14.5.4 Cases where there is a natural upper or lower barrier

In the last section it was possible to have readings outside the SLA we are using. We don't want them, and so we set the process mean accordingly. Even so, unacceptable readings may still occur, albeit in small numbers.

In contrast, some situations make it impossible to have readings beyond a certain level. For example, response times cannot be negative. We can have response times that are early, i.e. negative in that they are being measured above and below an agreed target. We cannot have items being processed in negative time. In other words we cannot process something until we have it to hand. For example, if the USL for the process is 5 days, then we do not want any items to take more than 5 days, and this is the limit to be used in the C_{pk} calculation.

In the same way, we might have a natural upper limit of 100%. In writing a book, for example, the publisher accumulates the material chapter by chapter. There is a natural upper limit of 100%, – you cannot put more in the book than is there. The lower limit on the process may be 85%, i.e. the publisher does not progress on putting the book together until he has received a minimum of 85% of the material. Here the limit to be used in the C_{pk} calculation is the LSL of 85%.

Both these cases are one-sided, and the interpretation of the C_{pk} formulae is amended accordingly. *Fig 14.15* shows the two alternative one-sided cases, and the C_{pk} formulae that should be used.

Be careful here. You might be tempted to follow the guidelines provided earlier and use the limit nearest to the mean value. Don't do so. Use the SLA that is present, and not the natural barrier.

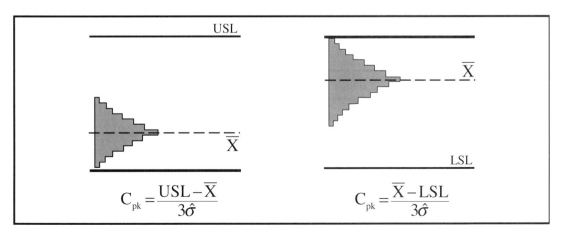

$$C_{pk} = \frac{USL - \overline{X}}{3\hat{\sigma}}$$

$$C_{pk} = \frac{\overline{X} - LSL}{3\hat{\sigma}}$$

Fig 14.15 *Alternative one-sided cases and the C_{pk} formulae that should be used.*

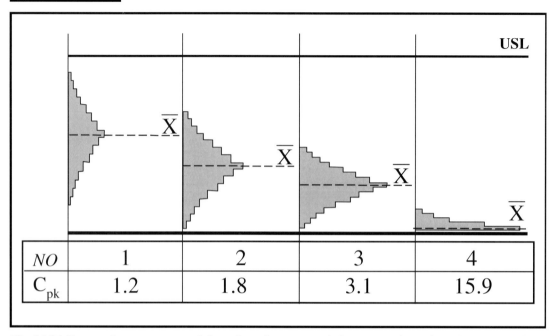

Fig 14.16 *Process improvement and C_{pk} values for a one-sided process where the USL is critical.*

The reason for this is that the C_{pk} formulae here have been so devised to register improvement in two ways – increasing the distance of the mean from the SLA and reducing the standard deviation as the process gets 'squeezed' against the natural boundary.

Fig 14.16 shows this sequence, using a USL as the SLA.

The previous four sections have made use of an (X, Moving R) chart. How is this changed if we use an ($\overline{X}$, R) chart?

14.5.5 C_{pk} calculations based on an ($\overline{X}$, R) chart

We use the same formulae as before as introduced in Section 14.5.1, except that the process mean is now $\overline{\overline{X}}$ and not $\overline{X}$. Otherwise, the expressions for C_{pk} are the same, and the rules for deciding on which form of C_{pk} to use are the same.

If the nominal is critical, then we use either: -

$$C_{pk} = \frac{USL - \overline{\overline{X}}}{3\hat{\sigma}} \quad \text{or}$$

$$C_{pk} = \frac{\overline{\overline{X}} - LSL}{3\hat{\sigma}}$$

Similarly for the special cases discussed in Sections 14.5.3 and 14.5.4. We replace $\overline{X}$ whenever it occurs by $\overline{\overline{X}}$.

14.6 Capability for attributes

The indices C_p and C_{pk} only apply when we are dealing with measured items, such as times.

When analysing attributes, we make use of two other capability indices.

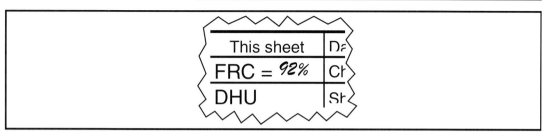

Fig 14.17 Completed FRC box on a multiple characteristics chart.

14.6.1 First Run Capability (FRC)

This index is used when we are considering documents, for example, and we are analysing the number of documents that are unacceptable.

If we are not careful here we could be pulled into detail on the different types of attribute charts. We therefore keep things very simple and make use of this capability index only in association with the multiple characteristics chart.

Suppose the data for producing a Multiple Characteristics chart produces a mean reject level of 0.08, i.e. on average 8 documents out of every 100 are unacceptable

In an attribute sense this is equivalent to a mean proportion $\bar{p}$.

The capability index we use is calculated from: -

FRC = $(1 - \bar{p})$ x 100%

Hence, knowing that $\bar{p}$ is 0.08,

FRC = $(1 - 0.08)$ x 100 = <u>92%</u>

The interpretation of the FRC is that if $\bar{p}$ is zero, then the FRC is 100%.

As usual, there is a section on the Multiple Characteristics chart to record the FRC and *Fig 14.17* shows the completed box.

Never ending improvement is interpreted here as reducing $\bar{p}$ in stages so that the FRC gets closer and closer to 100%.

14.6.2 Defects per hundred units (DHU)

We use the DHU index when we are considering documents, for example, and we are now analysing the number of errors, or defects in the documents, as opposed to the number of documents in error. In other words, we recognise that if a document is unacceptable, it could be because it is carrying 1, 2, 3 etc errors. Monitoring errors requires a different capability index.

Suppose we find that the data used in producing a Multiple Characteristics chart based on a mean sample size of 25 documents gives a mean error rate of 4.

By proportion, therefore, we would have 16 errors in 100 documents.

This is the DHU figure.

The interpretation of the DHU is that it is an index that should approach zero as the process improves, i.e. the error rate decreases.

Again, there is a section on the Multiple Characteristics chart to record the DHU and *Fig 14.18 (overleaf)* shows the completed box.

14.7 Making the choice

You may feel confused at this stage, particularly in terms of variables, as to which capability index is appropriate.

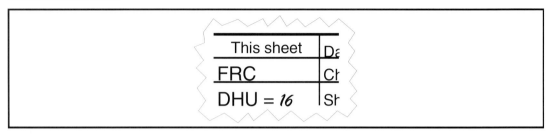

Fig 14.18 *Completed DHU box on a Multiple Characteristics chart.*

When do we use a C_p index and when a C_{pk} index?

The flow chart shown in *Fig 14.19* should help. No allowance for attribute choices has been made. The flow chart shown offers alternatives based on the use of capability studies for measured quantities only.

Having discussed capability mainly in terms of a histogram, we come back to the control chart in the final section.

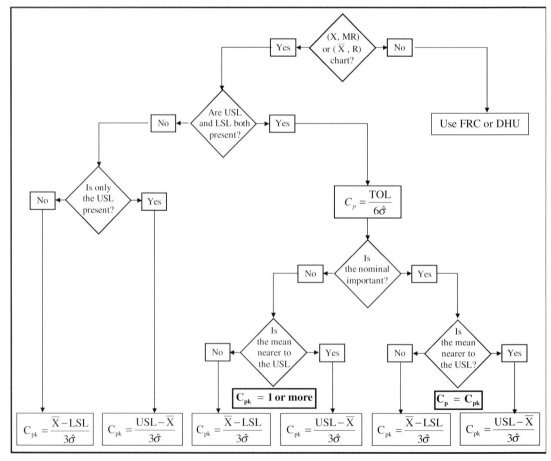

Fig 14.19 *Flow chart for choices relating to C_p and C_{pk}.*

14.8 Control, capability and improvement

The visual relationship between control limits and specification limits is another interpretation of capability indices.

This is represented in *Fig 14.20* which is based on Don Wheeler's definition of the four states of a process.

Fig 14.20 (a) shows a state of chaos. The process is out of control in that a special cause is present. The process is also incapable because there are values outside the specification limits. Calculation of

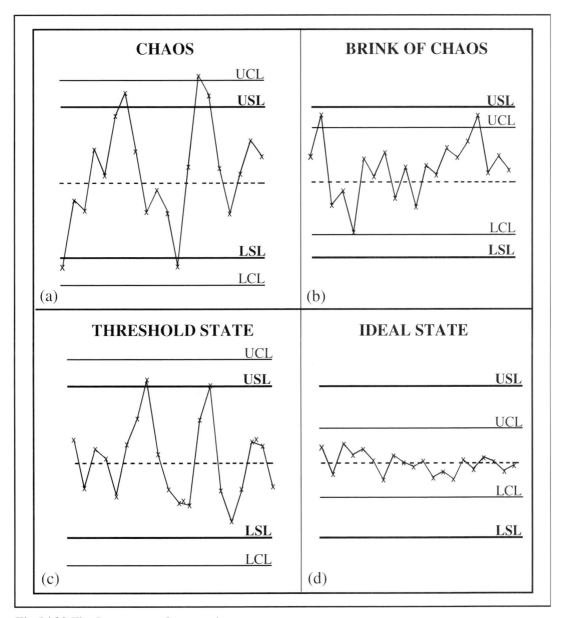

Fig 14.20 *The four stages of process improvement.*

capability indices is not allowed because the process is unstable. The only way to make an improvement is to work on removing the special causes so that the process becomes predictable.

Some improvement is shown in *Fig 14.20 (b)*, although it is still on the brink of chaos. The new process now seems to be capable because no readings fall outside the specification limits. However, the process is out of control, which means instability and the danger of moving back into chaos.

There is no alternative to removing special causes. *Fig14.20 (c)* shows the original process but this time with no special causes present. It is still incapable but because it is now stable a C_p value could be calculated, and would be found to be less than 1. This is because the natural variation of the process is greater than the difference between the specification limits.

Further improvement on the process shows the situation represented in *Fig 14.20 (d)*. The process is under control, capable and with a C_p value greater than 1.

The description of the process as ideal needs to be taken with caution. It depends on whether the nominal is more important than either the USL or LSL. Even then, the Deming view is that there may be an opportunity to reduce the variation even more.

14.9 Misuse of capability indices

In Section 14.4.1 a process was defined as being capable if the C_p value was 1 or more. This is a minimum requirement, and one generally used to introduce the idea of a capability index.

Some organisations adopt other minimum requirements for C_p. For example, it may be that C_p must be greater than 1.33 or 1.67, reflecting the fact that the process is improving. There may be some marketing benefit in being able to claim that we can perform against tighter SLAs, but it can cause confusion. If we redefine the SLAs from time to time, then the values for C_p and C_{pk} become meaningless.

In another sense the indices are sometimes used as targets. Management says that it wants the C_p value for a certain process to increase from 1.5 to 2 in a couple of months, yet they make no resources available to improve the system. It is no surprise that the implications of C_p and C_{pk} are not understood when the more basic understanding of the relationship between variation and the system is not there.

14.10 Summary of symbols and formulae

Symbols

C_p	Capability index used for variables
C_{pk}	Capability index used for variables
p	Proportion
$\bar{p}$	Mean proportion
FRC	Capability index used with attributes
DHU	Capability index used with attributes

Formulae

$$C_p = \frac{TOL}{6\hat{\sigma}}$$

$$C_{pk} = \frac{USL - \bar{X}}{3\hat{\sigma}} \quad \text{or} \quad \frac{\bar{X} - LSL}{3\hat{\sigma}} \quad \text{for (X, moving R) chart}$$

$$C_{pk} = \frac{USL - \bar{\bar{X}}}{3\hat{\sigma}} \quad \text{or} \quad \frac{\bar{\bar{X}} - LSL}{3\hat{\sigma}} \quad \text{for (} \bar{X} \text{ , R) chart}$$

$$FRC = (1 - \bar{p}) \times 100\%$$

14.11 Key points and summary

- A process must be under control before capability can be assessed.
- Two capability indices are available for use with variables.
- The C_p index measures the potential ability of a process to satisfy customer requirements.
- C_p must be greater than 1 for a process to be capable.
- The bigger the C_p index the better the process.
- The C_p value gives no help as to the setting of a process.
- The C_{pk} index measures the location of a process.
- The C_{pk} index can be interpreted in different ways.
- If the nominal is critical, then the optimum is for C_p to be the same as C_{pk}.
- Choose the correct C_{pk} formula depending on the nearest specification limit.
- If one of the SLA's is critical then C_{pk} should equal 1.
- With natural one-sided limits, only use a C_{pk} value.
- There are two capability indices for attributes.
- FRC measures the reject level of items.
- DHU measures error rates.
- 'Wheeler's four states' gives a useful summary of process improvement.
- Some improvement programmes have different minimum definitions for C_p.
- Don't use capability indices as targets.

A great deal of technical material has been covered in this chapter. These capability indices, particularly C_p and C_{pk}, are used extensively in manufacturing organisations, and there is a commonly expressed view that they don't really apply in administrative processes. This is erroneous. External customer requirements, or SLAs provide customer-driven limits in exactly the same way as traditional production specifications. Hence improvement in office-based processes can be reflected in the same way by using C_p and C_{pk}.

There is little use in setting up control charts unless we react to signals. Control charts do not solve problems, but the presence of special causes, for example, or the need to reduce common cause variation requires the application of problem solving techniques.

The next two chapters give you a tool kit of other useful techniques that can be used to support the control chart.

THE JOURNEY TO IMPROVEMENT
A FRAMEWORK FOR PROGRESS

15.1 Introduction

Control charts will help you highlight areas for improvement but they won't tell you how to go about making this improvement. Solving problems in a logical way is a requirement if we are to make progress in improving our various processes.

This chapter is entirely devoted to a specific problem-solving process. It explains an 'eight step process' which can be adopted when choosing a problem, deciding on an appropriate solution, implementing it, and then going round the sequence again in order to improve it even further.

The 'eight-step process' is a development of the Shewhart cycle, shown schematically in *Fig 15.1*. It is also sometimes referred to as the Deming cycle. The diagram represents, in a readily understood way, the sequence of steps involved in improving any process. This 'Plan Do Study Act' sequence is often referred to as the PDSA cycle.

The 'Journey to Improvement' is the process improvement and problem-solving approach devised by Catalyst Consulting Ltd, who hold the copyright.

15.2 The Journey to Improvement

As with any journey, you won't always need the map, but it's a comfort to know you've got one! The 'eight-step process', described in the next few pages, provides a framework that enables you to make improvements in a planned and logical way.

The process is represented by the diagram shown in *Fig 15.2*.

At each step you'll find a number of questions to consider and answer. These will keep you on track, though there will almost certainly be other questions for you to determine. And you will certainly need

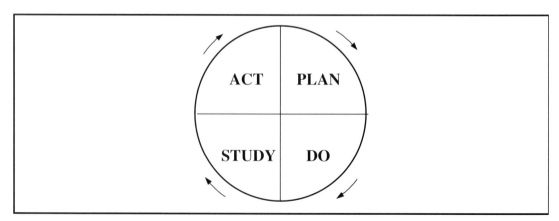

Fig 15.1 The Shewhart Cycle.

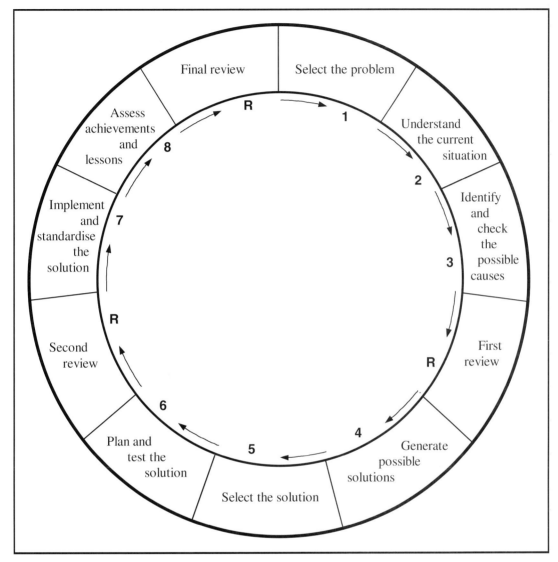

Fig 15.2 *Diagram representing 'The Journey to Improvement'.*

to use a range of tools and techniques to help you on your journey.

We've already covered a number of these, including, for example, flow-charts, and the next chapter provides at least an outline of some of the others you will need to help you on the way. Remember that different problems may need different tools. And some problems may not need a formal approach. Tailor things to suit your particular problem and experience.

The help of a facilitator is recommended generally, but particularly for the inexperienced team.

If you have some process improvement experience, you'll find it relatively easy to see 'short-cuts' in that you won't need to answer every question posed in the guide. You might also be able to jump some of the steps, though be careful you don't slip up.

Finally, remember the need to keep people up to date with progress and what's planned. The ***Improvement Journal*** is designed to help you here. This is covered in Section 15.14 and you will find a blank copy of this on Page 222. Use it to help keep track on what's happening, and to capture learning.

15.3 Step 1

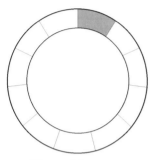

Select the problem

In the selection and prioritisation of problems to tackle, we need to be aware of the issues involved. For example, if possible choose the problem for your improvement journey relative to its impact on customer satisfaction, or cost. In particular, you need to clarify the following: -

- The problem or opportunity you are addressing.
- Why it's important to work on this now.
- How much improvement is expected, and by when.
- Who needs to be involved.

With this information and understanding, you can agree an 'Issue Statement' or 'Improvement Project Charter' that will help start you in the right direction. And answering the questions that follow (in bold), will help you start from the right place. Answering every question is probably unnecessary. But there may well be some other questions you'll want answered.

Experience will help you recognise the key issues for different projects. To assist you and your colleagues in answering the questions in bold, there are a number of other questions and prompts that you may find helpful.

So, what's the purpose of this project and what are we trying to do?

How do we know about it, and why? What's the current performance level and what should it be? What are the customer requirements? Are we sure? How do we know?

How will our customers be affected by the successful completion of this project?

Who are the customers and will they care if this project is successful? What's more, how will they know if it's been successful, and how will we know?

What other reasons are there for selecting this project?

What might happen if we don't take action? How does this project rank with other possible projects? Who thinks this project is important – external customers, internal customers, your manager, or your colleagues?

How will you know if things improve?

What measurement will you need in place and how will it relate to the customer requirements?

Although the detail will change, what's the broad plan for this project?

What do you think needs to be done? Who needs to work on the project and will they be able to? Who needs to be consulted for advice or information? And who needs to be kept informed? What's the scope of the project and the limits on authority and resources? When should the project start and finish? How will you document work and progress? Who will champion this project and provide support or 'clout' if it's needed?

By now, you should be in a position to agree an 'Issue Statement' or 'Improvement Project Charter', though it will probably change as things become clearer over time.

When you first start an improvement journey, it's very easy to rush off in the wrong direction and waste time. The charter will help start you in the right direction by providing a clear description of your project and what you hope to achieve.

It will also help you identify some of the additional information and data you'll need to complete the journey. As you find out some of these, you'll need to update and amend your 'Charter' – often the first draft will be at quite a high level. The 'Journey to Improvement' includes a number of reminders for you to review and update your 'Charter' as you find out more about your problem and its likely solution.

There are five main elements in the 'Issue Statement' or 'Charter':
- A business case – an explanation of why it's important to do this project.
- A problem and goal statement – a description of the problem and the objective. As far as possible, these should be in clear, concise and measurable terms.
- The project scope – this should define the parameters for the project, and identify any constraints.
- Milestones – the key steps and dates to achieve the goal.
- Roles – the people involved in and around the project, expectations of them and their responsibilities.

Let's look at each of these elements in a little more detail:
- **The business case** describes the broad area(s) of concern for an improvement team project and the rationale for doing it.
  - So, why is this project worth doing?
  - Why is it important to do it now?
  - What are the consequences of not doing it?
  - How does it fit with the business strategy, initiatives and targets?

In agreeing this, your team will understand the business imperative for the project and you'll also know why it's been selected ahead of other potential activities.
- **The Problem Statement** describes what's wrong.
  - So, what is wrong or not meeting our customer's requirements?
  - When and where do the problems occur?
  - How big is the problem? And what's its likely impact?

Early on in the project, you may not have enough information or data to provide all the detail you'd like. Remember that our whole approach to improvement should be based on fact, so if you don't yet have the information don't guess it! Leave gaps or keep things at a high level; you can update the statement later on.

One of the things you'll soon discover is that working on the charter quickly helps you identify the information and measurements you'll need on the project.
- **The Goal Statement** should focus on the results or impact you hope to achieve. It should not make assumptions about the causes of the problem; nor should it prescribe the solution! Ideally, it should start with a verb, for example:
  - Reduce
  - Eliminate
  - Control
  - Increase

And there should be a measurable target and completion date. In checking the effectiveness of your goal statements, make sure they are **SMART:**
  - **S**pecific
  - **M**easurable
  - **A**ttainable
  - **R**elevant
  - **T**ime bound

- **The Project Scope** defines the boundaries and resources of the team's improvement effort. If the scope is too broad, a team can waste effort by proposing solutions that are outside its influence or resource capability. But if the scope is too narrow, it can lead to limited and often disappointing solutions. It's a question of balance.

The following questions should help clarify things:

- What processes will the team focus on?
- What are the boundaries of the process we aim to improve?
- What's the start point and end point?
- What resources are available to the team?
- What, if anything, is out of bounds for the team?
- What, if any, constraints must the team work under?
- What is the time commitment that's expected of the team members?

And what happens to their 'regular duties' while they are working on the project?

- **Milestones** are needed for the key steps and activities on your journey. They should provide a sense of urgency and a feeling of accomplishment. But like the 'Goal Statement', they should also be SMART.

Again, it's worth remembering that these will probably be high-level best guesses at the start of the project. As you get a clearer picture of what will be needed for your journey they should become more accurate.

- **'Roles'** is the fifth and final element in the 'Issue Statement' or 'Improvement Project Charter'.

It doesn't matter how many improvement tools and techniques you know inside out, if the team doesn't work well together, the project will not succeed. Well defined roles help ensure smooth working relationships within the team, and with key influencers in the organisation. The following questions might help you clarify things up front:

- How do you want the management champion, or project sonsor, to work with the team?
- Is the team's role to implement or recommend?
- When must the team seek approval and from whom?
- What authority does the team have to act independently?
- What and how do you want to inform the management or project sponsors about the team's progress?
- What is the role of the improvement team leader?
- In terms of both function and hierarchy, are the right people on the team?

The 'Issue Statement' or 'Improvement Project Charter' should not be complicated or bureaucratic. Keep it simple, and recognize its value in helping you get off on the right foot. Ideally it's one side of A4, two at the most.

15.4 Step 2

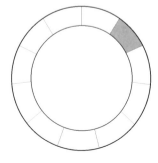

Understand the current situation

This step looks to ensure that your 'Issue Statement' is sensible. To do that, it's important to understand what's meant to happen, and why? And what's happened in the past? Gathering this information can help focus your improvement efforts and prevent you going off in the wrong direction.

So, what has happened in the past?

Is this a new problem – when did it first occur? If improvements have been tried before, what effect did they have and why? What problems or circumstances shaped the current process? Do they still exist?

What's meant to happen now?

What are the objectives of the process and are they clearly understood? What are the key input, process and output measures? What are the requirements of the process? How might a picture of the process flow help? (What about using a deployment flowchart, for example?)

What really happens now? And what do we do when we see the symptoms of the problem?

How well are we meeting the requirements of the process? How well are the procedures followed? What are the key measures telling us? And do we have an effective balance of input, process and output measures? What messages are we receiving from our customers and what signals are we sending back?

Where in the process do the symptoms of the problems appear? And when?

Where and how is the problem noticed? When does it occur? When doesn't it occur?

Who is involved? Who isn't? Who else needs to be?

Which customers and suppliers are affected? And which aren't? But be careful here, this isn't about finger pointing and blame. We are trying to see what patterns might exist, particularly if we segment the data.

With an improved understanding of what's been happening, you may need to consider who else you need to involve in this project and who else you need to keep informed.

15.5 Step 3

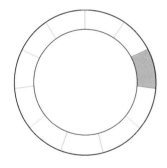

Identify and check the possible causes

It's now time to generate ideas on what might be causing the problem, but don't jump to conclusions. It's important to check the possible causes, using data to verify the ideas generated and manage by fact.

Identifying and removing the root causes of a problem will prevent it happening again.

What are the possible causes of the symptoms described in Step 2?

Remember the importance of getting to the root causes. And remember we're not looking for solutions, not yet at least!

How can these possible causes be verified? What measurement data do we need?

It's very easy to jump to conclusions, particularly when 'everyone knows the answer'. They might do, but let's prove it, and manage by fact. So what's the data telling us and what additional data do we now need?

What's the best way of presenting the data?

Pictures, graphs and, bearing in mind the message of this book, control charts are preferable to words and numbers.

What's the data telling you?

Which possible causes are verified by the data? Are there any surprises? Does the data suggest some other cause?

What are the possible deeper causes?

Make sure you really get to the bottom of the problem. Ask "Why?" five times. Initial answers are often superficial.

Who needs to be working on the project now?

Has the data and the identification of the causes affected who now needs to be involved? It really is time to review our progress.

15.6 First review

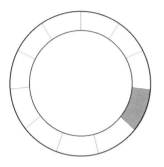

> **Review progress**

We need to check our progress and see if we are still on course. We also need to determine what we have learnt, identifying the things that have gone well and the reasons why.

How are we doing?

How well are we working as a team? Are we on track? How well have we kept our focus on the problem identified in Step 1? Does our 'Issue Statement' need amending?

What have we learnt?

What's gone well, and why? What could have been done better? How can we apply these lessons?

What are the next steps?

How many root causes are there? Remember Pareto's 'vital few'? Who else might we need on board? What about communication? Who needs to know where we now are?

15.7 Step 4

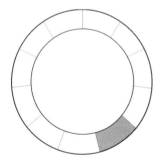

> **Generate possible solutions**

Depending on the size of the problem, it may be sensible to tackle the root causes one at a time or, at least, not all at once. Either way, we now need to generate some ideas to solve the problem. And, if possible, pilot them on a small scale.

What are the possible solutions?

Take time to generate as many ideas as you can; it's too easy to jump to conclusions.

What are the advantages and disadvantages of these?

Why do some of the possible solutions seem better than others? What knock-on effects might there be? What's important for the customer? Are there issues of time, cost or resources that are limiting the choice?

Which possible solutions seem to best address the root cause(s) identified in Step 3?

Keep your focus on the problem identified in Step 1 and the root cause(s) identified in Step 3. Don't forget your 'Issue Statement'.

How can the solution(s) be tried out as a pilot?

How can you try out some ideas in parallel? How will you measure their effect? What do you expect the result to be? Where would a good pilot site be? What are the barriers to a pilot?

15.8 Step 5

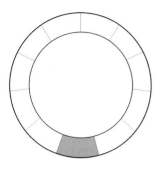

Select the solution

If we've tested out a number of solutions, we now need to evaluate the results and choose the most effective, taking account of any known restrictions on resources. Implementation can then be planned and actioned, taking account of the test results and any potential barriers to the solution.

Which of the possible solutions is the most effective? And is it viable?
What worked well and why? Are there any resource, cost or time implications affecting your solution? Naturally, the costs shouldn't outweigh the benefits!

How did the results compare to what you expected?
How does the solution need to be amended? What lessons have been gained from the pilot? What knock-on effects were there?

Have you learnt anything that might be helpful in tackling other problems?
Are there other problems, either in your own area or somewhere else that could benefit from the solution? Have you developed a computer program, for example, that has wider application?

15.9 Step 6

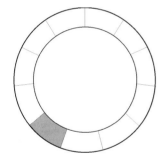

Plan and test the solution

We need to make sure your solution is going to be implemented properly. A well-conceived plan helps avoid misunderstandings or mistakes. Ideally, the opportunity is there for you to carry out a small test or pilot and iron out any teething problems in a safe environment. But we don't always have that luxury.

What's the implementation plan? And who needs to approve it?
What's the plan, and how well will it meet the objectives agreed in Step 1? Who will do what, when, where, and how? What training will be needed, who will do it and how? What barriers might there be to your plan and how can these be overcome?

How will the results be measured?
What are the key process measures? How do they relate to the customer requirements? What are the important signals to look out for and do the people in the process know what they are? How do they know?

How will the plan be communicated?
Who needs to be informed and in how much detail? Would it be sensible to arrange a 'walk-through'?

The Improvement Journal

Our team:

Lessons and output from reviews:

i)

ii)

iii)

1. Our Issue Statement for the problem

5. The solution:

Remember to review progress – are we still on course?

2. The current situation:

6. Planning and testing the solution:

3. Identifying and checking out the possible causes:

Remember to review progress and stay on course

7. Implementing and standardising the solution:

4. Possible solutions:

8. Assess achievements and lessons:

Final – Review - how did we do?

Fig 15.3 The 'Improvement Journal'.

15.10 Second review

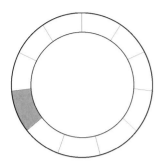

Review progress

Carrying out a review of progress will help avoid the 'ready, fire, aim' approach that wastes so much effort. We need to take stock again to check we are still on course, to identify what's been learnt and to make sure we haven't forgotten anything?

How are we doing?
Are we on track? How well have we kept our focus on the problem identified in Step 1? What have we learnt?

How comfortable are we with the solution?

Are we confident that all the reasonable options have been considered? Is the team's recommended solution soundly based and logical? Will it work and does it fully address our 'Issue Statement'?

How confident are we with our plan?
Is it comprehensive? Do we have the approvals and authority we need? Is there anything that might prevent or slow down the implementation? And if there is, what do we need to do about it?

15.11 Step 7

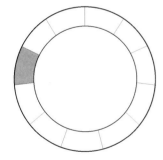

Implement and standardise the solution

It ought to be straightforward now to 'just do it', but after all the hard work to date, it's worth making sure you've followed your plan and not missed anything important on the way.

Following any adjustments from the pilot, what is the new standard method, process, product or service?
Remember Kipling again. You should use his honest serving men to check your plan covered all it should. That includes making sure you've told everyone you should tell about the changes. Communication is key.

Have all the people who do this work been trained?
If not, when will they be trained? How will new people be covered?

How will the measures you've put in place help you monitor on-going results and prompt further improvement actions?
Does the training include the importance of the measurements and the signals to look for? Will people recognise when the measures, and the control charts, indicate a problem and will they know what to do?

How have the changes to the documentation been standardised? Are there any implications for internal or external audit?

Do you need to update manuals or printing records, for example? Do you need to destroy old stock and what do you do if someone uses it?

15.12 Step 8

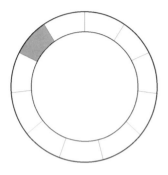

Assess achievements and lessons

This is the 'Study' part of the 'Plan, Do, Study, Act' cycle. The team needs to take stock of the journey and, where appropriate, prepare to update the project sponsor(s). We want to know if there any root causes or symptoms left. And we want to see how well the plan worked and determine our lessons from the project. Given all the hard work and effort, it's also time to celebrate and say thank you.

How well do the results match our expectations?

What were the objectives agreed in Step 1? How well have they been met? What are the key input, process and output measures telling you? What are your customers saying? Which root causes still need to be addressed?

How well did the plan work?

Is recognition due? What went well? What 'adjustments' were needed and why? How could it have been improved? And how will you share the experience?

How can the solution be improved? Is there scope for prevention?

What can be done to 'error-proof' the process? Is it possible to prevent things slipping again? How can the documentation be improved? What further training is needed?

15.13 Final Review

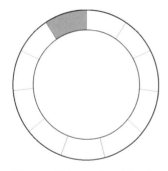

Review progress

This is the 'formal' post implementation review involving the project sponsor(s) or steering committee. The questions are very similar to those in step eight, but they take a wider 'business perspective'.

How satisfied are we that the problem has been solved?

How well have the objectives been met? What's the data telling us? Which root causes still need to be addressed? What other residual issues are there for the business to resolve?

What benefits have been realised or are in the pipeline?

Again, what's the data telling us? How do the benefits compare to what was predicted and are the costs in line, too? Have any other benefits been achieved?

Are there lessons, ideas or 'best practices' that can be applied elsewhere in the business?
What's been learnt and where else in the business might these lessons be helpful? Are there similar problems in another area where the solution might be applicable?
What should happen to the team now?
Should it be disbanded, or retained to tackle any outstanding root causes or address a new problem?
What should we do to suitably recognise the team's success and efforts?
Recognising success and effort is an important element in creating a culture of continuous improvement. Don't lose the opportunity presented by this project and remember that even a simple 'thank you' letter from the Chief Executive can have a significant impact on motivation and morale.

15.14 The 'Improvement Journal'

It's sensible to keep a log of the journey, particularly the key points from each of the steps and the lessons en route. If possible the 'journal' can be put up in the team's work area, perhaps as a poster or storyboard to provide a communication vehicle.

15.15 Key points and summary

- Try to choose the problem that has most impact on customer satisfaction.
- Recognise the importance of the 'Issue Statement' or 'Improvement Project Charter'.
- Make sure you gather information that can help focus improvement effort.
- Generate some initial ideas on what might be causing the problem.
- Provide some suggestions on how to solve the problem.
- Evaluate the results of initial tests and choose the most effective.
- Prepare to properly implement the suggested solution.
- Implement and standardise the solution.
- Take stock of what has been achieved to date.
- Review the problem-solving process at regular intervals.
- Use the 'Improvement Journal' to keep a log of the steps undertaken in solving the problem in order to maximise learning.
- Recognise the importance of recognition.

At various stages in this 'eight-step process' tools are available to support the activity. Some of these tools and techniques have already been referred to, e.g. the Pareto principle. Others are covered in the next chapter.

THE JOURNEY TO IMPROVEMENT SOME OTHER TOOLS

16.1 Introduction

Throughout this book we've included reference to a range of tools and techniques to assist in your improvement activities. The descriptions should help you try out most of the techniques, but for some it's likely you will need some specialist help to get started.

There is a range of tools available to support your journey to improvement. Many are quite simple, some less so, but we won't concern ourselves with the latter here. The Pareto principle, for example, is not difficult to understand and, as important as anything in the context of this book, has a close tie up with the multiple characteristics chart.

In this chapter we cover various problem-solving techniques which can be used to support the control chart and all its implications.

In Section 16.3 you will find detail on the basics of brainstorming, which leads naturally to the use of a fishbone diagram, dealt with in the next section. Two more advanced tools – the affinity diagram and the interrelationship diagram – follow in Sections 16.5 and 16.6. In Section 16.7 you will find material on a different technique altogether – Force Field Analysis. Two other techniques, the XY grid and paired comparisons, follow in the next two sections. Lastly, in Section 16.10, there is a description of the scatter diagram – a technique that has a direct relationship with the control chart, as described in Section 17.2 in Chapter 17. Finally, Section 16.11 illustrates how the various problem-solving tools can be used to support the different needs in assessing a process.

16.2 Other problem – solving techniques

As well as techniques already covered, such as the Pareto principle, there are, of course, other tools and techniques that can help. You should, for example, find out about 'the seven new tools for management and planning'. These will be particularly useful in looking at a large or complex project or issue. This chapter covers two of the tools, the Affinity and Interrelationship diagrams, and a selection of others that in total provide you with a tool-kit for your journey.

Even so, still one of the most important, yet simplest of approaches is to ask questions and in particular ask "Why?" five times. We referred to this in Chapter 2, using Kipling's poem to illustrate the point.

All too often, people have forgotten why something is done the way it is. And all too often, the reasons are no longer relevant! But, nothing will change if the right questions aren't asked. The six 'honest serving-men' provide an effective framework for a series of open questions. Use them all, but particularly "Why?" as often as you need to get to the real answer, i.e. beyond the initial, often superficial first response.

Having recommended asking questions, it's important to remember one thing. Questions are cheap, but answers can be expensive, so it helps to make sure you ask the right questions and the purpose of the questions is clear. Ask yourself, "What am I going to do with the answer?"

16.3 Brainstorming

We've made several references to 'brainstorming' and it's very likely that many of you will have come across this technique in one form or another. Unfortunately, and all too often, it's not used to its full potential.

Managers often enough say they understand brainstorming, but when you search deeper it transpires that they don't. Often their interpretation of brainstorming is 'barnstorming', – a thinly-veiled attempt to seek every-one's views but in reality it is a cover for pushing through the manager's own inclinations.

Brainstorming is a means of generating ideas from as many sources as possible in as short a time as possible. It involves all the members of a team, and will probably need up to 15 minutes to get the ideas out. A facilitator helps, but isn't essential, provided some simple rules are followed.

There are a number of different approaches. This section covers some of them although you might evolve your own approach.

16.3.1 Some sensible ground rules

- Review the subject to be brainstormed and ensure everyone understands the purpose of the brainstorming session. What question are we addressing?
- Allow a minute or two of silence to think about the question.
- Generate ideas.
- Capture ideas.
- Never criticise or at this stage discuss the ideas. The 'silly idea' often spawns a creative approach to an issue.
- Review the ideas, and perhaps group and present them as a fishbone diagram, as shown in Section 16.4.

16.3.2 Generating ideas

Generating ideas can be done in any of the following ways: -

Structured

In this method, the team members each give an idea in turn, or 'pass' until the next round. When, say, 3 or 4 people 'pass' in a row, open it up for general input.

Unstructured

Here, team members simply put forward their ideas as they come to mind. It's a less formal approach, but there's a danger of someone dominating the session.

Silent

This approach helps ensure everyone is involved. The team members write their ideas onto Post-it Notes – one idea per Post-it Note.

16.3.3 Capturing ideas

Capturing ideas is usually actioned by one team member writing the various ideas onto a flipchart. This should capture the speaker's words and not be the interpretation of the recorder. Writing onto Post-it Notes can be sensible as these can be displayed on a wall or flip chart when everyone has finished writing ideas, and can then be reviewed and grouped in a relatively easy way.

Sometimes, generating ideas can be made more fun, and more effective, by carrying out a negative brainstorm. You might, for example, brainstorm ways to ensure meetings are a disaster, or customers are unhappy. 'Changing the signs' can provide a list of actions to help/achieve your real aim. You might also ask the question "How many of these are we doing?"

PROBLEMS OF IMPLEMENTING SPC

Time to implement

Organisation not right for it

Conservatism

Resources needed

Unsure of perceived benefits

Lack of selection

If implemented, then needs financial support

Economics may outweigh SPC introduction

Resistance to change – both up and down

Lack of time / too busy / fear of job loss

Initiative overload / too many / motivation / delegation

Need to start with something that gives a good result

Negative attitude / don't want to know / scepticism – what, another initiative?

Data accumulation

Accuracy of data

Change of company policy

Training further down the line

People expect quick fixes

Got to deliver from top

Lack of spending on equipment

What's in it for me?

Politics

Not my job

Fig 16.1 *List of ideas following a brainstorming session.*

Fig 16.1 shows a list of ideas following a brainstorming session. The ideas related to the problems of introducing SPC following a training course. In this particular case, the session followed an unstructured format because it was felt that the culture of the organisation was sufficiently open. However, one or two of the responses amongst those listed might suggest something different.

Once the ideas have been produced, they need to be analysed in a structured way. This is where we might make use of a fishbone diagram.

16.4 Fishbone diagram

The Fishbone, or 'Cause and Effect' diagram is an effective way of grouping and presenting ideas from a brainstorm. It allows us to display the possible causes of a particular effect. Using Post-it notes during the brainstorm will make this easier.

Take care to remember that cause and effect will be separated by time. One doesn't always immediately follow the other. Indeed, there could be months, or even years between the two! Remember, too, that conducting a 'negative fishbone' can be a creative way of doing this.

The causes can be grouped together under whatever headings you choose. Typical headings generally adopted are 'People', 'Equipment', 'Method', 'Materials', and 'Environment'. In manufacturing, the traditional headings used are – 'Manpower', 'Machines', 'Methods' and 'Materials'.

The group headers can also be useful in prompting ideas during the brainstorm.

We construct the Cause and Effect Diagram by: -

(a) Placing 'the problem statement' or 'effect' in the box on the right-hand side of the diagram.

(b) Drawing the traditional major cause headings on the left-hand side of the diagram.

(c) Placing the brainstormed ideas under the appropriate major categories, and

(d) For each possible cause ask, "Why does it happen?" and list the responses as branches off the

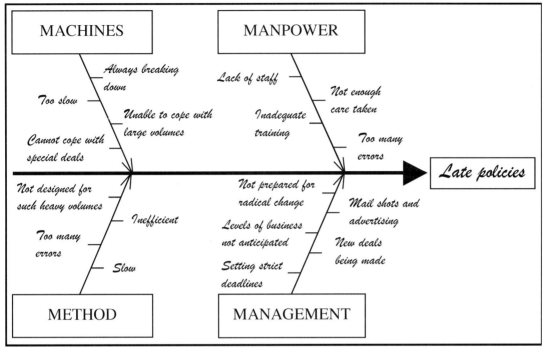

Fig 16.2 Fishbone diagram for analysing reasons for late policies.

major causes. In doing this, remember to ask "Why?" five times so as to get at the real reason.

The resulting diagram should look a bit like a fishbone!

The fishbone diagram is often used in conjunction with a control chart. It may not be easy to readily identify the reason for an out-of-control signal. A brainstorming session, followed by the use of a fishbone diagram, is more than likely required.

This was the case with the process relating to *Fig 16.2*. The original control chart plotted the proportion of policies issued which were not satisfying the required standard. Several out-of-control points were found, and as a result a brainstorming session was held with the group of people involved with the process.

As it happens, the fishbone diagram made use of the traditional 4M headings with 'Materials' replaced by *Management*', but, as stated earlier, in office areas the categories chosen are often quite unique to the environment concerned. For example, a fishbone diagram looking at renewal accounts in a bank made use of the categories 'System', 'Bank', 'Customer' and 'Economic Climate'.

The fishbone diagram is often called an Ishikawa diagram. It is worth making the point here that Ishikawa's role in initiating this technique in Japan, as part of the massive programme of problem solving training, has been much underplayed.

Having set up a fishbone diagram and analysed it, your next step will be to look for possible causes that appear repeatedly, and to identify where perhaps you need to gather additional data through measurement.

Pareto analysis, brainstorming and the fishbone diagram are three well-documented problem-solving tools. The affinity diagram and the interrelationship diagram, as described in the next two sections, are two of the 'seven new management and planning tools'. They're particularly appropriate for large issues and projects. These tools emerged from Japan and are an ideal first step in a project that will help improve the understanding of what needs to be done before rushing off and producing the project plan.

16.5 The Affinity diagram

The purpose of the affinity diagram is to generate, pull together, and organise a potentially extensive and unorganised amount of information. This could be a mixture of facts, opinions, ideas and intuitions, but the technique leads to consensus and ownership of the way forward, usually on quite large issues and projects.

Essentially, it is a silent brainstorm on a grand scale. But there's a difference, as the steps below show:

1. Take time to agree an issue statement or question to brainstorm around. Clearly define what the statement or question means and, perhaps, what it doesn't mean. Everyone must agree on the statement or question before you can proceed. These usually begin with words like: -
   - "Factors that influence…."
   - "Elements of…."
   - "What are the issues involved in…?"
   - "What are the barriers or problems involved in…?"
   - "What makes x effective?"

   In introducing SPC or a culture of continuous improvement, you might well find yourself using this technique with a statement on the following lines, *"What are the issues involved in introducing and deploying the application of SPC throughout the organisation."*

   Silently brainstorm the ideas, capturing each idea on a Post-It note. There should only be one idea per Post-It Note, written clearly to ensure everyone can read it. One word entries are not very helpful usually, but nor are those with too many words. Using a noun and verb will help.

3. When everyone has finished writing, the process of clustering can begin – but only when everyone has finished. Once they have, everyone, all at the same time, and still in silence, put their various Post-It Notes on the wall and in any order they wish! It helps to have some large sheets of brown paper on the wall.

4. It's time to step back, possibly in amazement, and read the different entries, still in silence! Reading the various Post-It Notes might prompt some more ideas and additional Post-It Notes can be written at any stage.

5. This next step can be quite entertaining. Everyone, all at the same time and still in silence, start to move the Post-It Notes around, putting them into what they perceive to be groups or clusters of similar ideas or themes. Some of these might be quite lateral, rather than the more traditional headings associated with the fishbone, for example. But you might feel happy to use the fishbone as a framework and if you do, then fine.

6. There might be some stragglers at this stage, Post-It Notes with no apparent home. Do not worry about them just yet, but do not forget about them either.

   Remember, at any stage, additional Post-It Notes can be written; and there might well be a case for one idea to appear more than once and in different clusters.

   It might also be appropriate to break the silence;

Fig 16.3 Post-It Notes at the ready, but not a word please.

the facilitator will determine the right time to do this. Almost certainly there'll be a need to clarify what an idea or a Post-It Note means, or the thoughts behind a particular grouping that's emerging. The facilitator will also determine when it's appropriate to move to the next step in the process.

7. This looks to agree a definition or description for each of the clusters and produce 'a header'. This may sound easy, but it's really important that the header can stand by itself in describing the content of the cluster. As before, one-word entries are unlikely to be helpful.

Back to the stragglers without a home. There are 3 possible actions here: -

- You might find a home now the headers have been agreed for the others.
- A single Post-It Note might well form its own cluster and some further brainstorming could then generate some ideas to go with it, or, if everyone agrees…
- A Post-It Note could be discarded.

The big advantage of the affinity diagram is that it generates a lot of ideas creatively and comparatively quickly. What is more, the ideas aren't lost (as can so often happen in brainstorming), and everyone owns the finished result.

That sense of ownership and understanding increases significantly with the use of the next technique, the interrelationship diagram.

16.6 The Interrelationship diagram

The purpose of the interrelationship diagram, often known as the 'I.D.' diagram, is to identify the logical and sequential connections and relationships between the clusters that were generated in the affinity diagram. It can also be used in the same way to look at the ideas within a cluster, or even the whole affinity diagram. That said, that would be quite a challenge!

So, at this stage, at least, let's keep it simple and stick to using the technique at the cluster level. Even this can be hard work, but the end result will be worth the effort.

What we're trying to do is to determine whether there is a cause and effect relationship between each and every pair of clusters. And if there is, which cluster is causing the effect.

Typically, it will be on the lines of: -

- "Must this happen here before that can happen?"
- "You must do this first in order to achieve that."
- "Does one item tend to help or influence the other?"
- "Does one item tend to follow the other?"

The process is as follows:

1. Take the header cards from the affinity diagram and place them in a circle, perhaps on a flipchart. Remember that these were meant to stand on their own in terms of capturing the sense and content of the various clusters. Let's see if they do!

2. Essentially, it's a question of looking at each pair to determine if there's a relationship. So, if the headers are A, B, C, D and E, we would start with A and look at AB, AC, AD and AE. Then we would move to B and look at BC, BD, BE and so on.

3. Where there is a relationship, we draw a line connecting the two headers.

4. We then need to determine the causal cluster and turn the line into an arrow, by drawing the arrowhead into the header that is being affected.

5. Once all the headers have been reviewed in this way, we count the 'arrows out' and the 'arrows in' for each header. This will enable us to identify the key causal factors. Hence a code of 3/1 in a header means that three arrows lead out and one arrow leads in.

6. From this, we can determine the likely sequence of actions now needed to progress the project. Certainly we will have identified the key driver to concentrate on.

There are a few simple rules to keep to. They're simple, but you'll find it difficult to stick to them!

- No matter the temptation, do not allow 'two-headed arrows'.
- Don't use thin lines and thick lines, or dotted lines. There's either a relationship or there isn't.
- That said, it could be sensible to use a pencil until everyone is sure on the lines and the direction of the arrows.
- If you reach an impasse, skip it and come back to it later. By that time it might be easier to resolve.

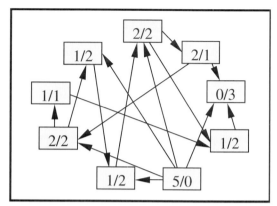

Fig 16.4 *A typical interrelationship diagram.*

Fig 16.4 shows a typical I.D. diagram with the arrows completed. It would suggest that the header (5/0) is worth tackling first.

The I.D. is hard work, but it really does increase understanding and provide insights that will help ensure the subsequent success of the project.

16.7 Force Field Analysis

Whether you're looking at problems or their solutions, Force Field Analysis is likely to be a helpful tool in improving your understanding of the issues involved.

One of Isaac Newton's Laws is at the root of this tool i.e.

"For every force, there is an equal and opposite force."

In another sense: -

"A positive force often has an opposing negative force."

Force Field Analysis helps identify those forces that are for and against change – the supporting and driving forces in favour, and the resisting barriers against. Some of these 'forces' are likely to be individual people, and the diagram can be a helpful step in developing influencing strategies and tactics that build on someone's positive view of the project, for example, or seek to overcome those who are against, perhaps by helping them see the 'what's in it for them' advantages.

These are brainstormed and appear either side of a vertical line drawn down the centre of the chart as the example in *Fig 16.5* shows.

The problem being analysed here is the state of morale in a department. The current perception is that it is low, whereas, obviously, it should be high.

HELPING	HINDERING
Individual training plans in place	No pre-management development
Recognition programme	Inconsistent recognition
SPC charts being utilised	Management doesn't understand variation
Problem solving teams in place	Managers not actively supporting problem solving

Fig 16.5 *Table showing positive and negative issues relating to morale in a department.*

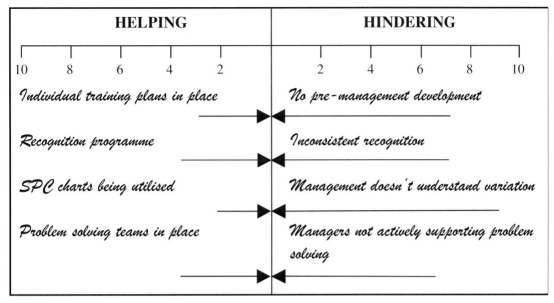

HELPING	HINDERING

| 10 8 6 4 2 | 2 4 6 8 10 |

Individual training plans in place → ← *No pre-management development*

Recognition programme → ← *Inconsistent recognition*

SPC charts being utilised → ← *Management doesn't understand variation*

Problem solving teams in place → ← *Managers not actively supporting problem solving*

Fig 16.6 *Completed Force Field diagram.*

When the various issues have been brainstormed, discuss the relative strength of their 'force' and draw arrows to correspond. The longer the arrow, the stronger the force. It might be helpful to draw in some sort of scale across the top of each side of the diagram, for example one to ten.

Fig 16.6 shows the data of *Fig 16.5* with the scale added and arrows drawn in as suggested.

The Force Field diagram now gives a good indication of how the group feels about the morale in the department, using data that is somewhat measurable as defined by the lengths of the arrows.

Once the arrows have been drawn, you can discuss and agree ways to build on the positive forces and maximise their potential, and/or reduce or remove the negative barriers and constraining forces.

16.8 The XY Grid

One way or another, the use of control charts will prompt the need for process improvement. Unfortunately, SPC won't tell you how to go about solving problems and improving processes. And it isn't always easy to 'just do it', especially if the individual or team is inexperienced at problem solving.

What's more, it isn't always easy to prioritise the various improvement opportunities. One way to help determine priorities for action is to present information in an 'XY Grid', sometimes referred to as a Boston Box. The example provides a means of identifying performance against the customer's priorities for a service or product. The XY Grid is appropriate to present a range of items, including the results from a self-assessment against the EFQM's Excellence Model.

Naturally, you're looking for high performance against the customer's priority requirements. If you're not achieving that, but are performing well in an area of low priority, it might be sensible to review the allocation of resources.

Either way, by determining the importance of the customer's requirements and the capability of your processes, you can quickly determine your own priorities for improvement.

Of course, it may well be that the decision is driven by the 'bottom line' and many organisations will look to prioritise according to the potential for cost savings. Phil Crosby's Price of Non-conformance (PONC) can be helpful here.

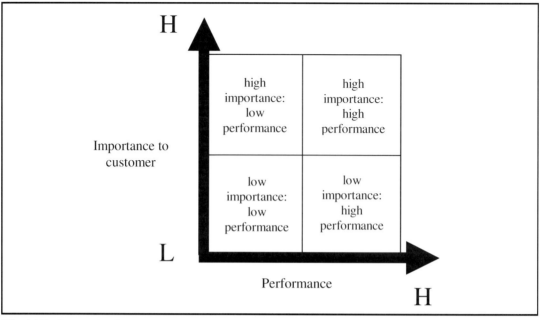

Fig 16.7 The XY Grid.

One useful way of deciding priorities, or selecting solutions, is to make use of a technique called 'paired comparisons'.

16.9 Paired comparisons and N/3

Paired comparisons provide a relatively straightforward way to determine priorities and select an improvement action to take, or problem to tackle. Here, you are looking at each pair from a list of ideas or problems. These may well have resulted from a brainstorming session.

Quite simply, you're asking the participants to compare A with B and decide which is their preferred choice, probably against one or other of the following questions:

- "Which item is the greater cause of customer dissatisfaction or non-conformance cost?"
- "Which action or idea do you feel will solve the problem and/or improve the position?"

This process continues by looking at A and C, A and D, A and E, B and C, B and D, and so on. You could do this openly, by going round the table, or by issuing a 'voting grid', along the lines shown in *Fig 16.8*.

Participants should circle their choices in each of the comparisons. The combined results will then

Item No.	Description	Options			
A		A/B	A/C	A/D	A/E
B			B/C	B/D	B/E
C				C/D	C/E
D					D/E
E					

Fig 16.8 Typical voting grid used in paired comparisons.

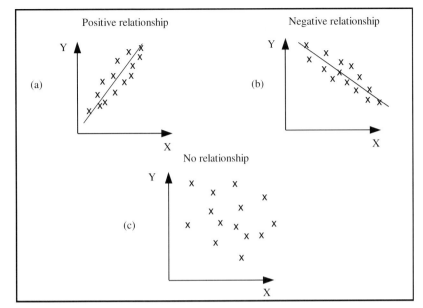

Fig 16.9 *Scatter diagrams showing different relationships.*

point to the agreed priorities for action.

If you're trying to select from a large list of brainstormed ideas, you might want to prune the list down before using paired comparisons. N/3 is a simple way of doing this.

N is the number of items in your list. So, divide N by 3 and give that number of votes to each member of the team to select their top choices – one vote per idea. You can then use paired comparisons on the reduced list.

The last technique we look at has a very close relationship with a specific type of control chart. Perhaps it is the most mathematically-based technique we make use of in the book, but don't worry, you should be able to see how useful it is without any need to get into detailed mathematics or statistics, which are handled automatically by spreadsheet software.

16.10 The Scatter diagram

The scatter diagram takes us back to measurement and the presentation of data.

A scatter diagram helps identify whether there's a relationship between two variables. What's more, we can put a value on the relationship if there is one. We're talking cause and effect, X's and Y's. It's used to help verify potential root causes.

We're looking to see if a change in the cause values (the X's) will produce a change in the effect values (the Y's). If our suspected cause is a real one, the Y variable will change as the X variable changes.

The dependent Y variable is always plotted vertically; the independent X variable is plotted on the horizontal axis. **The data is plotted in pairs -** so when X = 'this value,' Y = 'that value.'

Scatter diagrams are a useful and simple way to see if there is a relationship between two variables, for example sales and advertising activity, or productivity and investment in training. But do be careful! You can create diagrams showing a correlation for items with no real cause and effect connection at all.

So, for example, when England win at cricket, the error rate on processing new business applications in a sales office reduces.

Scatter diagrams are easy to produce using spreadsheets like Excel or programs like Minitab. But it's important to be aware of some of the common errors and pitfalls associated with them. These include: -
- Mixing up the X and Y variables and axes.
- Data is incorrectly paired.
- The diagram is not square because of inappropriate scaling.

CHAPTER 16

- The scaling is not sensitive enough for the data.

Ideally, there should be 5 - 15 increments of equal width on each axis. If you use Excel, beware of 'autoscaling' that ignores this requirement.

If you are collecting data in 'seconds' then plot the data in 'seconds,' not in minutes or hours. Rounding data up or down may mean the scale is not sensitive enough and this can lead to unusual patterns.

Finally, the biggest mistake can be the assumption that correlation always implies causation. This won't always be true, as our cricket example demonstrated – use common sense to draw your conclusions.

DIAGNOSTIC	TOOL(S) REQUIRED
I need to understand **how the process works**	"Ask questions" Flow-charts
I need to **quantify the problem**	Check sheet Control chart
I need to **present data**	Pareto principle Scatter diagram XY Grid Control chart
I need to **generate ideas**	Brainstorming Affinity diagram
I need to **group ideas**	Fishbone diagram Affinity diagram
I need to **understand the connections** between ideas or issues	Interrelationship diagram Force Field diagram Scatter diagram
I need to understand **the pro's and con's**	Force Field diagram Paired comparison
I need to **determine the priorities or sequence for action**	XY Grid Force Field diagram Interrelationship diagram Paired comparison

Fig 16.10 Table showing the relevance of various problem-solving techniques.

The correlation co-efficient is expressed as **r.** In a perfect positive correlation, r = + 1; in a perfect negative correlation r = - 1. r^2, expressed as a percentage, shows the percent of variation in Y explained by the effect of X. So, if r = 0.7, the variable is causing 49% of the variation in Y; if R = 0.8, the value increases to 64%. Your spreadsheet software can give you this value which is a key factor in confirming the vital few root causes.

Fig 16.9 shows three types of relationships that exist.

The line through the points is called the 'line of best fit'. There is a detailed mathematical way of obtaining this line and, you will be pleased to know a much simpler practical alternative.

The detail on this appears in Chapter 17 when considering how to handle what we call 'drifting processes'. Sales, over time, should be represented by a pattern shown in *Fig 16.9 (a);* i.e. there is a positive relationship in that sales increase over time.

16.11 Putting it together

As we've said, there are references to a number of tools and techniques throughout this book. The table shown in *Fig 16.10* provides a summary of them and highlights when they might be used.

16.12 Summary of symbols and formulae

4 M's   Manpower, Method, Materials, Machines.

I.D.   Interrelationship diagram.

XY Grid   Grid relating process performance to a customer's requirement. Sometimes called a Boston Box.

16.13 Key points and summary

- Don't underestimate the value of asking "Why" repeatedly.
- Use the brainstorming approach which best suits your organisation and group.
- Remember that brainstorming is not the same as barnstorming.
- Use a fishbone diagram in association with a list of brainstorming ideas.
- Reasons for special causes on a control chart can often only be determined by means of brainstorming and a fishbone diagram, with the possible causes then verified by data.
- Affinity and interrelationship diagrams have their uses in tackling large improvement projects.
- A Force Field Analysis can also be used in conjunction with a brainstorming session.
- The XY Grid can help present the relationship between process performance and customer satisfaction.
- Use paired comparisons as a method of determining priorities.
- Scatter diagrams provide a simple graphical representation of relationships and help identify whether an independent variable (the X), is influencing the results of a dependent variable (the Y).
- Use the various problem-solving tools as appropriate.

The last two chapters have covered various problem-solving tools that can support the use of a control chart.

The main thrust of this book has to do with SPC, and so it is appropriate that the next chapter returns to this theme.

Various items are covered in Chapter 17. It is almost a pot-pourri of the different technical issues to do with the control chart which have not yet been covered. It also begins to wrap things up, in preparation for some summary points to be made in Chapter 18.

SOME FURTHER ISSUES

17.1 Introduction

We are almost there in covering the various technical aspects to do with control charts. This chapter tidies up some remaining issues that we have yet to deal with.

Several times throughout the book reference has been made to patterns which occur on a control chart, and in this chapter we devote a significant number of pages to considering three unusual patterns. In Section 17.2 we discuss how to handle what we know as a drifting process, one where the points move linearly in an upward or downward direction. This is immediately followed by a Case Study showing how the technique has been used in practice. Another typical pattern is a cycle, covered in Section 17.4, with a relevant Case Study to follow in the next section. The third pattern we deal with is 'bunching', in Section 17.6, and again we have a Case Study to match.

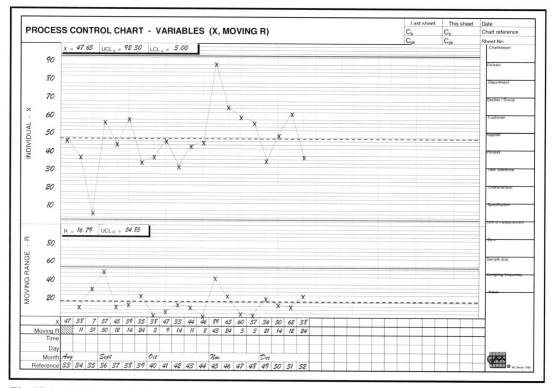

Fig 17.1 *Final control chart to be used for monitoring ongoing sales.*

A common problem associated with SPC is sampling, and all that it implies. The Case Study described in Section 17.9 covers various issues to do with the practicalities of sampling documents.

In Section 17.10 we deal with one of the most important issues when using a control chart i.e. when do we recalculate the limits?

Finally, there is a brief reference, and no more than that, to other types of attribute charts.

17.2 Drifting processes

17.2.1 The problem

Sales figures that show natural variation within the control limits represent a process that we now know is under control, stable and predictable.

Fig 17.1, which is a copy of *Fig 8.17* that we developed in Chapter 8, represents such a process.

Although the sales figures are under control, this does not mean that the situation is satisfactory. As it now stands, the organisation could be in real trouble with this product. Management would feel a lot more comfortable if the sales figures increased over time.

Fig 17.2 shows a table of sales figures that reflect a much healthier pattern.

Unlike the pattern of sales figures shown in *Fig 17.1*, these figures indicate a steady increase over time.

When developing the control chart to deal with these figures, as we have done before we follow a series of steps to set up the chart.

17.2.2 Step 1 – Record the readings

The twenty sales values are recorded in the data boxes on the (X, Moving R) chart in the usual way.

These are now to be used as a guide to determine the scale to be used for the X section of the chart.

17.2.3 Step 2 – Choose the scale

The way to do this is to locate the middle value of the sales readings, which is approx. 150, and fix it on the mid point of the vertical axis. Then choose an appropriate scale that will comfortably allow the initial and final sales figures of 128 and 174 to be plotted. Make sure that you leave sufficient room below the value of 128 and above the value of 174 so that the control limits can be drawn in eventually.

17.2.4 Step 3 – Plot the results

With the scale determined, the sales figures can be plotted.

The run chart for these numbers is now shown in *Fig 17.3(overleaf)*.

Some explanation is required here.

Up to now, it has always been emphasised that plotting the points should never take place until the control limits have been worked out. These limits then suggest the right scale to use.

Here, it is different. The logic of developing the control limits requires us to first draw in a line which represents the drift over time, and since this line is going to represent the points, then we must plot these first. Hence we have to use a pragmatic approach to fix the scale.

Sales	128	132	131	137	136	139	144	143	153	147	152	160	160	158	161	168	165	172	171	174
Month	Mar	Apr	May	Jun	Jul	Aug	Sep	Oct	Nov	Dec	Jan	Feb	Mar	Apr	May	Jun	Jul	Aug	Sep	Oct

Fig 17.2 *Table of sales values (in £1000's) for a certain product over the months.*

We now need to derive control limits to monitor these values. In doing so, the drift has to be taken into account.

17.2.5 Step 4 – Calculate the 'line of best fit'

We need to obtain a line that allows for the drift in the process. In other words, we need a procedure that takes into account the position of each point in the run chart in producing an inclined straight line. This line is sometimes referred to as the 'line of best fit'.

Two ways have been traditionally used to obtain this line.

First, there is a mathematical way. We don't intend to cover it here. "*SPC and Business Improvement*" contains technical detail on the mathematical calculations involved if you wish to know more. Software packages are available which carry out the routine.

At the other end of the scale of complexity is a typical rough and ready approach to obtaining the line. Use a transparent ruler, and then adjust its position so that it provides what seems to be the right balance i.e. the line to be drawn falls nicely between the points and reflects what seems to be a good optimum position.

Want we want is a balance between these two methods – one that is not too technical yet adequate enough to provide a good reliable estimate of the true position of the line.

Fortunately, there is such a method. Don Wheeler, in an article entitled "*Avoiding man-made chaos*", suggests the following: -

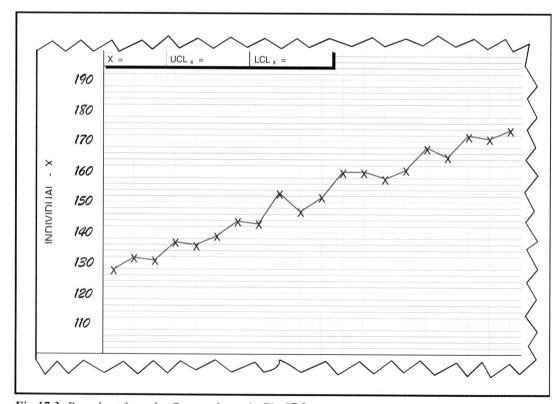

Fig 17.3 *Run chart for sales figures shown in Fig 17.2.*

Take the first four values of the sequence and calculate the mean of these four. We call this. X_1.

In our case this gives: - $X_1 = \dfrac{128+132+131+137}{4} = 132.0$

Mark this value on the chart corresponding to the mid point on the horizontal scale, i.e. between April and May.

Now take the last four values in the sequence and calculate the mean of these four, which we call X_2.

With our figures this gives: - $X_2 = \dfrac{165+172+171+174}{4} = 170.5$

This value, in turn, is marked on the chart corresponding to the mid-point on the horizontal scale between August and September.

Finally a line is drawn joining these two marks, extended at each end to cover the span of twenty points.

Fig 17.4 shows the run chart with the line of best fit drawn in.

17.2.6 Step 5 – Calculate moving ranges

Having transferred the twenty sales figures into the corresponding boxes of an (X, Moving R) chart, we calculate and record the nineteen moving ranges in the usual way.

The results appear in *Fig 17.5.*

17.2.7 Step 6 – Calculate mean values

First of all, note that here there is no need to work out $\overline{X}$. If we did, then we gain nothing by drawing it in as a horizontal line. We know the process drifts, and that we need an inclined line which we have allowed for and determined.

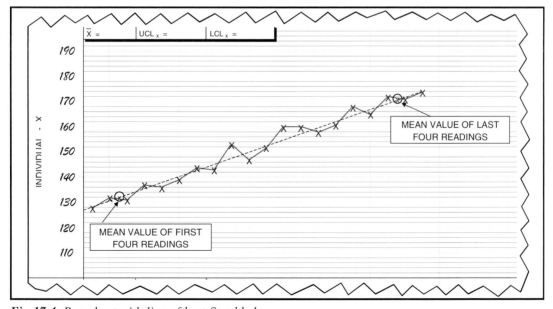

Fig 17.4 *Run chart with line of best fit added.*

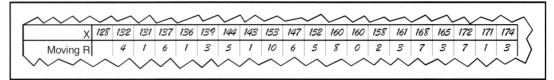

| X | 128 | 132 | 131 | 137 | 136 | 139 | 144 | 143 | 153 | 147 | 152 | 160 | 160 | 158 | 161 | 168 | 165 | 172 | 171 | 174 |
| Moving R | | 4 | 1 | 6 | 1 | 3 | 5 | 1 | 10 | 6 | 5 | 8 | 0 | 2 | 3 | 7 | 3 | 7 | 1 | 3 |

Fig 17.5 *Section of control chart showing completed data boxes.*

However, we do need the mean moving range in order to work out the control limits.
Using the nineteen moving ranges in *Fig 17.5*,

$$\overline{R} = \frac{\Sigma R}{19} = \frac{76}{19} = 4.0$$

17.2.8 Step 7 – Determine control limits
In Chapter 8 we explained that for the X section of the (X, moving R) chart, the values of the control limits are given by: -

$$UCL_X = \overline{X} + 2.66\ \overline{R}$$
$$LCL_X = \overline{X} - 2.66\ \overline{R}$$

With the figures we have, the line is drifting, and so we need to place the control limits at a distance of 2.66 $\overline{R}$ on either side of the line.

It is necessary to go into the detail of how to do this.

We know that $\overline{R}$ is 4.0

∴ 2.66 x $\overline{R}$ = 2.66 x 4.0 = 10.64

We now draw a line at right angles to the line of drift at the beginning of the line, so that the length of this line is 10.64 units on the vertical scale.

Fig 17.6 provides some explanation.

A similar line is drawn on the other side of the line of best fit, and then two other lines drawn in the same way at the other end of the line of best fit. The inclined control limits can then be constructed, and the final control chart is shown in *Fig 17.7*.

17.2.9 Step 8– Interpret for process control
The usual rules are applied, except that they are interpreted using the line of best fit as a reference. For example, a run of seven above or below the central line now means a run of seven above or below the line of drift.

The process is under control, and the inclined lines can be projected ahead to monitor the sales figures.

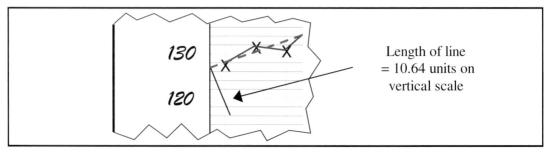

Fig 17.6 *Section of control chart showing how the position of the angled line is determined.*

17.2.10 Inclined lines for ($\overline{X}$, R) chart

The technique is not restricted to the (X, Moving R) chart. A similar approach is adopted when dealing with samples, as in the ($\overline{X}$, R) chart.

The line of best fit allows for the drift in the $\overline{X}$ values. Control lines are then set at a distance of $A_2\overline{R}$ out from this line.

17.2.11 Use of software packages

A growing number of calculators now provide routines to calculate the line of drift based on the X and Y values of the points.

If you have access to these packages, then make use of them. They are based on the more technical method referred to in Section 17.2.5. Don't worry about the mathematics. Just press the buttons to get the answer.

Unfortunately, it is rare to find packages that calculate the position of the angled control limits. Even if they do so, they might not use the correct 2.66 $\overline{R}$ expression. So, again, be careful.

The following case study shows how 3M Healthcare has introduced SPC into the sales and marketing function, and made use of angled control limits in monitoring the performance of its sales figures.

The description includes some non-technical material relating to the culture issues that impinge on the use of charts in newer, more difficult areas such as sales and marketing. The experiences of the company may be of benefit to others in this respect.

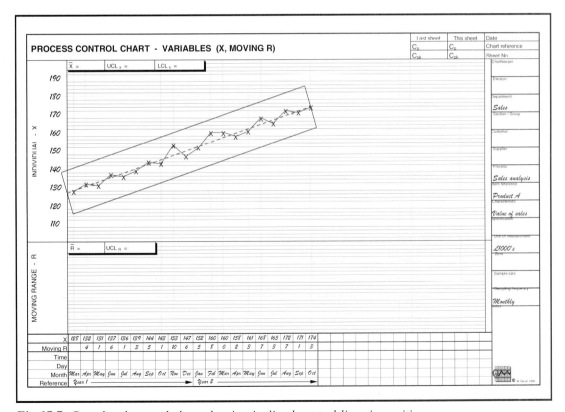

Fig 17.7 Completed control chart showing inclined control lines in position.

17.3 CASE STUDY 18 3M Healthcare

PROCESS CONTROL MEASUREMENT WITHIN THE SALES ENVIRONMENT

17.3.1 Background to the company

3M Health Care Limited has its UK headquarters in Loughborough, Leicestershire, and is a leading supplier of products and services to the health care industry. It is a full-service company with its own dedicated manufacturing, research, personnel, financial and marketing operations.

In the UK, the company markets a diverse range of over 1,400 products including ethical pharmaceuticals, surgical devices, hospital and community medical products, diagnostics, consumer health care, dental and animal care products.

Research and development are integral components of 3M Health Care's activity. The company has a reputation for expertise in specialist areas such as the development of drugs for respiratory diseases, systems for the delivery of drugs, restorative dentistry and many others.

3M Health care is part of the multi-national 3M organisation which has its headquarters in St Paul, Minnesota, USA and operations in over 60 countries. With a reputation for innovation, 3M currently produces over 50,000 different products for industrial, commercial, health care and consumer markets world wide.

17.3.2 From data to information

A key part of any Continuous Improvement Programme is the acceptance that everything we do, and everything we think, can be described in terms of a process. This basic understanding focuses our attention on processes, and their interrelationship one with the other. These relationships are not linear, and considerable work is needed to identify how various processes are linked within a system.

As our work develops on systems thinking, we have identified the additional needs to study the effect of how people inter-relate, together with their capabilities and competencies.

All of this has caused us to study the Theory of Variation. Work by Walter Shewhart, W. Edwards Deming and Donald Wheeler has guided the numerous groups across the whole company in this endeavour.

The application of Shewhart charts to data generated by many of our processes has helped to identify their capability. Where these processes have been technical or manufacturing, this technique has been widely applied. In the business areas, sales, marketing, customer service, finance, and others, the application of Shewhart charts has been slow.

There are many reasons for this. Much of the data currently collected is financial, and by volume. As all of this has been collected in financial groups, it is generated monthly, and aimed at satisfying the needs of monthly balance sheets. The data is also mainly collected at the end of the process – the 'finished goods' stage. Very little is historically available which reflects the process activity.

As people in non-manufacturing areas were helped to view data in chart form, as opposed to rows and columns of numbers, their first comments were about the time delays in confirming 'special causes' which indicate a process being out of statistical control.

The early stages of working with a sales group, looking at the variation within their processes, needed to handle these early concerns. The groups were encouraged to start to consider the key sections of the process, and look for ways to measure their performance.

The following document, represented in 17.3.3 and 17.3.4, is from a Regional Sales Manager who is at the early stages of studying the sales processes within his region.

17.3.3 The traditional view

Traditionally in the pharmaceutical industry, and in the sales environment in general, the view of sales results is usually 'black and white'. There are good months and there are bad months and generally not much else in between. As an individual, a region, or a company, if you are growing your sales it is seen as generally good, and if you are in 'negative growth' this is generally bad. There ends the sophistication. Occasionally some further analysis is applied, and 'double digit growth' is seen as extreme or extraordinary. Whilst viewing this information in its context is an option, there are not many tools to do this effectively, or often the will to look a little deeper.

17.3.4 The new view

Having been introduced to SPC some two years ago, there has been a slow, but definite integration of its use into our organisational culture based on the following reasoning;

Selling is a process. Changing the process produces visible results/outcomes.

There are many elements to the 'mix' – direct selling, marketing campaigns, resources etc, – and outcomes can be determined or affected by any one, or a combination of these.

There has to be a better way of looking at results than the good month/bad month scenario.

What did we do with the good month/bad month data except feel good or bad about it?

What do we do know, and what does it tell us?

When we view sales results, we now utilise SPC charts to organise and interpret the information that we have. This has several positive effects on what we do with the information, and also affects our thinking from a short to a longer-term view. In the old paradigm, a month that was extraordinary was met with a pat on the back from senior personnel, yet we did not know how extraordinary the data was. It may have been the case that we were congratulating ourselves for results that were, in fact, part of the natural variation of the process. It would be accurate to say that the reverse was also true, that we would be downcast because of a month in decline.

When we view our data now, we are looking for something very different – not volume growth but growth outside natural variation. We filter out the 'noise' and look for meaningful patterns.

This was an exciting and new concept. No longer did we fear or relish the issue of each month's results. We waited to view the data in its real context. Is natural variation present? Is there a special cause, and if so is it 'assignable'?

Therein lies the real elegance of viewing sales data in this way. In essence, what we need to do is capture a process that works, and broadly apply it. By viewing a special cause statistically, we are forced right back to the process to see what has worked, or view parts of the process for improvement when only natural variation is present. The other real benefit is that the short-term view (month by month) simply serves to punctuate the passing of the year without really looking at the broader over-view. Stepping back and viewing patterns over time, in and out of control, actually fits the nature of the selling process much better than a simplistic comparison of two figures. The clarity of thought that this tool has provided, both in terms of the analysis of data, and using data for prediction, is very powerful. Given that our goal is to 'break out' of the upper control limit, to exert our influence positively on the market, the use of charts with no growth element applied has been extremely useful.

The prediction of future sales, which can often be seen as more art than science, can be aided by using a growth element applied to the chart. In addition to that, when data is shown to be out-of-control, the process is then assumed to be producing an 'expected' growth. If the process stays the same, one could make the assumption that the results should continue to grow in a similar manner.

By using a growth chart, one can then ask a different question. We know that previous changes in process have pushed our outcomes out of the upper control limit – now let's look at further changes to those new outcomes and see what happens over and above the previous change in process. This helps not to confuse variation that you may have assigned to one change in the process when there is actually something else happening.

The challenges that we have in the sales environment are probably more to do with the determination of what those changes are! Large-scale changes, like change in marketing strategy, the introduction of new product competition, and the employment of new sales people are fairly easy to assign to statistical changes. The real skill in analysis is the determination of what has changed with individuals to promote a statistical signal.

Any sales organisation needs to capture a process that works, and transfer that success across the sales team. The use of SPC charts to view data, in addition to its many other benefits, focuses us to look very hard for the right questions. The variables in looking at, measuring and evaluating our processes, which is the stuff of human behaviour, is another challenge again.

17.3.5 Angled control limits

The majority of the control charts referred to in this case study made use of sloping lines.
Fig 17.8 shows one particular example. Note the different convention this package uses for the lines; control limits represented by the broken lines and the central line by a solid line.

For reasons of confidentiality, some of the figures have been modified or deleted. However, the figure shows a sales process which is under control and drifting upwards in a predictable way.

17.4 Cyclic processes

Instead of drifting in one direction or another, sometimes a process produces figures that show a cyclic pattern. For example, sales figures may vary over the four quarters of the year. Why? Is it due to sales targets being set which distort the natural pattern of the sales performance? If not, then it could be a seasonal effect, in other words, the true pattern of sales over time is cyclical, and this then becomes the natural pattern to expect. How do we deal with this?

One approach is to draw up separate charts for each month, accepting that February's figures, for example, come from a different process to those for March, and so on. You will need a lot of data points to set up the charts, so why not use weekly, or even daily sales figures, if these are available, and see what results these give you?

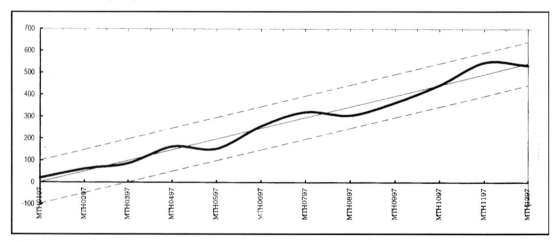

Fig 17.8 *Control chart for sales that drift over time.*

This feature whereby one month is different to the next also occurs in a similar way when analysing the number of customers attending an office. For example, the number of people visiting a bank in the period 9-30 a.m.– 10-30 a.m. is basically different to the number attending over the next hour and the next hour again. Separate control charts need to be kept for each hour across the day. Similarly, Monday's pattern overall could be different to Tuesday, and so on.

Cyclic patterns form the basis of the next Case Study.

17.5 CASE STUDY 19 Napp Laboratories Ltd.

INVOICE RUNS

17.5.1 Background to the company

Napp Laboratories Limited (NLL) distribute pharmaceutical products in the UK to wholesale chains such as Unichem, A.A.H., and Boots. They also supply to other small wholesalers, chemists and dispensing doctors.

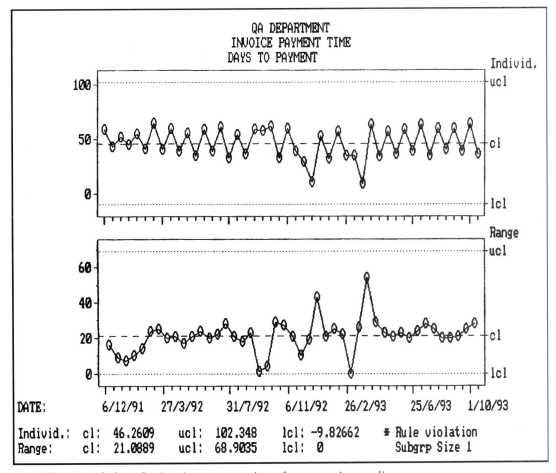

Fig 17.9 Control chart for invoice payment times for a certain supplier.

SPC was introduced through a series of project based training courses across a range of departments. This case study was prompted by the Production and Quality Director who was keen to apply SPC techniques in non-production areas.

17.5.2 The project

The rationale of the project was as follows: -
- It should not relate to production or quality.
- It should be a commercial or financial process.
- Data must be readily available.
- Data must not be currently in use.

With these points in mind, it was decided to analyse the time between the invoicing of orders and the receipt of payment. The value of current trade debtors amounted to £7.6M. With overdraft facilities to the company costing 10%, a reduction in this time would have clear benefit.

17.5.3 Invoicing procedure

Wholesalers are supplied on a two-week schedule and delivery is guaranteed within a three-day window. For the major wholesale chains an invoice is sent to each branch. Payment, however, is consolidated at Head Office.

17.5.4 The control chart

Fig 17.9 shows an (X, Moving R) chart for invoice payment times for a wholesaler. The figures represent the days to payment.

The first very notable feature is the clear cyclic pattern that is apparent on the X section of the chart. This is a direct reflection of the monthly payment system. Napp Laboratories require payment by the end of the month following the receipt of the invoice. The pattern on the chart reflects the time during the month when the invoice was received. It suggests that there are really two groups of readings, differing, on average, by about three weeks.

Whilst there are no points outside the control limits, there are two low points corresponding to payments of 9 days and 10 days respectively.

These were special discount deals for stocking and selling new products.

17.5.5 Potential savings

With an overall debt from the supply base of £7.6M, a calculation showed that if the number of debtor days could be reduced by one day then this would realise annual savings of almost £17,000.

Changing the day of the invoice run for weekly sales could make further savings. Normally the payment run takes place on a Friday, but in some instances this could be to NLL's disadvantage.

For example, suppose we have a particular month when Friday is the first day of the month. In this case the supplier has a month's leeway before payment is required. By changing the invoice run to a Thursday, then payment is required four weeks earlier. With sales of approximately £1,000,000, a saving of over £8,000 is possible for each month when the Thursday corresponds to the last day of the month.

17.5.6 Further action

As a result of the information provided by this approach, a review of the end of month invoicing took place and recommendations were implemented.

Further actions were set in place as follows: -

1. Terms and conditions were to be reviewed
2. Meetings were arranged with major customers.
3. Targets for debtor days were set and performance against these would be monitored, increasingly by the use of control charts.
4. Procedures prior to specifying a new computer system would be reviewed and finalised to see to what extent the system could automatically present data using control charts.
5. Potential cash savings were to be identified and quantified.

This case study provides an excellent example of recognising an unusual pattern, and then using this information as a basis for measuring the cost benefits that can accrue. As this example shows, the savings can be substantial.

Drifting patterns and cyclic patterns are not the only ones seen when producing control charts. Bunching is another feature that sometimes occurs.

17.6 Bunching

Bunching, sometimes known as grouping, or streaming, is seen on a control chart by the presence of groups of readings at the same level.

Fig 17.10 shows an (X, Moving R) chart where grouping was later found to be a factor.

The control chart is being used to assess the times taken to complete successive projects.

At first glance the process appears to be under control. Further analysis of the distribution of points, however, indicates that there are three groups of points, running at levels of about 3, 9 and 19. These levels tend to correspond to three distinct types of projects, each of a different level of complexity. The

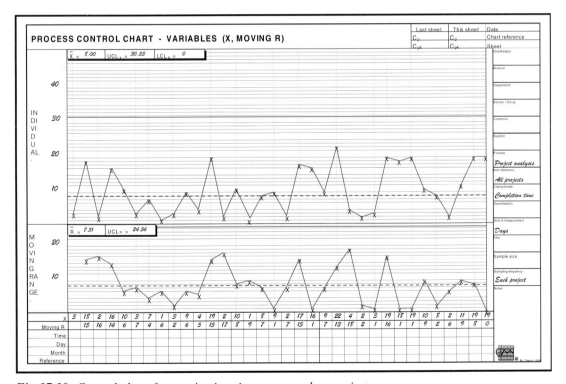

Fig 17.10 Control chart for monitoring times to complete projects.

next step was to segregate the readings corresponding to each project type, and then develop three separate control charts.

Be careful when looking for grouping because in some cases we may believe it is present when in fact it isn't. We could finish up treating groups of common causes as special causes, and in so doing dismantle the natural variation in the process.

Grouping seemed to be an issue in the next Case Study, but in fact there were other factors at work.

17.7 CASE STUDY 20 GEC-Marconi Avionics

ANALYSING GOODS RECEIVED NOTES

17.7.1 The company
Sionce this project was set up, GEC-Marconi Avionics Limited has become part of BAE SYSTEMS. The Customer Support Group comprises five businesses which together employ more than 15000 specialist support staff. The integration of expertise drawn from the various GEC-Marconi companies has created one of the largest dedicated support organisations in Europe.

Customer Support Group provides services ranging from Integrated Logistic support, through to customer training, technical representation, provision of support equipment including the design and manufacture of test and diagnostic systems, spares, provisioning, repairs, calibration, EMC testing and post design services, including product enhancement.

Customer Support Group is the industry leader in Contractor Logistic Support, through to customer training, technical representation, provision of support equipment including the design and manufacture of test and diagnostic systems, spares, provisioning, repairs, calibration, EMC testing and post design services, including product enhancement.

Customer Support group is the industry leader in Contractor Logistic Support, as exemplified by its Tornado GR4 Augmented Logistic Support contract with the Royal Air Force, which offers guaranteed availability of avionics at the aircraft's main operating bases.

17.7.2 Introduction
The area selected for this project was the Goods Inwards Department.

The department is responsible for all the material being received into Customer Support Group's Edinburgh site. This includes purchase order receipts that represent approximately 65% of all material received. On average, 770 Goods Received Notes (GRN'S) are raised each month. No accurate information on processing times for GRN's was known, but it was thought to be around one working day.

The supervisor responsible for Goods Inwards decided that monitoring GRN's would be a suitable project for SPC analysis. It would enable him to focus his attention on the working procedures and gain more accurate data on process times.

The characteristic to be measured was the time taken between packages delivered onto the loading bay and being made available to the factory.

17.7.3 The control chart
The ($\overline{X}$, R) chart seemed the obvious choice. The data was variable and available in blocks.

17.7.4 Data collection
Collection of the data was discussed with the Goods Inward clerk and a daily tally sheet was drawn up. When goods were delivered, the time received was recorded on the package. When the goods were

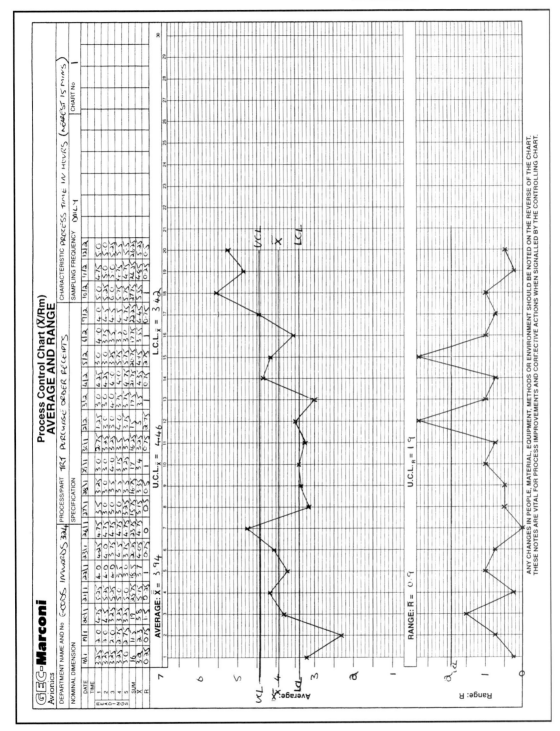

Fig 17.11 *Control chart for time, in hours between delivery and availability.*

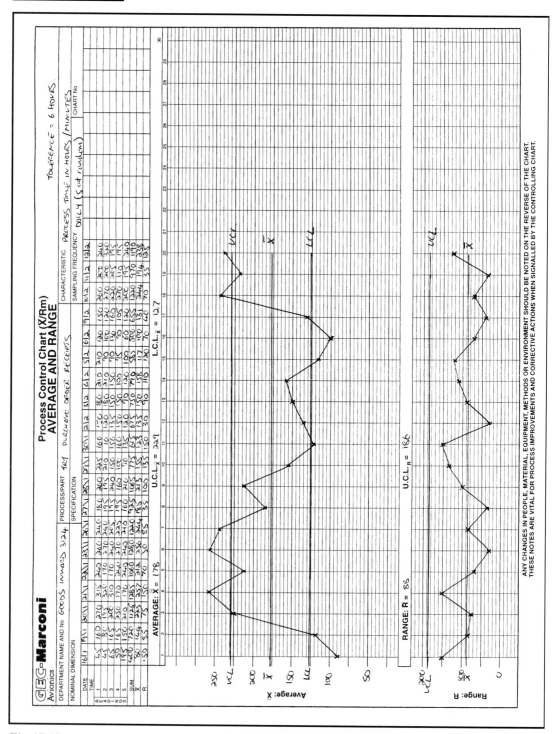

Fig 17.12 *Control chart for time, in minutes, between delivery and availability.*

later matched up with the GRN, the received time and the matched time were recorded on the tally sheet and the time difference recorded. The sheets were made available to the supervisor, who would then randomly select a block of five receipts each day and plot appropriate results on the chart.

Initially the data received, although accurate, was not representative of normal departmental through-put times. The readings were taken over the Christmas and New Year period when activity levels were unusually low. As process times of around 15 - 45 minutes were being recorded, it was decided not to use this data. In addition, some process times had been missed or not completed.

Data collection commenced again on Jan 16th 1998.

17.7.5 Chart results

The first twenty readings produced the control chart shown in *Fig 17.11*.

The process was clearly out of control, and further analysis was needed. It was found that although the process times varied considerably from day to day, they were all similar within each day. This, in turn, produced a low value for the mean range. As a result, there was a narrow control limit band for the $\overline{X}$ values.

The low range values were the result of batch working, and rounding up the process times to the nearest 15 minutes. Readings 18, 19, and 20 were influenced by the Goods Inward Clerk calling off suddenly on compassionate leave. Alternative labour was put in place at the expense of another process area.

17.7.6 Further analysis

It was recognised that rounding off the times to the nearest quarter of an hour could well distort the control chart.

As a result, a new control chart was set up using exact times in minutes. The control chart appears in *Fig 17.12*.

This chart seemed better, in that the control limits were wider apart. Even so, the process was out of control because there were still points outside the control limits.

Where next? Was the correct chart being used? Was the sampling procedure correct?

The process was clearly unstable.

In cases like this a short-term solution is to switch to an (X, Moving R) chart.

Fig 17.13 (overleaf) shows a control chart where the sample means have been considered as individual values to be used as X's in an (X, Moving R) chart.

The chart is now seen to be in control. However, that does not necessarily imply satisfaction with the results. An (X, Moving R) chart had been used in a short-term situation where the process was inherently unstable. If nothing else, the control chart shown in *Fig 17.12* enabled really wild values to be picked up.

A longer-term approach requires a more detailed study of the source figures.

The process shown in *Fig 17.12* was out of control, and the root cause for this needed to be determined.

Analysis of the control chart shown in *Fig 17.12* suggested that there was 'bunching' in the readings, indicating possibly that different process results are being combined to give an overall chart.

In fact, this was not an issue. Investigation showed that the results did not represent different types of GRN's. There was no indication that there were different processes operating. Some other factor was influencing the results.

It was very likely that the cause of the problem was the way in which the samples were being taken. If the samples of five, taken daily, are not taken in a random way that adequately represents the natural

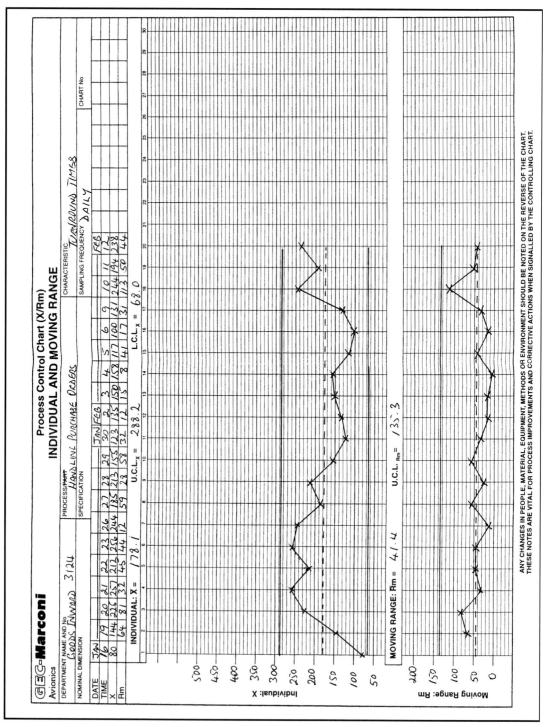

Fig 17.13 (X, Moving R) chart for time, in minutes, between delivery and availability.

variation, then any conclusions must be considered with some suspicion.

This factor directed the next stage of the analysis.

A new set of twenty samples was to be taken. Each sample of five was to make use of individual readings that would be a genuine representation of the process at the point of data gathering.

This Case Study has highlighted various problems associated with control charts.

Rounding off values can produce a control chart with control limits that are not a true indicator of the variation in the process.

Is the chart suggesting that 'bunching' is taking place?

Is the sample a genuine random sample?

All these issues were being taken on board in progressing the application of SPC in assessing turn-round times for GRN's.

In this recent Case Study, and throughout the book in general, problems to do with sampling have emerged.

It is a common issue, and so this next section could well be of interest.

17.8 Problems of sampling

One of the difficulties associated with tracking features such as document processing times has to do with sampling. Is the sample representative of the group? How do we actually take the sample?

The following Case Study brings out these learning points by narrating the experiences of a major organisation.

17.9 CASE STUDY 21 GEC-Marconi Avionics

TURNROUND TIMES FOR INTERNAL RELEASE NOTES

17.9.1 The company

Information on GEC Marconi, now part of BAE SYSTEMS, is the same as that detailed in Section 9.3

17.9.2 Introduction

Various metrics were available which could be used as a basis for applying SPC. After some discussion within the group responsible for initiating the SPC programme, it was decided to initially concentrate on turn-round times for Internal Release Notes (IRN's). A file of these covering the period 1st Jan 1997 to 30th Sept 1998 was obtained from the computer system.

A first attempt at statistical analysis made use of the histogram in representing the data. The histogram indicated very wide variability, and some initial concerns as to what the data was actually showing and how it could best be used.

In order to make the data more manageable, the project leader decided to make use of mean values, rather than the individuals. As a result, the mean of every ten readings, taken in sequence, was calculated, and these results then represented as a second histogram.

Having got this far, there was then some debate as to how to progress further. For example, there was concern that the data was not symmetrical, i.e. it could not be represented by a normal distribution, and therefore control charts for measured quantities could not be applied. It was understood later that this should not have been an issue.

IRN turn-round times, from initiation to despatch, involved a combination of several smaller times. Concentrating on just one element of the overall response time would mean that more useful progress could be made. Initially, therefore it was decided to concentrate on the time taken to progress IRN's through the despatch department.

17.9.3 First attempts

Appropriate data was extracted from the system and a control chart set up using the means and ranges of the first set of twenty sequential groups of ten readings.

The result is shown in *Fig 17.14*.

The chart represented a process that was clearly out of control. It raised a lot of questions. Was it the correct chart? Were samples being taken correctly? Was the correct parameter being used as the basis of the control chart? With limited practical experience of SPC available within the group at this stage, it was unclear as to how valid the chart was. Help was required in order to make sense of the chart.

17.9.4 Where next?

After further discussion, and reference to various texts, it was decided to switch to using an attribute chart. Any IRN that was in despatch for more than three days was to be defined as a defect. For the first attempt, a type of attribute chart known as an np chart was used. The approach led to a reasonable chart, i.e. one that in a general sense seemed to be the right one to use. Somewhat encouraged by this, the group decided to explore the use of attribute charts a bit further. This resulted in the use of the p chart. It was thought that the chart would be better, because it does not require a fixed sample size. This made sense to the group, because the number of IRNs going through despatch varies from day to day.

17.9 5 Training

There was no lack of enthusiasm for applying SPC, but there was limited SPC knowledge. This was becoming a particular issue because of the involvement of BAe (now BAE SYSTEMS) as a major

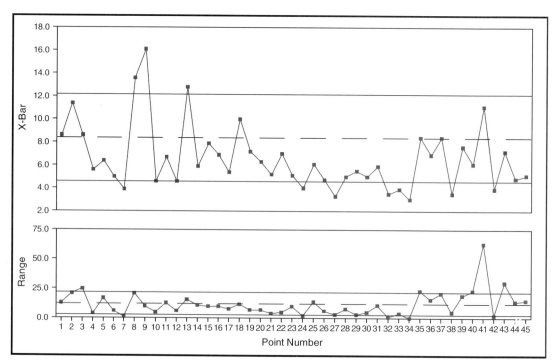

Fig 17.14 Control chart for time taken for IRN's to progress through the despatch department.

customer. BAe's programme of supplier development required that personnel are comfortable with SPC, can use it, and understand it. This could only be achieved by training, and consequently key staff were trained by attending a project-based SPC course.

17.9.6 Further developments

Following the training course, it was felt that whilst a p chart was providing some useful information, it was not giving data on a key characteristic. In other words, rather than plotting the proportion of IRN's that are beyond a certain cut-off value, more benefit would result from plotting the actual response times.

As a result, the project owner decided it was better to revert to using a variable chart. However, two changes would be made from the approach that resulted in *Fig 17.14.*

First, samples of five would be used, in line with the usual convention. There was no reason to use ten.

Secondly, these samples would be taken each day and in a way which represented all the IRN's which related to that day. For example, all the IRN's initiated on Jan 15th were listed, and a sample of five taken at random across the readings for that day. The same thing was done for the next day, and so on for twenty days.

Previously, the samples of ten had been taken in sequence, i.e. the first ten, then the second ten, and so on. This was in fact 100% sampling and was not the correct way to sample to bring out the variation over time. This was a major cause for the control limits shown in *Fig 17.12* being closer than they should be.

Results were plotted and a control chart drawn. Two points were found to be outside the control limit. These were associated with items that were for export and required more processing.

After discussion with the despatch supervisor, it was agreed that UK deliveries should be separated from export deliveries, and two charts kept in future.

17.9.7 Other issues

1. Taking the sample

The layout of the source data did not make it easy to take a random sample of 5.

Fig 17.15 (overleaf) shows a section from a page of the data.

With the response times ranked in order of magnitude for each day, it was not possible to choose a random sample because the randomness had been distorted by the ordering. In order to choose a worst case scenario, five readings in each sample were picked at equal intervals across the set, and which included the least and the greatest of the readings. For example, for the sample with a start date of 8th Jan 97, the five values chosen were 29, 7, 7, 4, 3.

The resulting control chart is shown in *Fig 17.16 (overleaf).*

The process is under control for the $\overline{X}$ section of the chart. For the R section, there is an out of control signal on Jan 8th, corresponding to an individual time of 29 days. Investigation indicated nothing unusual about this reading and so it was taken to be part of the system.

2. Effect of sample size

A considerable amount of data was available for analysis each day. Even so, there were occasions, such as on Jan 9th when less than five samples were available.

If these are rare events, as in this case study, then there is nothing lost by accepting there are fewer than five readings and working out the sample mean and range using the limited values which are available.

If the sample size is frequently less than five and varies a great deal, e.g. 3, 4, 2, 4, 3 etc, then it would be best to handle every reading and use an (X, Moving R) chart, rather than an ($\overline{X}$, R) chart.

The control limits are wider than they would be if the samples of five were taken at random, and the next step in this analysis was to arrange for the source data to be produced in a form which made it easier to take a representative sample.

3. The Question of Normality

The group initially thought that the ($\overline{X}$, R) chart was not suitable because the data was skewed.

The training course that the GEC Marconi Avionics staff had attended emphasised the Shewhart and Deming approach to control charts, i.e. that readings do not have to fit a normal distribution in order for a control chart to be applied. Average and range charts continued to be used on this topic, and, in addition, the use of the chart was extended to other applications.

This project raised several issues.

In the first place, people have difficulty in deciding what sample size to take. Having found out by trial and error that it is advisable to stick with five items, then taking those five requires the data to be available in its natural form.

Secondly, it is a common misconception that in order to apply SPC the process must provide results

REFERENCE DETAILS			STARTED	COMPLETED	TIME (DAYS)
36088	AN 188428	A103584	07-Jan-97	27-Jan-97	14
36095	AN 118401	A103581	07-Jan-97	27-Jan-97	14
36058	AN 118399	A103580	07-Jan-97	27-Jan-97	14
36096	AN 118408	A103580	07-Jan-97	27-Jan-97	14
36101	PXR0029405	LS4131	07-Jan-97	15-Jan-97	6
36098	29404	LS4131	07-Jan-97	15-Jan-97	6
36073	FG 25986	LS4109A	07-Jan-97	14-Jan-97	5
36074	FG 25887	TOR11A/3034	07-Jan-97	14-Jan-97	5
36045	FG25885	LS2897	07-Jan-97	13-Jan-97	4
36085	FG 25890	LS1306	07-Jan-97	13-Jan-97	4
36084	FG 25889	LS1306	07-Jan-97	13-Jan-97	4
36078	FG 25887	LS2611	07-Jan-97	13-Jan-97	4
36076	FG 25886	TOR11A/3034	07-Jan-97	13-Jan-97	4
36050	FG 25878	LS2611	07-Jan-97	13-Jan-97	4
36166	AN 119106	P28922/FC	08-Jan-97	18-Feb-97	29
36140	AN 118776	PO4193	08-Jan-97	08-Feb-97	23
36161	AN 118218	7490	08-Jan-97	17-Jan-97	7
36144	AN 118217	SO3746	08-Jan-97	17-Jan-97	7
36133	AN 118216	10512	08-Jan-97	17-Jan-97	7
36154	AN 118219	P73382J	08-Jan-97	17-Jan-97	7
36120	AN 118215	T14929	08-Jan-97	17-Jan-97	7
36112	FEI/006/97	TOR11A/3034	08-Jan-97	17-Jan-97	7
36119	FG 25881	LS2413	08-Jan-97	13-Jan-97	3
36128	FG 25880	LS2611	08-Jan-97	13-Jan-97	3
36212	FG 25933	TOR11A/3036	09-Jan-97	20-Jan-97	7
36221	FG 25910	LS3924H	09-Jan-97	15-Jan-97	4
36222	FG 25907	LS4190	09-Jan-97	15-Jan-97	4
36192	AN 118125	LS1964	09-Jan-97	14-Jan-97	3
36254	AN 118719	BEL 10518	10-Jan-97	07-Feb-97	20

Fig 17.15 Section from source material used to set up the control chart.

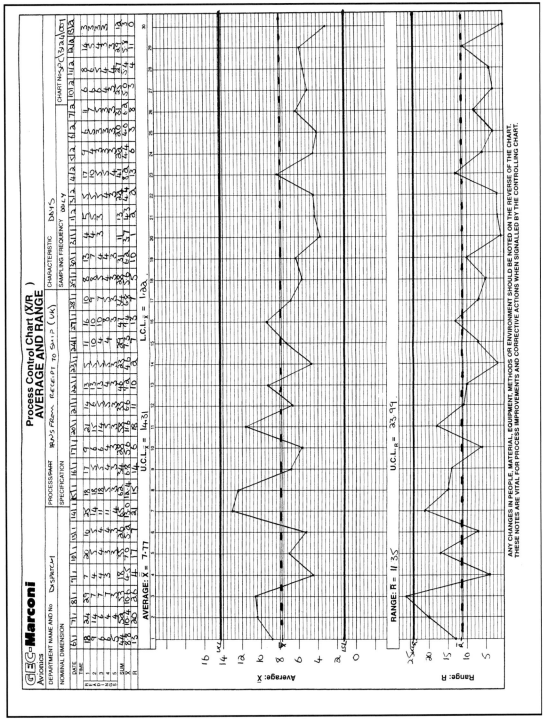

Fig 17.16 *Final control chart for processing times for IRN's which relate to UK deliveries.*

that are normally distributed. If we follow the Shewhart and Deming line, then this statement is not true. It has been said before but it is worth saying again. Education in classical statistics, rather than being a help, is more likely to be a hindrance in understanding some of the building blocks of SPC.

Thirdly, the discussion as to whether the item being analysed should be classified as a measure or an attribute. If the feature is naturally a measure, such as a document processing time, then use a variable chart. By converting to an attribute chart valuable information is being lost.

17.10 Recalculating control limits

If there is a genuine change in the process, then we start afresh after the change and use the first twenty readings under the new conditions to determine new control limits. This situation was shown in *Fig 1.9* in Chapter 1 where a process review had been carried out.

Problems arise when we do not use genuine signals from the control chart and recalculate control limits without the necessary control chart information in place to justify doing so. For example, Section 6.6.3 in Chapter 6 provided the example where, in some organisations, new control limits are worked out as each new blank sheet is introduced. In other instances, chart keepers recalculate the limits almost as the spirit takes them. In one organisation control charts were issued with control limits already printed on the blank sheets. Not much chance of applying never-ending improvement here.

We need strict rules, underpinned by a control chart pattern, in order to recalculate limits.

You may need reminding that we only recalculate on the basis of a signal that is associated with an improvement to the process. If the signal is indicating something associated with a process going out of control in a bad sense, then we do not recalculate to cater for a deteriorating situation.

We will look at three cases, corresponding to the three types of charts we have used.

17.10.1 Recalculating limits for an ($\overline{X}$, R) chart

You might wonder why we start with the ($\overline{X}$, R) chart rather than the (X, Moving R) chart. There is a reason, best explained as we go through the analysis.

We learned in Chapter 10 that the control limits for the $\overline{X}$ section of the ($\overline{X}$, R) chart are given by:

$$UCL_{\overline{x}} = \overline{\overline{X}} + A_2 \overline{R}$$
$$LCL_{\overline{x}} = \overline{\overline{X}} - A_2 \overline{R}$$

We suggested that, unless there was a specific reason otherwise, you keep the sample size fixed at 5 so that A_2 is always 0.577.

Whatever, the control limits are always placed a distance $A_2 \overline{R}$ outwards from the central line $\overline{\overline{X}}$.

If we are to improve the process, in the sense of reducing the variation in the process, then we need to reduce $\overline{R}$. If we can reduce $\overline{R}$, then we can pull in the control limits on the $\overline{X}$ chart.

Signals on the R chart will therefore be a cause for investigation. Is there something unusual, and beneficial happening? Hopefully, we can find the reason. We don't recalculate yet. We need to be certain that there is a factor operating. Seven points in succession is a good indicator. If we get eight, nine, ten points below $\overline{R}$, then we become more and more certain that a genuine change has taken place, and that we can find the reason for it and recalculate.

With a new value of $\overline{R}$, we can calculate new values for $UCL_{\overline{x}}$ and $LCL_{\overline{x}}$.

We then go through the same routine again. Seven points below the new value of $\overline{R}$ could mean a signal associated with further improvement. A further recalculation of $\overline{R}$ means drawing in the control limits for $UCL_{\overline{x}}$ and $LCL_{\overline{x}}$ yet again, and so on through the improvement cycle.

Fig 17.17 illustrates the stages we go through.

A second signal will be a value of R below LCL_R on the R section of the chart.

This is not an option with a sample size 5 because LCL_R is not present until n is seven or more.

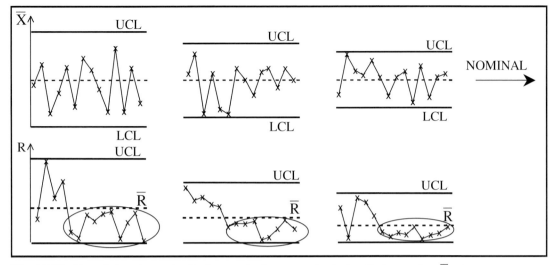

Fig 17.17 *Use of signals on the R chart to indicate recalculating limits on the* $\overline{X}$ *chart.*

If that is the case, then a value of R which fell below the LCR value is possibly an indication of improvement in that the mean on the R chart has reduced.

In this analysis we have assumed that the aim of the improvement programme is to always have the central line $\overline{\overline{X}}$ as close as possible to the nominal, and the nominal does not change over time. In administrative processes involving turn round times this will be unusual. It is much more likely that the nominal will reduce over time. Never ending improvement then requires two approaches.

We use the R chart to give us signals to reduce the variation to make the turn-round times more consistent. At the same time, we work on reducing the nominal. The control chart could help us here, but in a different way. For example, if we have a run of seven or more points below $\overline{\overline{X}}$, then this could indicate a special cause associated with a lower mean response time. Alternately we may need to be more proactive in reducing $\overline{\overline{X}}$ by using other techniques, such as a flowchart, for example.

17.10.2 Recalculating limits for an (X, Moving R) chart

In principle, the same analysis is followed as summarised in *Fig 17.17*. The $\overline{X}$ chart is replaced by the X chart and the R chart is replaced by the Moving R chart. We use the Moving R section of the chart to provide signals for improvement.

Unfortunately, these are not going to be so obvious because of the limitations of the Moving R chart, described in Section 8.15.2. A run of seven points below the mean on an R chart becomes a run of fourteen points below the mean on the Moving R chart. We can still use this amended rule, but it is not as helpful as before.

17.10.3 Recalculating limits on a multiple characteristics chart

The multiple characteristics chart is typically used to monitor attribute quantities, i.e. errors, complaints, faults etc.

Never ending improvement means reducing these to zero. Improvement is indicated on the control chart by a run of seven points below the mean. After confirmation that a special cause has been found that is associated with a reduction in the level of errors, complaints etc, then recalculation takes place and a further signal looked for.

The sequence for recalculation is identical to that shown on the lower part of *Fig 17.17,* except that attributes are now being plotted and not R values.

17.11 Other attribute charts

We have deliberately not gone into detail on specific types of attribute charts. We have avoided the issue by treating all attributes as single readings and using an (X, Moving R) chart.

However, we cannot just gloss over the fact that there are specific charts for dealing with attributes, and as a result four more formulae are available for working out control limits. It is good practice for some one in your organisation to be familiar with this, to provide a resource for moving from an (X, Moving R) chart to the correct attribute chart as and when it is felt appropriate. If you are interested, then '*SPC and Business Improvement*' will give you the detail you require.

17.12 Summary of symbols and formulae

np   Specific type of attribute chart
p   Specific type of attribute chart

17.13 Key points and summary

- Sales figures must increase over time for profitability.
- A stable predictable process isn't necessarily a satisfactory one.
- Cyclic patterns may require the data to be split into hourly, or daily groups and separate control charts plotted.
- Rounding off readings can produce misleading control charts.
- Use separate control charts for the groups of readings that show bunching in an overall chart.
- Make sure that the sample you take from a large number of documents is a random one.
- Always use a variable chart for measurable data. Converting the data to attribute format results in loss of information.
- A distribution does not have to be normal in order to make use of a control chart.
- Only recalculate limits when you have a statistical signal to guide you.
- Refer to other more detailed attribute charts at the appropriate time after you have some experience of charting.

This chapter completes the technical contents of the book. The following, final chapter deals with some of the more general practicalities of introducing SPC into an organisation, and offers some suggestions on how to commence the programme.

INTRODUCING SPC INTO AN ORGANISATION – PROBLEMS AND OPPORTUNITIES

18.1 Introduction

This last chapter provides a chance to comment on some non-technical issues not yet covered and also pulls together many of the ideas expressed earlier in the book.

The role of management is crucial to the use of control charts, and Section 18.2 deals specifically with that. Once a decision has been taken to introduce control charts, then you need some ideas on where to start the initiative. Section 18.3 may help you here. Section 18.4 reinforces the need to manage by fact, and includes a further flow chart combining two used earlier in the book. Management by fact implies better management reporting, and the Case Study in Section 18.5 shows how one organisation makes effective use of a control chart as part of a report. In the next section you have some pointers for success, followed in Section 18.7 by material on the training implications of SPC. After some brief comments on the alternatives of software or manual charting, Section 18.9 provides the last Case Study involving a relationship between training, software and management reporting. Section 18.10 provides examples on the wider opportunities for SPC. We reverse the usual sequence so that the Key Points and Summary follow next. This is because we finish with a page from the diary of an Operations Director, typical of a non-process orientated activity that will remain the norm if we don't opt for a change in the way we run our organisations.

18.2 SPC and management

Hopefully, you have read this book and you have become convinced of the benefits and potential of using SPC. And hopefully you're ready to put it into practice in your own organisation.

If so, and if you are the Chief Executive, you'll probably be successful. If you are not the CEO, it will be that bit harder. Certainly you will not realise the full potential of SPC without the genuine support and commitment of management. Of course, if a culture of continuous improvement is already in place, then SPC will help to make things even better, and its introduction should be relatively straightforward.

With fond memories of 'CJ' in "The Fall and Rise of Reginald Perrin", it's unfortunate that so many managers find themselves where they are today as a result of being reactive and directive. People who appear to get results by putting out fires, never mind that the fires should have been prevented! And, remembering the time gap between cause and effect, people who moved up the ladder before anyone understood what was really happening and the price being paid.

To paraphrase Rosabeth Moss Kanter, the former editor of Harvard Business Review, SPC isn't something the top tells the middle to do to the bottom. It's something that needs to be integrated into the whole operation. It can work at team level or in a department, in a function or a division, in a business unit or in a whole business. But it needs to be a natural part of 'the way things are done around here'.

Linked to continuous improvement and problem solving, SPC can be introduced top down and bottom up. But the top down factor is vital if we are to achieve the full potential. In theory it's all very simple. If you accept the principles of variation, then management behaviour must demonstrate that.

Management meetings and decisions should be supported by data that puts the voice of the process in the context of the voice of the various stakeholders. Managers should manage processes by working on the performance of the process using the knowledge and experience of the people who work in the process. And the results of the process should be viewed precisely as that – the results of the process.

If the results aren't good enough, then look at the process. But don't look at why this week's results are better or worse than last week's, or this week's last year. In other words, demonstrate an understanding of natural variation. If managers decide to ignore the principles of variation, then they will not realise the full potential of SPC. What's more, and mixing metaphors, any bottom up initiatives are likely to wither on the vine or be strangled at birth. It really is as simple, or complex, as that. Indeed, if SPC is introduced, but managers fail to change their behaviour, then, as far as the organisation is concerned, you might as well not have bothered.

18.3 Starting the programme

So, how, and where, do you start? Not surprisingly, there are a number of options – and you will need to decide what is best for you.

You could start with a pilot, perhaps in a function, division or business unit. This is a worthwhile approach if you are not sure of the support you are likely to get from higher management. Senior executives sometimes look for good initial applications, providing convincing examples of the potential for using SPC. "*Show us it works,*" they say, "*and we'll give you the backing.*"

There is an element of caution required here, however. It is likely that some of these senior executives are driven by cash implications, and are looking at measuring financial gains over a relatively short time span. If that is the objective, then the programme will almost certainly fail. Successful SPC programmes usually bring their financial rewards over a longer time span. It's worth remembering Deming's views on hidden costs and hidden benefits, benefits that an individual gains by learning about a control chart, improving decision making, enhancing teamwork. It may not be easy to provide financial data to measure these. On the other hand, it is possible to quantify financially the results of applying a control chart. For example, in analysing errors in documents it is possible to cost the time involved in rectifying errors of different types. For the larger organisation, when this time is multiplied by the number of staff involved, and the number of errors in total, this will mount up considerably over the year. A similar approach has been used in analysing the costs involved with handling accidents in an organisation as a result of first using a multiple characteristics chart.

You could start in the middle, providing a high level of awareness for the managers and equipping a selection of teams to try out SPC. This is a common approach, and is likely to prove the best bet. Without doubt if this is the strategy you adopt, then training for the senior staff will need to follow at some stage, preferably sooner than later.

You might be fortunate to work in an organisation with a really enlightened Chief Executive – one who has been exposed to SPC through training earlier in his or her career, understands all the system implications of the programme, and is now in a position to run an organisation using control charts backed up by a supportive approach along the Deming lines. These people are rare, but thankfully, there are some about. It takes a bold executive in a large organisation to initiate a programme that might only blossom after he or she has moved on to other responsibilities.

That is why starting in the middle is often the best option and for two reasons. First, staff trained at middle management level are the future chief executives. If they can be convinced of the power of SPC, then when they reach executive status they have the confidence, and the authority, to get the organisation to all operate along the same lines. Secondly, by training the middle, you provide a solid group who can begin to create influence. There is a momentum generated, and if it has being going long

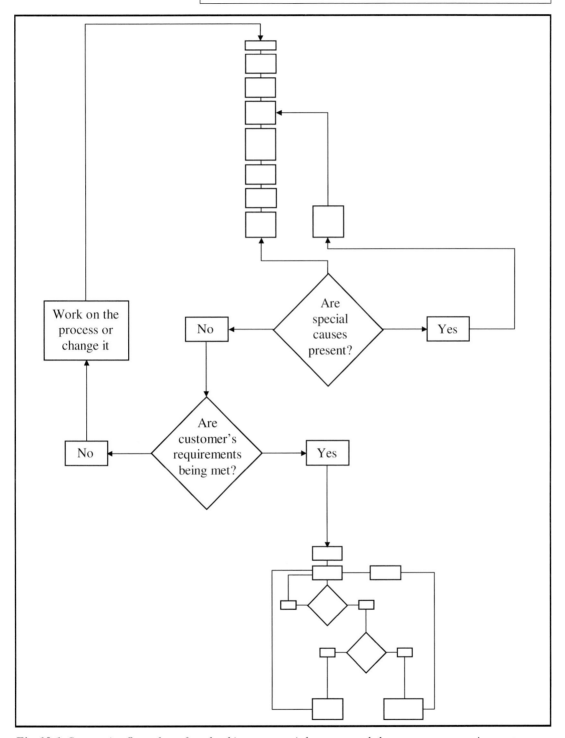

Fig 18.1 *Composite flow chart for checking on special causes and then customer requirements.*

enough, a new Chief Executive will find it difficult not to fall in line with the growing majority who are operating in a new, better way.

But why not start with an issue statement from an affinity diagram? This might be on the lines of *"What are the issues involved in successfully introducing SPC into our organisation?"* You will need to develop and agree your own. What falls out is the framework for your solution in your organisation, taking into account your culture and experience. You might find the material in *Fig 16.1* helpful here. It refers to typical problems likely to be encountered when introducing SPC.

18.4 Managing by fact

What you will be looking for is an evolutionary approach where continuous improvement thrives and where SPC enables you to manage by fact. Management information will be produced and presented as control charts, or at least as snap shots of control charts. It is worth noting that a couple of organisations have developed rather neat management reports which are miniature sections from the original more comprehensive range of control charts. Some reports are produced which integrate a control chart with other problem solving tools, as shown in the Case Studies in this chapter.

Management decisions will be made by getting processes under control and then checking that they satisfy customer requirements.

In line with the approach in earlier chapters, we can use a flow chart to indicate the choices.

Fig 18.1 shows a composite flow chart, making use of two flow charts shown previously. The miniature at the top of the diagram corresponds to the flow chart shown in *Fig 6.6* for setting up and interpreting a chart.

We now add a new section that provides the alternatives to follow if the process is under control. If the process is meeting the customer's requirements, then we can progress into the flow chart shown at the bottom of *Fig 18.1* which is a miniature version of *Fig 6.10* to use when handling special causes in an on-going sense. If it is not meeting the customer's requirements, you need to do something fundamental and then start again at the top of *Fig 18.1*.

Managers don't necessarily need to get into the nitty-gritty of the miniature flow charts in *Fig 18.1*, but they do need to concentrate on the two questions. Is the process under control? Is it satisfying the customer's requirements?

If they do that, then discussions won't be wasting time comparing data points that represent simple natural variation in a process. It's a very different meeting and a very different organisation.

In a climate of trust and openness, where fact replaces opinion, processes and data aren't distorted to meet arbitrary goals or to avoid a dressing down. The numbers are reported honestly, even if they do not always relay good news, and continuous improvement will be thriving from the office floor up. The people in the process really do know what's going on, and often will know what's needed to improve things. In this respect, the following extract from a quotation by Konosuke Matsushita says it all: -

"We are going to win, and the industrial west is going to lose. There is nothing you can do about it, because the reason for your failure is within yourselves."

With your bosses doing the thinking, while the workers wield the screwdrivers, you are convinced deep down that this is the right way to run a business. For you, the essence of management is getting the ideas out of the head of management and into the hands of labour.

For us, the core of management is the art of mobilising and putting together the intellectual resources of all the employees in the service of the firm.

"Only by drawing on the combined brainpower of its employees can a firm face up to the turbulence and constraints of today's environment."

We ought to take note of this and similar messages which have reached our Western ears over the last few decades. Sadly, we don't appear to have done so.

Management reports will be different. No longer should you be faced with making that tricky decision on how many pages your report should be. Too few and it won't be considered important enough. Too many and it's not likely to be read.

One particular organisation, in specific operations, has made use of an excellent SPC-based management report that forms the basis of the Case Study described in the following section.

18.5 CASE STUDY 22   ORGANISATION D

SPC AND MANAGEMENT REPORTING

18.5.1 Background to the company

The organisation concerned is involved with communications and has various offices across the world.

This case study shows how the technique has been used effectively in improving a service provision whilst at the same time prompting a more efficient layout for a management report.

18.5.2 The project

Abandoned telephone calls provide an ideal application for the use of SPC. An abandoned call is one where the caller has hung up for one reason or another.

At the start of 1996, some 28% of incoming telephone calls were abandoned. This was clearly an unacceptably high figure. A brainstorming session on the reasons for abandoned calls resulted in the development of a fishbone diagram, making use of the headings 'customer', 'focus', 'tools', and 'staff'.

Action was taken to work on the likely reasons for abandoned telephone calls. As a result, the level of these calls dropped to 18%. Further progress on driving down the response level resulted in a mean rate of 9%.

18.5.3 Management reporting

A summary sheet incorporating the control chart, fishbone diagram, a commentary and future action appears in *Fig 18.2 (overleaf)*.

The layout presents as neat a management report as you could wish to see. The control chart has prompted a series of actions which has directly resulted in an improvement in process performance. The interaction between the techniques is presented in a very effective way.

More than anything, the layout provides an excellent example of how a management report should appear. Bar charts and pages of descriptive material are replaced in a striking way by a one-page summary of how a process is behaving.

18.6 Some pointers to success

SPC works, but as you've probably already gathered, successfully introducing and integrating SPC into an organisation may not be so easy. The likelihood is there'll be resistance from people at different levels, so here are some tips to help ensure success: -

- Start by using Mr Kipling's exceedingly good questions as the framework for your briefing, so:
  - Ensure the managers and staff understand *what* is meant by SPC.
  - Explain *why* you are going to use it.
  - Explain *when* it will be introduced.

PERCENTAGE OF CALLS ABANDONED

Abandoned Calls

Commentary

Performance against this measure continues to follow the trend of the last 12 weeks, with all of the results, apart from 2, scoring below the $\overline{X}$ line or projected target line.

These two corresponded to particularly poor performance levels prior to the September shutdown with performance approaching the upper control limit which is set at 15%.

Call volumes for the weeks of September were 3849, 4102, 3932 and 3212

Actions

	By when	By whom
Help desk model R-2	15th Oct	T. Burridge
Revised Help Desk Model	31st Dec	T. Burridge

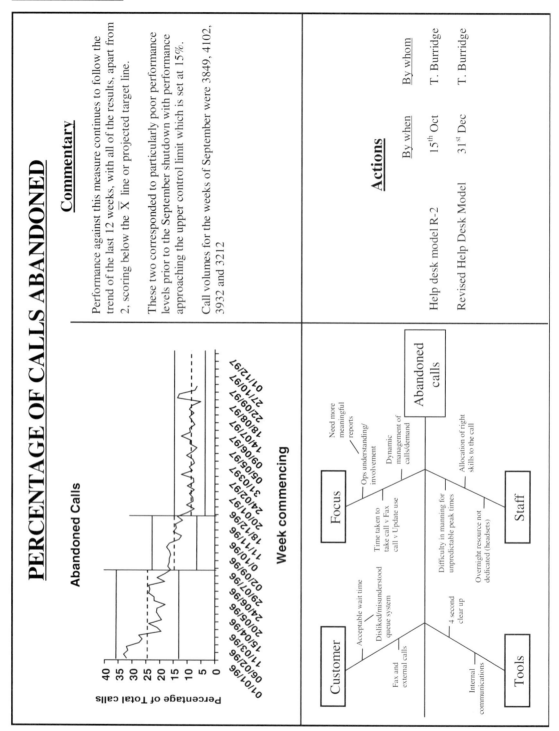

Fig 18.2 Management report incorporating a control chart and other techniques.

- Explain *how* it will be introduced and *how* it will be used.
- Explain *where* it will be used.
- And, of course, *who* will be trained, and *when*.
- Whatever you do, KISS (Keep It Simple Stupid)
- Make sure that SPC, and measurement generally, isn't seen as a hassle for people. Take an evolutionary approach and don't try to measure everything all at the same time.
- Make sure SPC comes to life: -
  - Display the charts for people to see.
  - Personalise the charts, in terms of labelling them for clear identification, and remember that you don't have to use a standard chart or a piece of graph paper. Why not let the chart keeper use their creative skills to have their own unique chart, so long as you don't finish up with a myriad of different varieties of a control chart used as part of the communication process? We could then find ourselves confused as a result of introducing unnecessary variation into the process.
  - Make sure the chart is being used! A clean chart is probably a signal that people are going through the motions, so write on it! The chart then becomes a living record of what's been happening in the process and the events that have been influencing results.
  - Charts on the wall are ideal, but computer produced charts also have their place, particularly in providing information and reports to management. Section 18.8 enlarges on this. The key, as with most things, is balance. If you use computer-produced reports, make sure they are not 'secret' and make sure they also have notes on them to make them a living record. Perhaps you will use both.
- Provide particular attention to management understanding and behaviour:
  - Managers must use the charts and manage by fact, ensuring that people recognise it's the process that is being measured, and not them.
  - Managers must be seen to use the charts, too, including physically going to view the charts on

PROFIT AND LOSS

REF. NO.	ITEM	PREVIOUS MONTH (June)		CURRENT MONTH (July)	
		FORECAST	ACTUAL	FORECAST	ACTUAL
001	Sales – Domestic	565	617	570	563
002	Sales – Export	125	103	130	129
003	Gross sales	690	720	700	692
004	Allowed discounts				
005	Net sales	690	720	700	692
006	Finished goods	270	280	270	265
007	Raw materials	35	34	35	35
008	Packaging	79	72	81	83
009	Wages and salaries	120	124	120	121

Fig 18.3 Section from a typical profit and loss statement.

display, using the opportunity to show their commitment to SPC and their support to the staff in achieving continuous improvement.

– Management information, weekly and monthly reports, for example, should encompass at least a snapshot of the control chart, so that the meeting is conducted using process data and in an environment free of blame.

It may be that you introduce a 'halfway house', particularly at senior executive level. In other words you devise a report that includes information as traditionally produced, i.e. a tabular row and column format, together with the same information presented as a control chart format.

For example, a section from a typical profit and loss statement appeared in *Fig 4.1* in Chapter 4, shown again for convenience in *Fig 18.3*. We take each item in turn and use earlier readings for the 'actual' figures to produce an appropriate (X, Moving R) chart. The June and July figures are then the last plotted points on the control chart.

Fig 18.4 shows a section from the final management report using the first four items on the profit and loss statement. The combination of the traditional approach and the newer one based on control charts provides an opportunity to understand some of the benefits of using a control chart. It goes without saying that far more information is available for decision-making using the charts than there was in the original format.

- If you haven't already done so, use the introduction of SPC as a catalyst to prompt the identification of your processes: -
- Make sure each process has a customer-focussed objective that takes account of the customer requirements.
- Develop the critical success factors and key performance indicators.
- Map the process and identify the requirement inputs, and in-process measures needed at the various interfaces.
- Make sure people are equipped and supported to take action on the prompts and information given by the charts. And remember they will need to feel able, as well as be able to take improvement action.
- Recognise their success in achieving improvements and communicate that success throughout the organisation. This will help to spread the word and to share lessons. It might also prompt ideas on what to measure in other parts of the organisation.

There is nothing particularly difficult about any of these tips is there?

18.7 Training

Our approach to training is to keep it simple and practical. Let's face it, many people are likely to be put off in the first place by the title. "*Statistical Process Control*" is very daunting. You can minimise this fear somewhat by some preparatory work, particularly when the training is for the operational staff. Appropriate pre-course reading is a help. An excellent article in this respect is the "*Germ theory of management*" by Myron Tribus – far and away the best article of its type. Free of statistical jargon, and carrying a really powerful message regarding management and its role in improving the system, it is a thought-provoking document that constantly receives complimentary comments from course attendees. It is also advisable to provide a covering letter, allaying some fears and trying to put people more at ease about attending what seems a very technical course.

Training is generally available in different forms – practitioner training, management overview, operational training, and so on. Senior executives typically feel that they cannot spare more than a half-day, or a day at the most, to attend an SPC course. It has to be said that more exposure would be better. Enlightened senior staff have no problems with attending a typical 2-day practitioner course, to

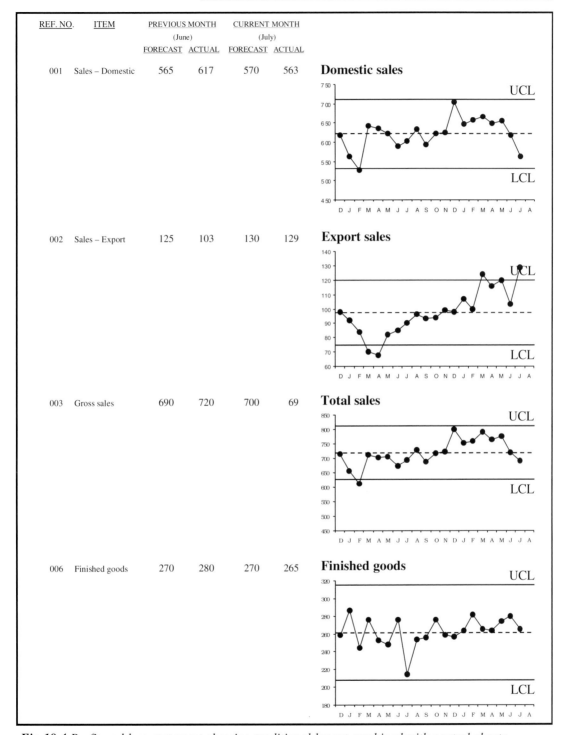

REF. NO.	ITEM	PREVIOUS MONTH (June)		CURRENT MONTH (July)	
		FORECAST	ACTUAL	FORECAST	ACTUAL
001	Sales – Domestic	565	617	570	563
002	Sales – Export	125	103	130	129
003	Gross sales	690	720	700	69
006	Finished goods	270	280	270	265

Fig 18.4 *Profit and loss statement showing traditional layout combined with control charts.*

271

be followed some six weeks later by a feedback day where the findings of pertinent SPC projects are presented. This 2 day + 1day format provides an environment in which attendees learn how to construct and interpret a control chart, learn a selection of problem solving tools and then do it, ideally using the 'Journey to Improvement' framework to ensure a systematic approach. Even more enlightened executives make a point of finding time to attend feedback days involving people who report to them. This is the support that others are looking for.

When senior executives and, more specifically at this stage, middle management feel very comfortable with control charts and all the management issues, then you can begin to think about training the operational staff. Yes, you can start pilot programmes before this stage, using clerical people to help in collecting the data, but in no way should SPC be introduced at the sharp end until the confidence and knowledge is present at middle management level. When you do train the operational people then it is vital that the training revolves around the exact data that staff use in their daily activities.

18.8 Software or manual charts?

Throughout this book there have been references made to the availability of software packages. Where and when do you use them? How good are they?

We have already commented that in our view people will only really understand the ins and outs of control charts if they actually work out the values of central lines and control limits, and record them manually on a chart. There might be a case for not getting them to spend time unnecessarily plotting points and joining up the crosses. On a two-day training course, for example, charts with the plotting already carried out are provided once the first chart has been developed from first principles. However we are convinced that a manual approach to control charts provides the best avenue to follow in developing understanding and confidence.

When this knowledge is there, then software can be utilised. In fact it is likely that in many cases software must be used if we are to be able to handle all the data that is available. However, there still remain many processes for which a single sequential result is required, and these single readings are easily obtained, for example the response time for a supplier, the weekly totals of errors in a document. Once the chart has been set up, it does not take much to keep it up to date. In addition, the display of a control chart on a wall carries a very powerful message, perhaps stronger than being displayed on a monitor.

When you do decide to acquire software then be careful. It is not our function to recommend one software package in preference to another, but one or two general points are worth heeding. Make sure that the package is user friendly, and not couched in statistical terminology. Some packages include more classical statistics than control charts, and provide values for complicated coefficients and indices that are very likely to put people off. Also, make sure that the packages use correct formulae, particularly when working out control limits. You really do need to check on this. An article by Don Wheeler entitled "*Charts done right*" is an excellent summary of the correct formulae to be used, and the dangers that lurk if you don't do so.

Training, combined with a very positive use of SPC software, provides the basis of the final Case Study.

18.9 CASE STUDY 23   AUCS

SPC TRAINING, SOFTWARE AND MANAGEMENT REPORTING

18.9.1 Background to the company

AUCS was until recently AT&T– Unisource Communications Services. It was formed in 1996 as a joint venture between AT&T of the USA, the world's network leader, and Unisource, the European partnership of KPN Telecom of the Netherlands, Swisscom and Telia of Sweden. AUCS provides pan-European communications services with global reach to corporate business users in Europe, mainly multinational and large international companies. Through its links with AT&T and WorldPartners in the USA, in Asia and elsewhere, AUCS is part of the world's largest and leading global communications alliance. Through this alliance the company can enable its European customers to reach over two hundred countries around the world.

AUCS offers a portfolio of voice and data products and services that can either stand-alone or be presented as an integrated offering, depending on the customer's requirements. For coverage outside Europe AUCS works with KDD of Japan and WorldPartners. AUCS is the exclusive provider of WorldSource services in Europe. The portfolio of WorldSource Services includes virtual network services for corporate voice services, highly reliable private line data services, and frame relay services for high-speed data transmission. WorldSource Services, introduced in 1993 and now being deployed in 32 countries, are seamless and global and provide customer support that includes a single point of contact for ordering, service provisioning and maintenance. WorldSource Services can be billed centrally or locally, as the customer requires. Each service is backed up by rigorous, consistent, world-wide standards for assured quality and superior performance. High reliability is achieved through a US 100 million dollar state-of-the-art networking platform for anytime, anywhere global network support, comprehensive customer network reports and three network management centres in Europe.

18.9.2 The training

From its inception in 1996, the company has introduced SPC to some of its processes with varying levels of success.

In 1998 a concerted drive was made to expand this knowledge base through the provision of three-day training courses. The first two days provided hands-on exposure to manual charting. Unlike other organisations, where the project feedback day followed some six weeks later, AUCS was keen to move straight from the training to applying the techniques in the various processes. With confidence in understanding control charts through developing charts manually, it was felt that process owners would be comfortable in making use of SPC software in handling their own data. They would need some exposure and training in the particular software package to be used, however. After considering various options, AUCS had decided on the SPC package that they would like to use. Subsequently, a presentation by the company representative was made during the first half of the morning of the third day.

Each delegate had come to the session armed with typical data relating to their business processes. After the presentation on how to operate the SPC package, there followed a period of some 2 - 3 hours during which each delegate got to know the system, either by importing their own data or by entering fresh data. A decision then had to be made on the correct chart to use, and the patterns resulting from the control chart(s) were then studied and interpreted.

Each delegate's control chart was downloaded onto a common disk. Then, in turn, each person made a presentation on his or her findings based on one or more type of control chart.

18.9.3 Applications

Various uses of the control chart were demonstrated during the feedback session. Following the day it was inevitable that some of the projects would fall by the wayside. Others were progressed. In addition, further applications of the use of SPC were introduced because AUCS had recognised that over time other newer measures would provide better information on how the company was progressing.

As a result of the training, management reports making use of SPC were increasingly being developed. A typical example is shown in *Fig 18.5 (overleaf).*

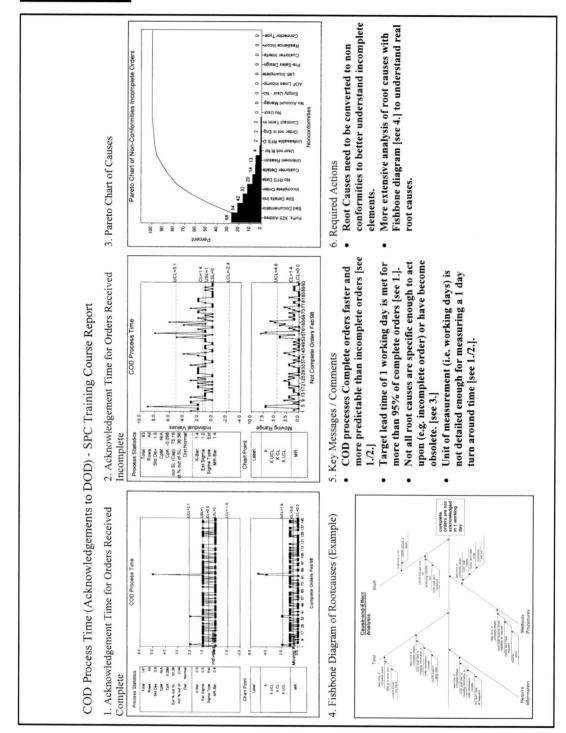

Fig 18.5 *Use of control charts as part of a management report.*

The control charts used in this report were used to monitor the time taken to process data orders arriving at the Central Order Desk (COD). Customer orders are created by Distributors and then sent to the COD using an Excel Workbook. Before orders are put into the order database, they are checked for completeness, using a checklist. Only complete orders are put in the database; incomplete orders are cleaned up first, after discussion with the Distributor.

The first control chart that was constructed was based on the process times of all orders. The process seemed to have a wide variation and appeared to be out of control. After combining the knowledge derived from the SPC chart with the experience of the people working in the COD, it was decided to monitor the two order flows separately (the orders defined complete upon arrival vs. the orders defined incomplete). This showed significant differences in cycle times between the two groups.

To improve the quality of incoming orders, a Pareto chart categorising the reasons for incompleteness was constructed. After that, the personnel of the COD carried out a Root Cause Analysis, facilitated by the Process and Quality team.

The project showed how a control chart was a catalyst in promoting: -
1. A different way of handling presentations on applying SPC following a training course
2. A better way of presenting a management report.

Certainly so far as the presentations were concerned, the Case Study has provided an example of an enlightened view of SPC training. It is rare for course attendees to move from a manual approach to using software for project presentations virtually overnight, and at the same time display confidence with both the technicalities of control charts and knowledge of the software product.

8.10 Wider opportunities

It is easy to develop a narrow stance about SPC and control charts. It is not helped by the traditional picture that SPC is a technique to be applied specifically in mass production processes.

Now that you have read this book, you should have a much wider view on what is meant by SPC, and where it can be applied in office areas. But don't stop there. There is almost no limit to where these techniques can be applied. Here are some thoughts as to where a control chart can be used.

Each week you walk through a shopping mall, where there is a florist with a central stall selling flowers. You make your purchase and the owner/assistant duly records a hand written entry in a book, identifying the sale and the amount involved. What an opportunity for a control chart.

You visit your favourite local restaurant. The owner needs to keep a record of meals served, and more importantly, the income and expenditure each night. He/she may also have customer complaints. Do you know of any restaurant that makes use of a control chart to monitor these and other figures?

You need to do some decorating, or repairs to your home. You visit a major DIY outlet near to you. What a source of data for using a control chart. You look in vain for charts on display indicating response times for orders, or nature of customer enquiries. This might be asking too much. Sadly, it is highly unlikely that charts are being used internally to monitor progress of the company.

You visit your doctor's surgery. At least they have a computer system that records patient needs in terms of prescriptions, and some other details. But is it enough? *"This computer system is so old-fashioned"*, says the nurse who is recording your details. And where are the control charts on patient numbers, call out requests, nature of request, you think to yourself? Not there. It would be a minor miracle if they were.

You travel by bus to town. Does the bus company use control charts which monitor the number of passengers carried, travel times, non-availability and reasons for it? Likely not.

You turn up at the appointed time at the outpatient's department of your local hospital. Your mind wanders as you count the number of people in front of you, and how long each will take to be seen. Patient waiting times – what good material for an (X, Moving R) chart. Perhaps the Patient's Charter might be helpful in this respect. Wrong again. The Patient's Charter, and similar charters, seem to be concerned only with the need to satisfy some arbitrary target. Issues relating to the relevant processes are lamentably missing.

You attend a parent's evening at your local school. A manager at a local company who happens to be a parent governor bombards parents with facts and figures which are isolated one-offs and presented in a way which few can understand. You know about SPC and how powerful it can be. You squirm at the presentation, recognising that most of the audience doesn't understand the situation. Is this familiar? Parents probably don't understand SPC either, but its odds on that the presentation could be much more interesting, and with a fair chance that, properly presented, the majority of the audience could have a feel for what was happening. People are not as daft as we sometimes suppose. Remember what Matsushita said as recorded in Section 4.

Your annual tax return is due, and you have the usual forms to fill in and send to the Inland Revenue? Again your mind wanders. Are they using SPC, you say to yourself? Are they using control charts on the no. of outstanding payments, no. of reminder letters sent out, no. of errors in forms and payments made, the nature of these errors? Probably wishful thinking, or is it?

You attend a local auction, a football match involving your favourite team. You walk across the Bristol Suspension Bridge, visit London Zoo, book a holiday at your local travel agent, and so it goes on. Data is all around us, yet few in a position to use it have the remotest idea of how to interpret it properly.

Wherever you go there are opportunities for using control charts, but they have not really been picked up. Are you prepared to join a growing number of people who wish to spread the message that this technique can be used almost anywhere? Without seeming overconfident, the authors of this book, and others beside, are now hard pressed to think of anywhere where control charts could not be used. That does not mean that we advocate using a control chart on anything, just for the sake of it. We need to be sensible. The main point is that any organisation, whatever its size and the nature of its operation, can ill afford to ignore the benefits that result from using a control chart.

It's not as if this is something new.

In 1950, C.A. Bicking wrote an article for the journal Industrial Quality Control. The article included a series of examples of SPC in the 'newer areas', some of which appear in *Fig 18.6*.

Where have we been?

Budgeting and cost accounting records	Personnel performance
Clerical work	Personnel placement
Cost analysis	Sales by area
Credit conditions	Sales by personnel
Customer sales	Sales by lines
Economic indices	Sales by totals
Error rates	Sickness rates
General business conditions	Traffic data
Inventory relationships and discrepancies	Training guide
Office and sales expenses	Wage structure

Fig 18.6 Examples of SPC in administrative areas quoted in a journal in 1950.

18.11 Are we ready for change?

So, is it business as usual, or shall we introduce SPC? If things stay as they are, there's every chance that the typical diary for the Operations Director will look a little like *Fig 18.7*.

It's your choice!

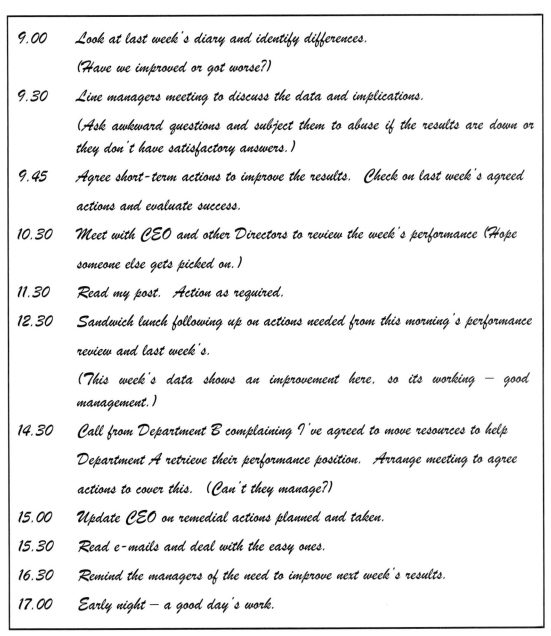

9.00   Look at last week's diary and identify differences.

        (Have we improved or got worse?)

9.30   Line managers meeting to discuss the data and implications.

        (Ask awkward questions and subject them to abuse if the results are down or they don't have satisfactory answers.)

9.45   Agree short-term actions to improve the results. Check on last week's agreed actions and evaluate success.

10.30   Meet with CEO and other Directors to review the week's performance (Hope someone else gets picked on.)

11.30   Read my post. Action as required.

12.30   Sandwich lunch following up on actions needed from this morning's performance review and last week's.

        (This week's data shows an improvement here, so its working — good management.)

14.30   Call from Department B complaining I've agreed to move resources to help Department A retrieve their performance position. Arrange meeting to agree actions to cover this. (Can't they manage?)

15.00   Update CEO on remedial actions planned and taken.

15.30   Read e-mails and deal with the easy ones.

16.30   Remind the managers of the need to improve next week's results.

17.00   Early night — a good day's work.

Fig 18.7 *Page from a diary of a typical Operations Director.*

18.12 Key points and summary

- SPC can work anywhere, given certain conditions.
- Senior management support is ultimately vital, but don't let that put you off starting to use a chart on your own process.
- Do stop making single figure judgements.
- Choose carefully how you start the programme.
- In many ways, starting in the middle is the best option.
- Make a control chart a necessary part of any management report, providing that there is a common level of understanding.
- Make use of the 'pointers for success'.
- Introduce the necessary training in a structured way.
- Don't jump into buying SPC software.
- Look around for all sorts of areas where SPC could be applied.
- Examples of SPC in office areas were referred to 50 years ago.
- Are you ready for change?

APPENDIX 1

DEMING'S 14 POINTS

1. Create and publish to all employees a statement of the aims and purposes of the company. The management must demonstrate constantly their commitment to this statement.
2. Learn the new philosophy, management and everybody.
3. Understand the purpose of inspection, improvement of processes and reduction of cost.
4. End the practice of awarding business on the basis of price tag alone.
5. Improve constantly and for ever the system of production and service.
6. Institute training.
7. Teach and institute leadership.
8. Drive out fear. Create trust. Create a climate for innovation.
9. Optimise towards the aims and purposes of the company the efforts of teams, groups, staff areas.
10. Eliminate exhortations for the workforce.
11a. Eliminate numerical quotas for the production. Instead, learn and institute methods for improvement.
11b. Eliminate management by objective. Instead, learn the capabilities of processes, and how to improve them.
12. Remove barriers that rob people of pride of workmanship.
13. Encourage education and self-improvement for all.
14. Take action to accomplish the transformation.

APPENDIX 2

TABLES OF CONSTANTS AND FORMULAE

The tables of constraints and formulae opposite is reprinted with permission from ASTM publications STP-15D, **Manual on the presentation of Data and Control Chart Analysis**, 1976, pp 134-136. Copyright ASTM, 1916, Race Street, Philadelphia, PA 19103

	$\overline{X}$ and R charts				$\overline{X}$ and s charts			
	Chart for Means ($\overline{X}$)		Chart for Ranges (R)		Chart for Means ($\overline{X}$)			Chart for Standard Deviations (s)
Sample Size	Factors for Control Limits	Divisors for Estimate of Standard Deviation	Factors for Control Limits		Factors for Control Limits	Divisors for Estimate of Standard Deviation	Factors for Control Limits	
n	A_2	d_2	D_3	D_4	A_3	c_4	B_3	B_4
2	1.88	1.128	-	3.267	2.659	0.7979	-	3.267
3	1.023	1.693	-	2.574	1.954	0.8862	-	2.568
4	0.729	2.059	-	2.282	1.628	0.9213	-	2.266
5	0.577	2.326	-	2.114	1.427	0.94	-	2.089
6	0.483	2.534	-	2.004	1.287	0.9515	0.03	1.97
7	0.419	2.704	0.076	1.924	1.182	0.9594	0.118	1.882
8	0.373	2.847	0.136	1.864	1.099	0.965	0.185	1.815
9	0.337	2.97	0.184	1.816	1.032	0.9693	0.239	1.761
10	0.308	3.078	0.223	1.777	0.975	0.9727	0.284	1.716
11	0.285	3.173	0.256	1.744	0.927	0.9754	0.321	1.679
12	0.266	3.258	0.283	1.717	0.886	0.9776	0.354	1.646
13	0.249	3.336	0.307	1.693	0.85	0.9794	0.382	1.618
14	0.235	3.407	0.328	1.672	0.817	0.981	0.406	1.594
15	0.223	3.472	0.347	1.653	0.789	0.9823	0.428	1.572
16	0.212	3.532	0.363	1.637	0.763	0.9835	0.448	1.552
17	0.203	3.588	0.378	1.622	0.739	0.9845	0.466	1.534
18	0.194	3.64	0.391	1.608	0.718	0.9854	0.482	1.518
19	0.187	3.689	0.403	1.597	0.698	0.9862	0.497	1.503
20	0.18	3.735	0.415	1.585	0.68	0.9869	0.51	1.49
21	0.173	3.778	0.425	1.575	0.663	0.9876	0.523	1.477
22	0.167	3.819	0.434	1.566	0.647	0.9882	0.534	1.466
23	0.162	3.858	0.443	1.557	0.633	0.9887	0.545	1.455
24	0.157	3.895	0.451	1.548	0.619	0.9892	0.555	1.445
25	0.153	3.931	0.459	1.541	0.606	0.9896	0.565	1.435

$$\text{UCL}_{\overline{X}} = \overline{\overline{X}} + A_2 \overline{R}$$
$$\text{LCL}_{\overline{X}} = \overline{\overline{X}} - A_2 \overline{R}$$
$$\text{UCL}_R = D_4 \overline{R}$$
$$\text{LCL}_R = D_3 \overline{R}$$
$$\hat{\sigma} = \frac{\overline{R}}{d_2}$$

$$\text{UCL}_{\overline{X}} = \overline{\overline{X}} + A_3 \overline{s}$$
$$\text{LCL}_{\overline{X}} = \overline{\overline{X}} - A_3 \overline{s}$$
$$\text{UCL}_S = B_4 \overline{s}$$
$$\text{LCL}_S = B_3 \overline{s}$$
$$\hat{\sigma} = \frac{\overline{s}}{c_4}$$

APPENDIX 3

LIST OF REFERENCE BOOKS

Amsden, R.T., Butler, H.E. and Amsden, D.M., SPC Simplified for Services: Practical Tools for Continuous Quality Improvement. Chapman & Hall, 1991.

Bissell, Derek, Statistical Methods for SPC and TQM. Chapman and Hall, 1994.

Burr, A., and Owen, M.H., Statistical Methods for Software Quality. International Thompson Computer Press, 1996.

Dale, B.G. and Plunkett, J.J., Quality Costing. Chapman & Hall, 1991.

Deming, W.E., Out of the Crisis. MITT Press, Cambridge, MA, USA, 1986.

Gitlow, H. And Gitlow, S., The Deming Guide to Quality and Competitive Position. Prentice-Hall, Englewood Cliffs, NJ, USA, 1987.

Hutchins, D., Just in Time. Gower

Ishikawa, Kaoru, Guide to Quality Control. Asian Productivity Association, Tokyo, 1976.

Joiner, B.L., The Team Handbook. Joiner Associates, Madison, WI, USA.

Kilian, Cecilia S., The World of W. Edwards Deming. Cee Press Books, Washington, DC, USA, 1988.

Kohn, Alfie, No Contest, The Case Against Competition. Houghton Mifflin, 1992.

Kohn, Alfie, Punished by Rewards. Houghton Mifflin, 1993.

Mann, Nancy R., The Keys to Excellence. Prestwick Books, Los Angeles, CA, USA, 1985.

Neave, H., The Deming Dimension. SPC Press, Knoxville, TN, USA, 1990.

Ott, E.R., Process Quality Control: Troubleshooting and Interpretation of Data. Mc-Graw Hill, 1975.

Owen, M.H., SPC and Business Improvement. IFS, Bedford, UK, 1993. Being reprinted. Contact the author.

Price, F., Right Every Time: Using the Deming Approach. Gower Press, 1990.

Rosander, A.C., Applications of Quality Control in the Service Industries. Marcel Dekker, New York, 1985.

Scherkenbach, W.W., Deming's Road to Continual Improvement. SPC Press, Knoxville, TN, USA, 1991.

Scherkenbach, W.W., The Deming Route to Quality and Productivity: Roadmaps and Roadblocks. Cee Press Books, Washington, DC, 1986.

Shewhart, W.A., Economic Control of Quality of Manufactured Product. Van Nostrand, New York, 1931.

Walton, Mary, The Deming Management Method. Mercury Business Books, 1989.

Wheeler, D.J. and Chambers, D.S., Understanding Statistical Process Control. Addison-Wesley, New York, 1990.

Wheeler, D.J., Understanding Variation - The Key to Managing Chaos. SPC Press, Knoxville, TN, USA, 1993 .

APPENDIX 4

LIST OF ARTICLES

Bicking, C.A., "The Application of Quality Control to Administrative Problems". Industrial Quality Control, 1950.

Nolan, T.W. and Provost, L.P., "Understanding Variation". Quality Progress, May, 1990.

Starkey, M.W., "Measurement with Meaning: Using Statistical Process Control to Improve Marketing Performance." Journal of Targeting, Measurement and Analysis for Marketing, June 1995.

Tribus, Myron, "The Germ Theory of Management". Paper presented at the British Deming Association National Forum, 1989.

Wheeler, D.J., "Shewhart's Charts: Myths, Facts and Competitors. ASQC Annual Congress, 1991.

Wheeler, D.J., "Charts done right". Don Wheeler, Knoxville, TN, USA.

APPENDIX 5

OTHER REFERENCES

AMERICAN SOCIETY FOR QUALITY

Quality Progress
Transactions of Annual Conferences
Details from:
    ASQC,
    611 E. Wisconsin Avenue,
    Milwaukee,
    WI 53202
    U.S.A.

    Tel: (414) 272-8575
    Email: @asq.org
    Website: www.asq.org

3M Healthcare   244

A

Absenteeism   117
Adding value   17
Aerospace Composite Technologies   182
Affinity diagram   230
An introduction to processes   11
Analysing Goods Received Notes   250
Analysis of downtime at an ATM   185
Analysis of weekly recorded shortages   182
Are we ready for change?   277
Asking questions   17
Asking the right questions   26
Assess achievements and lessons   224

B

Balanced Business Scorecard   27
Bar charts   35
Brainstorming   227
Bromley Council   189
Building the picture   46
Bunching   249

C

Calculating and recording the C_p index   200
Calculating and recording the C_{pk} index   204
Calculating results   66
Calculation of central lines   67, 93, 135, 167
Calculation of control limits   67, 93, 135, 167
Capability – can the process deliver?   196
Capability for attributes   208
Capturing ideas   227
Carrying out the required calculations   92, 134, 141, 166
Cases where there is a natural upper or lower barrier   207
Chart based on individual readings   75

Chart based on samples	80
Check sheet	23
Choice of correct formula for evaluating the standard deviation	100
Choice of sample size	143
Choice of SLA and target	29
Choosing a scale for the chart	168
Choosing scales for the charts	95, 137
Classifying the data	176
Collecting the data	65, 89, 131, 163
Commercial vehicle maintenance costs	114
Company cars	158
Company-wide processes	13
Comparison with reality	30
Complaints analysis	189
Computer-based records	34
Continue monitoring the process	100, 142, 171
Control chart format to be used	90, 132, 163
Control, capability and improvement	211
C_p index	198
C_{pk} calculations based on an ($\overline{X}$, R) chart.	208
C_{pk} index	201
Critical Success Factors	27
Customer requirements	12, 28
Cyclic processes	246

D

Daily call rates for sales personnel	111
Data available	76, 82, 84
Data not currently available and has to be collected	78, 82, 84
Data which is classified into different categories	82
Defects per hundred units (DHU)	209
Defining and interpreting the C_p index	198
Defining the process	64, 89, 131, 161
Deming's 14 points	182, 279
Deployment flowchart	22
Detecting unusual features	8
Developments in Japan	5
Developments in the US	4
Do we pay our suppliers too early?	151
Draw the central line and control limits	96, 138, 169
Draw the new central lines and control limits	142
Drifting processes	239

E

Equipment and facilities	13
Errors in letter writing	178

F

Final review	224
First Run Capability (FRC)	209
Fishbone diagram	228
Flowcharts	15
Force Field Analysis	232
From run chart to control chart	58
Further analysis	172

G

GEC- Marconi Avionics	106, 186, 250
Generate possible solutions – Step 4	220
Generating ideas	227
Getting the measure of processes	33
Giving up smoking	127
Glyph charts	39

H

Highlighting the major problem	172
Historical information	4
How are the processes doing?	197
How to measure. – the control chart - a step by step guide	64

I

Identify and check the possible causes	219
Implement and standardise the solution	222
Improvement Journal	225
Improving the process	144
Inclined lines for ($\overline{X}$, R) chart	243
Internal customer/supplier chain	11
Interpretation based on setting up the chart	68
Interpretation when using the chart in an ongoing situation	71
Interpret the chart	68, 99, 139, 142, 169, 185
Interpreting the standard deviation	56
Interrelationship diagram	231
Introducing SPC into an organisation – problems and opportunities	263
Invoice runs	247

J

Journey to improvement – a framework for progress	214
Journey to improvement – Some other tools	226
Journey to Improvement	214

K

Kerry Milling	104
Key Performance Indicators	27

L

Limitation of the Moving R section of the chart	101
Limitations of existing methods	42
Limitations of the C_p index	200
Line graphs or run charts	38
List of articles	283
List of reference books	282
Listening to voices	1
Looking at data in a different way	7

M

Making the choice	209
Making the right choice	86
Managing the fact	266
Manual records	33
Mapping and measuring the process	15
Mean	52
Measurement	33
Measures of the position of a process	52
Measures of variation	55
Measuring or counting?	44
Measuring the detail	24
Misuse of capability indices	212
Mode	52
Moving from sheet to sheet	73
Multiple Characteristics control chart – case studies	178
Multiple Characteristics control chart	161

N

Napp Laboratories Ltd	247
National Provident Institution	178
NatWest – UK Retail Banking Services	155, 185
Nominal is critical	201
Number or value?	176

O

Organisation A	117
Organisation B	127
Organisation C	147
Organisation D	267
Other attribute charts	262
Other charts	40
Other issues relating to the ($\overline{X}$, R) chart	143
Other issues relating to the (X, Moving R) chart	100
Other issues relating to the Multiple Characteristics chart	174
Other problem-solving techniques	226

P

Paired comparisons and N/3	234
People, skills and knowledge	13
Pie charts	38
Pointers to success	267
Plan and test the solution	221
Plotting and recording	67
Plotting sample results	96, 138, 168
Problems of sampling	255
Procedures	13
Process and the customer	22
Process control measurement within the sales environment	244
Process stapling	16
Processes and Business Excellence	18
Projecting lines ahead	99, 142, 171
Putting it together	236

R

R chart	144
Rainbow charts	38
Range	55
Recalculating control limits	260
Recalculating limits for a multiple characteristics chart	261
Recalculating limits for an ($\overline{X}$, R) chart	260
Recalculating limits for an (X, Moving R) chart	261
Recent developments	5
Record data on chart	91, 133, 163
Recording numerical values on chart	95, 137, 167
Recruitment selection tools	108
Removing values resulting in special causes	141
Repeating the procedure	174
Representing the data	46
Response times to customer transactions at the counter	155
Response times to task authorisation	106
Review progress	220, 222
Ronaldsway Aircraft Company	108
Rover Finance	151
Rule 1. Point outside the control limit	58
Rule 2. Run of seven	59
Rule 3. Unusual pattern	60
Rule 4. Middle third rule	61
Rules for special causes	58

S

Sample calculations	67, 92, 134, 166
Scatter diagram	235

Scores for training courses	119
Select the problem	216
Select the solution	221
Sensible ground rules	227
Service Level Agreements	28
Service Order Invoice errors	187
Setting up a new control chart	173
So what is a process?	11
Software or manual charts	272
SPC and management	263
SPC and managing reporting	267
SPC training software and management reporting	272
Spillers Milling	111, 114, 158
Standard deviation	56
Standard order processing times	147
Standards	13
Starting the programme	264
Statistical Process Control	3
Step 1 Record the readings	239
Step 2 Choose the scale	239
Step 3 Plot the results	239
Step 4 Calculate the 'Line of best fit'	240
Step 5 Calculate moving ranges	241
Step 6 Calculate mean values	241
Step 7 Determine control limits	242
Step 8 Interpret for process control	242
Supplier requirements	13

T

Tables of constants and formulae	280
Targets	28
Traditional methods of representation	34
Traditional sources of information	33
Training for Excellence	119
Training	270
Turnround times for Internal Release Notes	255
Two voices	197
Typical figures to work on	88, 130, 161

U

Understand the current situation – Step 2	218
Understanding the process	2, 12
Understanding the voice of the process	44
Unisource	272
Use of (X, Moving R) chart	174
Use of software packages	243

USL or LSL is critical   205

V

Variation   6
Variations in patterns   50
View of the customer   1

W

Water consumption   104
What does the histogram tell us?   49
What doesn't the histogram tell us?   50
Which chart to use?   75
Wider opportunities   275

X

(X, Moving R) chart – CASE STUDIES   104
(X, Moving R) chart   88
($\overline{X}$, R) chart – CASE STUDIES   147
($\overline{X}$, R) chart   130
XY Grid   233

BUSINESS BOOKS FROM GREENFIELD PUBLISHING

Winning Major Business – Marketing and selling projects, programmes and major products worldwide

by Alex Weiss and Stephen Willson
with cartoons by Matt Pearce.

ISBN   0-9523328-0-9

298 pages

£35.00 each including postage and packing. Quantities of five or more @ £30.00 each.

Winning Major Business is a ground-breaking book. It provides new ideas and practical approaches on marketing and selling to governments and other institutional purchasers. At last, a major text is available which deals with the specialised field of winning large contracts.

For the newcomer to the subject, and those facing the challenges of a recent promotion, it will provide a ready reference and accelerate their progress in this complex area. The experienced will be able to refresh their knowledge and review recent developments. For those in management, it should stimulate discussion on strategic issues and increase their contribution to the marketing and selling effectiveness of the organisation.

The book will be of particular interest to those supplying the aerospace, construction, defence, electrical and electronics, instrumentation, information technology, machinery, process control, public utilities, telecommunications and transport markets.

Alex Weiss has spent thirty years in a variety of sales and marketing roles in the UK electronics industry. Stephen Willson combines eleven years of marketing in North America with wide experience of industrial training. He is the principal of Marketing & Commercial Development, providing custom-designed training in industrial marketing.

ORDER FORM

ORDER FORM

To: Greenfield Publishing
P. O. Box 12, Kenilworth
Warwickshire, CV8 1ZS
UK

To obtain copies of this book, complete and return this page (or a photocopy), together with a cheque made out to Greenfield Publishing.

Please tick box if a receipt is needed ☐

Please mail me one copy of *Winning Major Business* @ £35.00 including p&p **OR**
Please mail me .....copies of *Winning Major Business* @ £35.00 including p&p (£30.00 if 5 copies or more)

I enclose a cheque for £.........

Name: ....
Job Title: ....
Company: ....
Address: ....
....
....
....
Postcode: ....

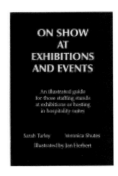

On Show at Exhibitions and Events – An illustrated guide for those staffing stands at exhibitions or hosting in hospitality suites

by Sarah Turley and Veronica Shutes with cartoons by Jan Herbert

ISBN 0-9523328-1-7   48 pages – 40 cartoons

£15.00 per pack of 5 copies including postage and packing.

On Show at Exhibitions and Events provides essential information, in a light hearted and amusing manner. Copiously illustrated with cartoons, the book deals with important issues and provides useful lessons and key reminders.It is essential reading for stand staff at exhibitions and those hosting in hospitality suites or at other social events organised for customers. There is also much useful information for stand and suite managers.

Moreover, the book provides vital material for those managers in sales, marketing and public relations who are trying to decide which exhibitions to attend, how to select and train suitable staff, and how to approach attendance at such events. A 3½" IBM PC compatible floppy disc is also available, containing cartoons and key bullets for use when briefing staff.

Sarah Turley has worked in various roles in public relations; much of the time organising attendance at exhibitions. Veronica Shutes worked in public relations up to management level for 17 years. She is an authority on hospitality suite management. Jan Herbert is a successful freelance graphic designer and cartoonist.

On Show at Exhibitions and Events contains essential information aimed at improving company effectiveness at trade shows and hospitality events. It is invaluable to directors and managers in marketing, sales and public relations, as well as their staffs. Amusingly presented, it provides useful lessons and reminders.

It enables people on stands and those hosting to:
- Communicate better with customers and guests.
- Avoid embarrassing situations.
- Cope with any eventuality.
- Avoid confusion and hassle.
- Prepare effectively for the event.

It will help management to:
- Improve the selection of events to attend.
- Convey a consistent image through staff behaviour.
- Brief staff effectively.
- Ensure appropriate handling for press and VIPs.
- Select the most suitable staff for each role.
- Provide checklists for stands, and hospitality suites.
- Create smoothly run events.

ORDER FORM

ORDER FORM

To: Greenfield Publishing
P. O. Box 12, Kenilworth
Warwickshire, CV8 1ZS
UK.

To obtain copies of this book, complete and return this page (or a photocopy), together with a cheque made out to Greenfield Publishing.

Please tick box if a receipt is needed ☐

Please mail me .... packs, each containing 5 copies of *On Show at Exhibitions & Events* @ £15.00 including post & packing.

Please mail me just one sample copy of *On Show at Exhibitions & Events* @ £3 including post & packing.

Please also send me a 3½" PC compatible floppy disc of briefing material on @ £5.00 including post & packing.

I enclose a cheque for £.........

Name: ....
Job Title: ....
Company: ....
Address: ....
....
....
....
Postcode: ....

ORDER FORM

ORDER FORM

SPC in the Office
Mal Owen and John Morgan

To: Greenfield Publishing
P. O. Box 12, Kenilworth
Warwickshire, CV8 1ZS
UK

To obtain further copies of this book, complete and return this page (or a photo-copy), together with a cheque made out to Greenfield Publishing.

Please tick box if a receipt is needed ☐

Please mail me .....copies of *SPC in the Office* @ £40.00 including p&p (£35.00 if 5 copies or more)

I enclose a cheque for £.........

Name: ....
Job Title: ....
Company: ....
Address: ....
....
....
....
Postcode: ....

FURTHER ASSISTANCE

If you are interested in training and consultancy in programmes associated with this book, then we would be pleased to help.

Please contact us as follows.

Mal Owen, Training for Excellence

Tel no: 01275 375096
Fax. No: 01275 375770
Email: mhowen@globalnet.co.uk
Web-site: www.trainingforexcellence.co.uk

John Morgan, Catalyst Consulting

Tel no: 01580 712760
Fax. No: n/a
Email: catalyst.jm@btinternet.com
Web-site: www.catalystconsulting.co.uk

We look forward to hearing from you.

READER FEEDBACK

Reader feedback is very important to us, the authors and publisher. It would be a great help to all if you could please let us have your response to this book.

On the next page you will find a brief questionnaire asking for your views on various aspects of this book. Could you please indicate your responses and add comments if necessary.

At the same time, we are interested in knowing something about the people who have acquired this book. Again, some details on yourself and your organisation would be very welcome. This data will not be released to any third party.

Could you please forward the completed form to: -

Mal Owen
1, The Manor Close
Manor Road
Abbots Leigh
N. Somerset
BS8 3RW

FAX No: 012175 375770

FEEDBACK FORM

Your time spent in completing this brief questionnaire would be much appreciated. Could you please complete the questionnaire, ticking the box as appropriate and providing written feedback for those sections requesting it. Many thanks.

	Not at all				OK					Highly

1. Usefulness
☐ ☐ ☐ ☐ ☐ ☐ ☐ ☐ ☐ ☐

Poor / OK / Excellent

2. Layout
☐ ☐ ☐ ☐ ☐ ☐ ☐ ☐ ☐ ☐

Not at all / OK / Highly

3. Relevance
☐ ☐ ☐ ☐ ☐ ☐ ☐ ☐ ☐ ☐

Poor / OK / Excellent

4. Level of content
☐ ☐ ☐ ☐ ☐ ☐ ☐ ☐ ☐ ☐

Poor / OK / Excellent

5. Value for money
☐ ☐ ☐ ☐ ☐ ☐ ☐ ☐ ☐ ☐

6 Any other comments?

Name: ....

Job Title: ....

Organisation: ....

Address: ....

....

....

....

Postcode: ....

Tel No: ....

E Mail: ....